FROM A BARE HULL

FERENC MATÉ

To My Dearest Friend, Candace,
without whose confidence and perseverance
I would still be dangling my feet
from a leaky old scow.

INTRODUCTION

It has been a long dream. I was thirteen when we used to gather in the basement of a friend to play billiards on a wobbly-legged table the size of an honest suitcase, with tiny clay balls so lumped and pitted that our games seemed more like exercises of faith and hope than displays of skill or concentration. The basement was home to a huge tin furnace that ate sawdust and wood and coal and thumb-wrinkled magazines. From one someone had torn a picture, a brown picture of a sailboat, a schooner I think, and nailed it to the rough inside of the cedar-siding. I don't know who put it there, it may have been I; but from that picture on I decided I was going to get that sailboat and just sail around the world for the rest of my life.

For most of the years since, I made no conscious effort towards this end. But somehow I had always been certain that sometime, probably any day now, I'd be stepping aboard my boat and doing whatever I needed to do to get her on her way and just go. The fact that I have had absolutely no money, not even enough to accumulate a single noteworthy debt, appeared to have very little bearing on the certainty of my future plans. On the other hand, I knew nothing about sailing boats or their costs so I was never threatened by the magnitude of the financial chasm between my brown paper schooner and me.

I did however, at the age of nineteen take a significant step. Upon a small, old, wooden scow with an irreparable starboard list, I built a smaller two room house. Its unlimited use of previously used material blended in splendidly with the tiny Vancouver bay and the surrounding junk.

It was a poor marina with sinking floats, stinking water, and sporadic bursts of electricity. But perhaps because of this lack of glamour it attracted a fleet of colorful, though sometimes rotting, old sailboats and a pack of sometimes rotting though unfinished new ones. Their owners almost without exception were very friendly and extremely talkative individuals (hence possibly the reason for the condition of their vessels) who were a great source of information regarding every imaginable aspect of sailboat theory, construction, refurbishing and surprisingly enough, maintenance.

Aroused by their endless discourses about toggles, garboards, pintles, and baggywrinkles I took a further step with the purchase of a then 32 year old Flattie, to which egomaniac owners refer as a Geary 18. The price was $100; high, but I did manage to pursuade a friend to assume half ownership for seventy-five. Since the boat was leaky and dirty and very slow and because he lived 97 miles from the water I considered the boat my own and abused it as such.

Sailing in the bay called False Creek was made illegal to succour the endless parade of trawlers, tug boats, and scows. I did have a small nameless motor but it ran for only eight minutes after I bought it so I had to abandon the idea of motoring out to legal sailing grounds. But there was always the night. The boat parade eased after the end of the workday so after dusk I hoisted my once-white sails and lurched into the darkness. The bay was unlit but after a few outings I learned where most things were and only when the scows were shifted without my knowledge did I run very hard into some unseen wire rope and huge poly-line. But the forestay was strong and it held. The hull wasn't strong and didn't hold when one night we were run over by a stampeding log boom. She had to be destroyed.

My following four years were spent continuing my mis-education; living and sometimes working on the wharves; prowling about sailboats; listening to the talkatives; hustling rides, sometimes across the bay and sometimes through the islands; and squatting on the float's end waiting for the miracle.

I then met someone who also wanted to sail. She was more practical than I, had sailed much longer journeys, had infinitely more drive and ambition, and was capable of actually organizing dreams. The other thing we had in common was no money. So we prowled together. Later we were married. Then we bought a Westsail 32 . . . in pieces.

INTRODUCTION

TABLE OF CONTENTS

LIST OF PHOTOS

LIST OF FIGURES

LIST OF TABLES

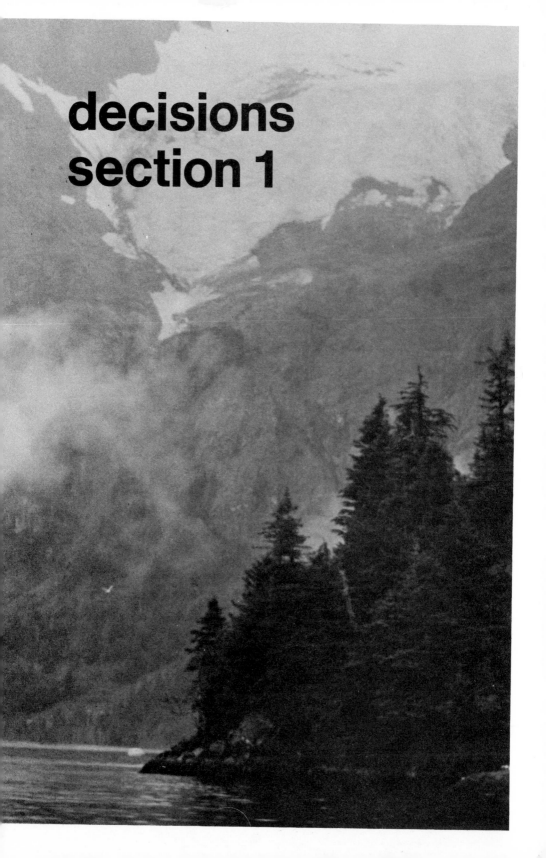

decisions
section 1

Chapter One
TO FIND A BOAT

The search seemed to last forever. We considered almost every new and used boat that was for sale and otherwise up and down the coast for a three year period. I even worked for a month and three days at a brokerage hoping to find the deal that never came. Finally by way of a corner ad in Sail magazine I found the ruggedly constructed Colin Archer double ender built in fiberglass in Southern California. It was available in parts and we could finish it ourselves.

I never wanted to build a boat. I always hated boat building. I actually hated people who were involved in boat building.

Most people will tell you that they do it because they love it, they love the accomplishment and they love doing things with their hands. I, however, never thought myself good with my hands. And if the thought ever entered my mind, my father chased it away with brief psychologically effective terms like "Oaf," "Ox," "Clumsy Oaf." and "put your hands in your pockets so they won't get in your way." The only thing I was allowed to do during his numerous undertakings around the house was to pull rusty nails from rotting boards, not exactly the most fulfilling preoccupation; so my fear of building turned into hate.

Others advocate that if you are to cruise you must build your own boat to know how and where everything was put together, so when something fails you know how to repair it. I always thought that if I left building my boat to someone who knew how to build the thing in the first place, I probably would never have to repair it.

When no arguments were left, the maniac builders threw out

the greatest raison d'etre: cost.

To a measurable extent, building your own boat can be very rewarding financially. They said that I would learn to love boat building and the giant project would be finished in no time. That last part of it convinced me. I knew they were wrong. I knew I could never learn to love it and I also knew that I could learn to hate it so much that I'd finish it in record time because I couldn't stand doing it anymore.

I bought a hull.

About the cost, they proved to be absolutely correct. A boat like ours when bought from the factory completely outfitted to the point that ours is, will run approximately $60,000. We have spent altogether, even with some additional hired out labor, no more than $29,000 and ended up with a boat with 10 sails, Aries self-steering, all winches, windlass, teak interior, teak decks, teak exterior, the large Volvo MD3B engine, windlass anchor chain, compasses, all bronze portlights, and other things too numerous to mention. The potential for savings is obvious.

The decision to build my boat was derived from a long search for the "right boat." The purchase of an old sturdy wooden sailing-ship seemed at first most reasonable. Some appeared to be financially within range and the traditional lines and romantic aura were difficult to resist. I should here explain briefly why I first excluded construction other than wood.

Used Fiberglass-Hulled boats, the few that could be considered structurally capable of offshore work, were all too new consequently much too expensive for our means. I must say that we drooled over the Cheoy Lee built Offshore 40, the Swedish Mistral 33, the Canadian Spencer 35 that the Roths employed so successfully in their Pacific cruises, and the whole line of meticulously-tooled Nicholsons from 32 to 38 feet. But the oppressive fact of our poverty emerged triumphant! We turned away.

Aluminum Boats were unavailable under forty feet (at least in the Pacific Northwest), and although there was someone starting hull production in of all places Squamish, British Columbia, we felt somewhat leery of the novicity of the operation. This experience was several years ago and since then the company may have matured, so if you're aluminum inclined you may consider further investigation.

We did fleetingly acknowledge the existence of a thirty-six foot STEEL-HULLED ketch which was being marketed at the ludicrous "sail-away price" of $13,000.00. But upon inspection the boat turned out to be poorly welded, under-constructed (the ribs were already showing, a characteristic one would be more accustomed to seeing on a thirty-year-old tug boat), and for some inexplicable reasons the builder chose to make his steel cabin with 5'9" headroom evoking emotions somewhat analogous to being in an iron lung. To support our skepticism of steel-hulled boats we had a friend who bought a beautifully sleek 48' sloop, peeled away the insulation from the inside of the hull, and found sunshine. I erased the existence of steel-hulled boats from my mind.

Ferro Cement was in irreconcilable turmoil, producing, aside from a few masterpieces, the most frightening herd of bestial mutation imaginable.

Trimarans I hate.

Thus, our first affair was with an ancient, world-proven Tahiti ketch. Hanna created a craft of fabulously simple design which in most cases is extremely heavily built, often proudly maintained, frequently available in differing degrees of refinement therefore cost, but agonizingly slow under sail. Some with the more ambitious Marconi rig are almost tolerable but the majority still flaunt the gaff main and this rig to windward is practically a joke. I'm not yearning to fly, if I did I would, but the number of additional days tacked onto already lengthy ocean crossings require additional space for water, stores, and above all somewhere to stretch one's self, none of which is available on this sturdy little ship.

Its sluggishness makes island-hopping tedious, often necessitating use of the engine, an occurrence which I detest. Some of course will say that when cruising, one should not have to worry about time. But there have to be limits to lack of exhilarating sailing. The lower end of my threshold is just above a Tahiti ketch. Apart from its slovenliness, its accommodations are marginal. The main cabin is almost adequate but with very little storage and only slouch-encouraging headroom. The forecastle with its gastly ventilation and no headroom is utile as a sail-locker only.

The rest of the ship, I must say, is unquestionable. The double-ender to me is the most seakindly craft. The displacement and beam provide a stiff comfortable boat, the small cockpit is ideal for mean-breaking waves; and the aft-hung rudder is large and brutal. While not quite indestructible, it is very accessible for repair. Prices ranged between ten and fifteen thousand dollars up and down the west coast. The largest selection was in San Pedro.

Initially the cost seemed attractive but when complimented by expenses for the usually-needed new suit of sails, rigging improvements, engine replacement (most have gasoline engines which I dread), enlargement of fuel and water capacity, and some interior modifications; apart from caulking, painting, etc. the sum to be expended climbed effortlessly beyond the twenty thousand dollar point.

Preoccupation with somewhat more recent and faster designs followed. We fell in love with a thirty-six foot cruiser-racer yawl named "Chica," memories of which still haunt me occasionally. She was a beautifully designed ship with slight tumble-home, not too fine an entry, and a graceful yet not excessive overhang. She was built in 1956. Her mahogany hull was immaculate, but the varnished house needed some care. The rigging was stainless, the spruce spars spotless, and the herringbone teak decks and brightwork below made us forget about our newly realized poverty. With its traditional skylight, varnished dinghy, and masterfully crafted cockpit, she was all we could dream of. BUT:

The forepeak was damp and dingy; the engine was a sputtering Atomic Four complete with a shockingly low 25 gallon fuel capacity and no room for expansion. Her sail inventory was made up of a 17-year-old main, a middle-aged jib, and Noah's canvas mizzen. To aid us in our rationalizing, she displaced twenty-two thousand dollars. But God she was a beautiful sight. I hope the varnished skylight leaks all over the new owner.

We began to overreact and immediately found the perfect substitute: a sleek looking 34-foot sloop built in 1945 and maintained in Bristol fashion by her original owner. Her price of $11,000 made us forget the gasoline engine, huge cockpit, and 7'10" beam because of which (we were told by a knowledgeable and reliable friend) she would sail constantly on her ear into the wind causing a most uncomfortable ride; and her deep heavily ballasted keel would result in a ceaseless pendulum-like roll downwind. Our attention was also brought to the mast which to me seemed to a frighteningly fragile head supported by a gastly number of struts, jumpers, and uncountable tiny bronze turnbuckles, all of which were dying to separate of fatigue at the first given opportunity. In short we were told that she would make an ideal island-hopper but only insanity could compel one to take her offshore.

I may at this point appear unreasonably picky but I lived around many disenchanted sailors who through their fallen dreams served as a perfect example of people insufficiently selective in their choice of boats resulting in harbor-bound fixers, rebuilders, reriggers, sellers, neurotics, and potential suicide victims instead of mariners sipping ancient coconut juice under a faded African Queen in green Tahitian waters.

Indeed I have so far refrained from mentioning a resurging fear which I attempted resolutely to suppress, but which accompanied

TO FIND A BOAT

me to every wood boat viewing: ROT.

Three good acquaintances purchased seemingly sound, thoroughly surveyed, and unquestionably approved wooden cruising boats during the time we lived in our float house. Their prices hovered about $15,000; with old gas engines, galvanized rigging, and very basic though efficient construction they could definitely not be considered bargains. At any rate, within a few months of purchase all three found extensively dry-rotted areas.

The couple in the Tahiti ketch, after remodeling the entire interior, decided to install new stanchions and found the bulwarks rotted. They had planned to go cruising shortly but instead tore apart the topsides, replaced the rot, got a divorce, and sold the boat. A lesser acquaintance bought a 36' Alden, I think it was. After passing the survey with flying dollars her stern post was found to be so rotten that the rudder was about to fall off. Repairs cost $2,700.

A closer friend bought a beautiful 36' gaff ketch with a mahogany hull. It was only twenty-years old, beamy, freshly-painted, spotless, and I turned green with envy. After installation of a diesel engine they were going off on a hand-to-mouth cruise for a long time. When he took out the old galvanized tanks to have the galvanizing removed for the new diesel, he found a rotten fir plank in the cockpit. Three weeks later he had finished tearing out the entire rotten mess and replaced it with fiberglass over plywood. Then he found rot in the starboard aft corner of the cabin, then in the port aft, then in all the corners, and then in the cabin top just aft of the main mast.

This mess resulted in innumerable weeks of labor, a lot of dead-cheap red-dry wine drinking, a badly needed skylight aft of the mast, and seemingly inexhaustible drunken discussions on the potential merits of musk-ox ranching in the Northwest Territories or perhaps Alaska.

I'm not faulting the buyers' choices in any of the three cases. Blame lies only with the incompetent surveying, although all three surveys were by reputable people. The point I'm trying to make is that our indecisiveness and indulgence in extensive wharf shopping were enhanced by this fear of rot, which seemed ominously unavoidable.

It is certainly a problem which cannot be dismissed and to treat it tenuously is indeed the epitome of folly.

Here I will humbly make a note to the intransigent wood-boat maniac who is reading this book for the solitary purpose of fortifying his arguments against all fiberglass boats and who will, regardless of rot or toredo worms or the plague, purchase a wooden one.

Take care. After the surveyor has completed his olympic-record-shattering dash through your future headache, find a knife, a flat pointed one that doesn't leave much of a mark, then find at least two hollow days to crawl, creep, slither, and weave over every square, inexcessible inch of wood and poke the knife into it. There's no need for a back swing, just poke gently; if there is rot the knife will penetrate with little effort. When you have found the rot take the flat pointed knife and sink it to the hilt into the villainous marine surveyor. Take a giant back swing.

To the topic. The Tahiti ketch, the Swedish cruiser, and the sleek weekender are only three of about forty wood boats we viewed for possible purchase, but these three seemed to traverse the range of the type of boat we had in mind. We looked at no boat under thirty feet for we felt they were too cramped for extensive cruising, and we considered nothing over forty-five feet for with the increase in size come the increased problems of large-sail handling, the cost of maintenance, and the cost of repairs which escalate disproportionately. Most of all we did not want to rely on outside crew; we had enough difficulty tolerating each other without intensifying the charged atmosphere with a third victim.

The following mania centered on new fiberglass cruisers built in the Orient. The possibility of taking delivery of a boat there with the then valuable American dollar seemed very promising. The boats appeared of excellent craftsmanship (mainly joiner work); the designs were so varied that one's choice was practically unlimited; and of course the prices made them seem almost attainable. We went into deep research regarding different designs, different companies, and became involved even to the extent of exchanging a few night letters regarding delivery dates, modifications, color of cockpit cushions, etc. Then we began to hear horror stories. Most of them I'm certain were untrue, but they sufficed to demoralize us long enough to discover our present boat.

For the stories. Apparently we were then at the acme of the Oriental boat explosion, the world demand for them having become very intense. According to one story, one of the large manufacturers expanded from two hundred to thirteen hundred employees in one year resulting in crowded toilet facilities, chaos, hiring of inexperienced labor, and a fleet of substandard hurriedly mass-produced craft.

A smaller company was said to have cut back on their consumption of expensive fiberglass roving for hull construction replacing it with somewhat more traditional burlap. Another was said to have

TO FIND A BOAT

been less conservative and used newspapers, the quality of which is rather low in the Orient to start with. Companies which were known to turn out hand lay-up fiberglass of four to six laminations were now using chopper gun, the undesirability of which will be discussed later. The quality of stainless steel used for fittings and tangs was much below acceptable and the sitka spruce used for masts had become scarce resulting in either green or warping sitka lumber or knottier and heavier fir.

As I mentioned these rumors were all stories, few of them substantiated and even fewer first hand. I did however see one boat which had begun to expose its chopper-gunned hull by shedding its blue gelcoat in palm-sized flakes, an occurrence which struck me as somewhat unappealing in a boat only four months old.

Apart from flying over and examining the factories to disprove the claims of the talkers we could do little else but dismiss the idea of an Oriental craft.

At this time we heard about independence and thought about building our own. We even considered lofting the hull ourselves. Many of our neighbors had done just that and some beautiful results were turned out in fiberglass, wood, foam sandwich, and of course the inevitable ferro cement. Designing one's boat to one's needs seemed attractive; building our own boat would be fulfilling and the final cost could be kept quite low. But there was one great frightening factor: The only boat which was anywhere near completion had taken its owner four years to build. He had an ideal system; four months of hoarding money on a freighter in the Arctic then eight months of twelve to fifteen hour days working on this William Garden designed "Porpoise."

The results were enviable, but four years is much too long a time for someone as unstable as myself to maintain interest, even if I could become familiar with the myriad of skills needed to accomplish completion. And four years was record time. A sobering example was our next-float neighbor living in a then seven-year-old concrete cave of a hull with a polyethelene deck and huge icicles in their main non-cabin as decoration. I didn't have the nerve to begin.

The only remaining alternative was buying a completed fiberglass hull and struggling on from there.

Chapter Two
TO FIND A HULL

I find something distinctively repulsive about the term "kit," evoking nauseating analogies to the "fix your own plumbing kit," "remove your own appendix kit," and the "save and cap your own teeth with old copper pennies kit." My lips tremble with embarrassment when the word trips reluctantly over them. I shall hence make reference to "bare hull" or "hull and deck" or "semi-completed boats," avoiding the "you know."

I shan't rave about our specific choice — William Atkin's "Eric" redesigned for fiberglass by naval architect W.I.B. Crealock and built by California's Westsail Corporation. The company's brochures are more than competent in this aspect, but I will mention the points which we found decisive.

Design

Being a double ender, as I mentioned in connection with Hannah's thirty footer, makes our boat very seakindly. It offers little resistance to following waves thus it will not be pushed to dangerously high speeds with the possible eventuality of diving into a trough. The pointed end will split large following seas while a transom stern is likely to disturb them and cause them to break. Excessive speed may cause any wave to break but I feel that every ounce of help is worthwhile.

Some people argue that double enders lack stern buoyancy, and thus tend to get pooped easily. This point of view is quite valid if the stern is lean and pointed, so be certain the one you choose is full and rounded.

The rudder is easily accessible, and like a Tahiti ketch more than sufficiently affixed with three hefty sets of gudgeons which have been known to withstand two whole days of the boat being thrashed against rocks by six to eight foot surf. The rudder did eventually begin to wear away so it was removed.

The beam is eleven feet which for a boat of only 27½' lwl yields vast amounts of living space below that can be utilized in various, very functional layouts (discussed extensively in chapter on planning).

The bow and stern are full and buoyant. The ample beam along with 7,500 lbs. of ballast gives great stability. And although she will heel somewhat if not reefed, she will at that point become stiff and settle into a fast comfortable ride with the long keel holding a steady course. This stiffness gives the helmsman a feeling of complete control without having to fight and struggle with the rudder. I have sailed on too many light, fin-keeled fiberglass boats which were prone to burying the rail and sometimes the cabin side. And although they never succumbed to a complete knockdown, they suffered a total loss of rudder whereupon the boat would swing wildly into the wind with madly luffing sails. Once full of wind she'd settle nicely on her beam then go down almost flat, lose rudder, come up madly luffing, etc. It can become very boring.

Apart from providing incomparable directional stability and pleasant turns at the helm, the long full keel has other advantages. Obviously it facilitates self-steering and eases the task of drydocking either on ways or on the shore beside pilings without threat of damage or danger of the boat falling onto her side. If the latter should occur, the large beam will maintain her in a sufficiently safe position until refloating on the next tide without the threat of cabin-flooding or wave-damage to the topside. One boat did run aground in Mexico and had to await the tide change. She suffered no damage.

Designs other than double enders are available in various stages of completion. Two manufacturers offer traditional clipper bows. On paper they look attractive; in real life the bows are lean and hungry, containing little if any buoyancy for the considerable amount of weight to be stowed there. Anchors, chains, and windlass amount to substantial mass and if not well supported by a buoyant bow could cause uncomfortably wild pitching which also retards the boats progress.

The lack of bow and stern buoyancy recurs in yachts other than these clippers and one should definitely be on the lookout for them for it is a sign of poor design and can result in a violent ride. As the lean bow plunges it is checked by a halting yank as the better-

TO FIND A HULL

rounded more buoyant section of the hull is introduced to the water. Motion like the above is wearing not only on the crew but also on the rigging, mast, and fittings and could result in premature loosenings of fasteners, tangs, and bonds.

Hulls of narrow beam (under 9 feet) should be carefully studied and measured up for accommodations. For although the designs may indicate a spacious tricabin layout with dinettes and lounge areas, upon evaluation one may find room for two quarter berths and a deep breath. (For actual measurements required for specific items and bodily positions please see chapter on planning.)

Everyone has his own phobias and intransigent beliefs even about sacred things like cruising boats. With kind permission of their authors, W.I.B. Crealock, N.A. and Herb David, N.A., we enclose their essays of thoughts at the end of this chapter regarding the "ideal" cruising boat. Somewhere between their varied point of view you should discover "your" cruising boat.

Construction

We found the aforementioned hull characteristics of our boat positive factors; yet the most heart-warming aspect was its construction. The thinnest place was ½-inch thick (at the sheer) increasing to a full inch in the keel. It is of hand lay-up fiberglass, see photo 1. Other factories, who also supply partially completed boats, will expound the glories of their ¼-inch-at-the-sheer hulls which will, at the gentle nudge of a forefinger, vibrate prolongedly like the well-tuned cross-cut saw of the bald Italian on the Original Amateur Hour.

So thin a hull can result in "panting" once the boat is completed. Excessive panting will cause loosening of bulkhead bonds, deck fittings, and hull-to-deck attachments. Very excessive panting will cause bulkheads to literally pop out in rough seas or cause the hull to collapse like the crushed side of a soft aluminum can. Panting, of course, can be eliminated by honey-combing the hull with bulkhead upon bulkhead, but it is rather a thoughtless last resort which could have been avoided by constructing a sufficiently strong hull in the first place.

The argument that the thickness of the hull as an indicator of strength cannot be relied upon is to a point acceptable. A ½-inch thick hull with only, say three layers of mat and roving (or much worse — cloth) is in fact weaker than another hull utilizing the same number of laminates of equal weight with an accumulated thickness of ¼-inch. It's obvious that the difference in thickness had to have been made up by resin which in itself has little strength. The

Photo No. 1 — Hull being hand laminated.

strength of all fiberglass products comes from the tensile strength of the fibers of the mat or roving or cloth laid in the resin. (A simple experiment with a cube of set resin dropped from even a modest height onto a solid surface will by shattering, demonstrate the above point.) But a well-squeegeed lay-up of five or six paired layers of adequate laminates like two ounce mat and 24 ounce roving will result in a solid dependable hull.

1. Mat, Roving, and Cloth

Mat — an unwoven conglomeration of loose, approximately four-inch long fibers laid upon each other.

Roving — long fibers woven into a thick but loose pattern.

Cloth — very tightly woven long fibers resulting in a much finer material than roving.

It would seem at first obvious that to attain maximum strength the strongest of the three materials should be used, putting cloth, because of its high density fibers on the top of the list. But a hull of pure cloth, apart from being ridiculously expensive to lay-up due to the number of individual layers required to achieve sufficient strength, would lack adequate stiffness, a quality provided by the use of alternate layers of mat. Then, of course, it would seem the choice should be cloth and mat. Yet this procedure has a major flaw for, unless absolutely meticulously squeegeed, the cloth would,

TO FIND A HULL

upon catalyzation of the resin, give a finish so smooth that the following layer would not find sufficient irregularities to provide a good bond. As in the case of any adhesive, the glossier the surface, the weaker the bond.

The next "obvious" choice would then be a hull of pure roving for it would give the rigidity required because of its sufficient resin holding ability due to its loose fibers. It would also, with its heavily textured surface, supply ensuing layers with a good-bonding, rough face. But it is because of this textured surface that roving must be combined with mat for an ideal bond. If one looks at roving one will see the surface riddled with hollows. If the following layer of unyielding-to-contour roving is added the depth of these hollows is doubled and they will contain either unreinforced resin or much weaker air. When mat is alternated, the shorter fibers of this material will easily conform and fill the hollows of the old layer of roving as well as provide a supple base for the hard protrusions of the next layer, which must be applied before the resin in the mat has catalyzed.

2. Chopper Gun

Although people exist who advocate the chopper gun method of lay-up, they base their argument on the fact that mat, because of its poly-directional strength, is the strongest of the three reinforcing agents. This statement must be cautiously let out the other ear.

Mat is indeed indiscriminately strong in all directions because of the random pattern of its fibers. But mat used in hand lay-up has long overlapping strands in even layers, whereas chopper gun by its very nature must utilize shorter fibers in a resin-rich mixture which tends to yield a product more closely resembling the shattering resin cube.

A hull containing by weight, less than thirty percent reinforcing fibers is considered weak by most experts. Yet with the resin dependent chopper gun it is almost impossible to achieve a fiber content close to thirty percent. At the same time a well squeegeed mat and roving hull can have up to 38 to 40% glass content. A mistake which I myself tripped upon is to surmise that a difference of 8 to 10% can hardly be considered significant. On closer examination one must realize that this 8 or 10% actually makes up almost 30% of the fiber content, thus resulting in a hull stronger or weaker by that percentage. Apart from actual strength, the short fibers will not provide the resilience and flexibility of hull supplied by the long fibers of cloth or roving.

3. Lamination Procedures

It may be worthwhile suggesting to all those who will have a chance to inspect the incomplete hull of their future boat that they look for proper laminating procedures. The obvious thing is to inquire into the weights and numbers of layers of material used. One should ascertain that full lengths of the material run the entire length of the hull. Although this procedure may slow production compared to a set-up where a number of short pieces are over-lapped, it will, through the single continuous fibers, add great strength as well as prevent difficult-to-work-around lumps in the hull.

4. Miscellaneous

Once the above has been confirmed one should check for the following:

Lumps. Although the exterior of a hull may be completely fair, bumps and lumps may be evident inside it, indicating an accumulation of resin either through poor squeegeeing or catalyzing before the excess could be effectively removed. Apart from what is obvious from the discussion of unreinforced resin, these spots could be areas of weakness because of the trapped air they may contain. Subsequent layers may hide the obvious air pocket, so if a suspicious lump is encountered one should tap it to ascertain whether or not a hollow exists. One should not look for tiny gnat-sized ripples. But a major lump, the size of half an orange, should serve as a warning.

Gloss. Smooth glossy areas, unbroken by the contour of the fibers beneath, are also indication of poor squeegeeing or poor catalyst-resin mixing. Again, slight patches are bound to occur in any boat due to the sensitivity of the medium to any vacillation in temperature or humidity. But a frequent recurrence should at least prompt one to make serious inquiries. If the builder shrugs it off as irrelevant, interpret this reaction as a sign of ignorance which is likely to infect his entire product. Shop elsewhere.

White fibers. This argument is the last straw one can cling to with tenacity. They may be visible through the resin and again they are an indication of improper procedure with a resultant loss of strength. The cause of this occurrence is probably shrewd and not poor judgement. A manufacturer may use very heavy fibers in long layers and may even end up with a beautifully textured, glossless, lumpless surface through which the white unsaturated fibers are visible.

Visible white fibers are a result of too rapid catalyzing. While the mixture was "cool" enough to remain workable to a fair end result, it did go off prematurely in a sense that all the fibers had not sufficient time to be saturated. Premature catalyzation is done only to save waiting time, i.e. time during which a mold must be left unused awaiting catalyzing before the next layer can be applied. Since a manufacturer has only a limited number of costly molds his motivation for accelerating catalyzation is obvious. To see the ridiculous extreme of what may result, take a piece of unresined fiberglass cloth and crumple it in your hand . . . not too seaworthy is it?

I must note that the above occurrence would likely be encountered in a quality boat yard, one using heavy roving which is the most difficult to saturate. If white fibers are discovered in a boat yard using light cloth or mat (a place where a self-respecting cruising hull buyer should not be found to begin with) head for the nearest exit, for absolutely no excuse can be acceptable here.

Our hull contains six layers each of two ounce mat and 24 ounce roving and it seems to lack most of the above-mentioned flaws. Some say that such conservative procedure adds unnecessary weight and unnecessary cost. They believe the hull to be overbuilt out of ignorance. Tell it to a 65-foot whale.

5. Ballast

If a fiberglass cruising boat is to last any length of time the ballast should be internal. A heavy bolt-on keel will require monstrous mechanical attachments all of which will in time work loose from their fiberglass bed regardless of its thickness. The ballast, whether lead pigs, steel punchings, or a solid casting should be bonded into the hull to provide stiffness and prevent unnecessary motion and work in the keel area. And if you go belly up a well bonded ballast will spare the pretty lamp on the ceiling.

Externally ballasted boats do have one undeniable advantage. If they go aground lightly on rock or coral the lead may get badly gouged but no structural damage will be caused. An internally ballasted boat may have part of its fiberglass hull ground away or badly abraded necessitating very thorough repair.

If steel punchings or other rapidly oxidizing material is used for internal ballast it is necessary that it be carefully sealed from air and water by either tar or, better yet, resin. If this precaution is not taken the entire inaccessible ballast may in a few years turn to rust. For details on the above procedure see the chapter on ballast installation.

I have purposely avoided involvement in lengthy discussion about ballast ratios and their distribution. The books of Eric Hiscock and D.M. Street attack the problem verbosely and thoroughly. My attempt to reword their findings would I believe be superfluous.

6. Bulkheads

If you are purchasing a completed boat the following item will definitely concern you. If you are acquiring a hull only it is quite probable that you will have the main structural bulkheads installed. This procedure is a common one, inspired not by the human kindness of the manufacturer, but by the necessity of reinforcing the hull before it's extracted from the mold. Some companies use temporarily bonded in stiffeners obviating premature apprehension, for then you will install your own bulkheads and you will be able to do it properly.

"Properly" to me is a simple and inexpensive method that utilizes an angled piece of rigid polyurethane foam installed between the bulkhead and the hull, figure 1. The foam serves three purposes. First, if it is cut on a 45° angle the foam will create a gentle curve the lines of which will be easily followed by the bonding of mat, cloth, or whatever material comes on top. If the foam were excluded it is obvious that the bonding would have to make a sharp right-angular turn resulting in a brittle and delicate area.

Figure No. 1 — Bulkhead installation.

Second, the foam will absorb sudden jolts imposed upon the hull by heavy seas and, along with the flexible section of bonding which covers its angled surfaces, it will prevent the transmission of these jolts to the stiff ungiving bulkhead.

TO FIND A HULL

Third, the constant undulation of the hull could bring about chafe between it and the bulkhead. Admittedly this motion will not cause immediate problems with almost any boat but where two surfaces of an equal hardness are rubbing against each other, eventually something will begin to wear away. If foam is inserted this process will in no way be halted, but the victimized member will be the non-structural foam instead of the bulkhead or the hull.

On a stiffer hull, i.e. 3/8 of an inch thick or more, the use of foam is not necessary because of the unflexing rigidity inherent with such heavy construction. However, it is a simple necessity on anything thinner and if a boat yard deems it unnecessary, you and a small fee should have little trouble convincing them of its importance. If their appeal is that they've never used the method, show them this section and the one on "Plywood Parts Installation." Charge a small fee.

The material most commonly used for bulkheads is plywood. It must be the highest quality marine grade, and it has to be at least ¾-inch thick. Since in a fiberglass boat these bulkheads take the place of ribs, frames, and beams used in wood boats, the need for them to provide optimum stiffness and rigidity is obvious. Plywood less than ¾-inch thick is much too flexible; I recently almost became nauseated sitting in an Oriental "cruising" boat watching the 3/8-inch thick bulkheads undulate gently.

Deck and Cabin Mold

Unless one is a completely self-sufficient boat builder he should investigate further into the company whose hull is being considered for purchase. The major task in boat construction is, of course, the hull and if you feel competent to continue on your own from this stage, fine; I hope the pages on decking will serve as an aid.

If, however, you require a more completed boat before you take command you should look thoroughly into a molded cabin deck, which most hull manufacturers offer. Apart from the basic esthetics of their design, which I will leave to your taste, you should consider the following points: cockpit layout, method of construction, bulwarks, hull to deck attachment, mast step support.

1. Cockpit Layout

Although the size of the cockpit has been touched upon in previous discussion, I feel it important enough to elaborate. I must admit that a huge cockpit with comfortable seat-backs, upholstered cushions, and room for at least four to lie about in undisturbed stupor has its decadent attractions. Yet when cruising, the need to survive overwhelms the urge to satisfy one's perversions; thus the lounge-pit must give way to a thimble-sized hole sufficiently long for four erect adults, sufficiently narrow for the helmsman to brace his legs in stiff winds, and sufficiently shallow to hold no more than a few hundred pounds of ocean when brimmed. Dimensions of forty-eight inches by thirty by eighteen inches deep seem to me none too puritan; when one considers that a structure of such escetic dimensions holds almost a thousand pounds of water, one becomes very reticent to add even an inch in any direction.

While on the subject of the cockpit, another feature may be looked for. In most instances the engine and possibly the fuel tanks will be located somewhere below and around the cockpit area. To have the cockpit sole removable yet absolutely water tight seems to me an excellent idea. Marine diesels, reliable as they are, do break down and when they do so, they have to come out and when they have to come out they should do so by merely lifting the cockpit sole instead of ripping out the sink, sledgehammering the toilet bowl, disassembling the icebox and extracting the engine through the fourth drawer of the chart table, nut by bolt. How to seal the removable sole will be discussed under "Waterproofing." See figure 2.

Figure No. 2 — Removable but watertight cockpit sole.

　　　　　　　　　　　　　　　　　　　　　TO FIND A HULL

2. Method of Construction

To give glass reinforced plastic decks sufficient rigidity so that they will not whip and vibrate themselves to death, loosening deck fastenings, chainplates, hull-deck attachments, etc. in the process, a layer of sufficiently thick marine plywood should be laminated into them. On decks and cabin tops of boats below forty feet, plywood of ½-inch thickness is satisfactory.

The plywood should not be thrown in as undisturbed sheets, but it should be tapered at the edges where curves are to be encountered to enable placement of a smoothly fitting bonding not threatened by the impossibility of 90° angles, see figure 3. The removal of sharp edges is also vital to eliminate the corners against which the flexing glass must work. An untapered edge will in a disturbingly short period crack the glass, if not to the extent of jeopardizing the deck's structural integrity, then at least to the point where dreaded rain water may find its way to the plywood and cause dreaded rot.

Figure No. 3 — Tapered plywood core.

The quality of fiberglassing is just as vital here as it is in the hull. And although the thickness of the glass on either side of the plywood need not exceed ¼-inch, it should still be made up of a well worked mat-and-roving or mat-and-cloth combination.

Another vital aspect of construction is the radius of the curves of cabin-top-to-sides, deck-to-cabin-sides, and if applicable (and it should be) deck-to-bulwarks. Although curves of small radius appear to me more attractive partly because they're traditional and mostly because they are fairly easy to overlay handsomely with teak decks, teak cabin sides, or teak trim; the practicality of this method structure-wise must be questioned. A small-radius curve where the two adjoining planes approach 90° with little transition makes for a potentially weaker area than one with a larger radius which will, with its flexibility, transmit vibrations without having to drastically alter the form of the waves at one vulnerably angled point.

Again this philosophy may not be critical for a standard fiberglass boat which, designed partially for racing, is usually outdated and disposed of by the time the twentieth installment is paid. But for a cruising boat which hopes to establish a permanent relationship with its owner, any detail in design and construction that will increase its life expectancy must be considered a necessity.

3. Bulwarks

Bulwarks are to a great extent considered a phobia of the traditionalists; but quite apart from this undeniable truth they have great practical value. Obviously they keep the deck a little drier; how much so depends of course on their height and the amount of freeboard. On a major heel they can provide a good walking surface, or if not high enough, at least a ledge against which one can wedge one's feet. In any rough sea the psychological comfort they provide through their visual (and hopefully structural) massiveness, can with little imagination be analogous to the comforting sides of one's crib which reassuringly defined one's safe territory. But then this need for security may be an evidence of my own psychosis.

The best I have left for last, for the most vital service (and I am referring to the definition of vital "necessary to the existence, well-being and indeed continuance," the bulwarks can render is to reinforce the stanchions. Stanchions through-bolted in the deck, as in figure 4, will work loose even from everyday use like visiting behemoths yanking them from their base when boarding. They will definitely not last long enough to keep a hurtling body from going overboard. If you insist on using stanchions of this kind to support lifelines onto which you may snap your safety harness in a storm, have the decency to leave your foul-weather gear and good rubber boots down below so someone else can use them in the morning when you're gone.

If your stanchions are just screwed into the deck, remember to unscrew them at the onset of a storm and hide them in a safe place until the winds die down.

With bulwarks of any height you have the opportunity to install stanchions that will actually serve some purpose. The stanchions can be so fabricated as to bolt through the bulwarks at well spread points, see photo 2. If for some reason this construction is not favored, a standard deck-through-bolted stanchion can be sufficiently reinforced if a collar is attached to it at the top of the bulwarks, as

TO FIND A HULL

STANCHION

STIFFENERS

DECK

NUT AND WASHER

Figure No. 4 — Stanchions through-bolted to the deck.

in photo 3. This reinforcement will shorten the treacherous lever arm and make the term "lifelines" less of a joke.

4. Hull to Deck Attachment

Do not for an instant wrongly assume that because this heading appears late in this section it is of lesser importance. If this procedure is improperly executed consequences may vary from the slightly annoying inaccessible leak to the most embarrassing habit of "deck popping," one of which I have witnessed.

It was a gun-barrel-grey Vancouver afternoon and the Royal Yacht Club's 29ish footers were luffing, awaiting the start of their event. The rain had stopped. A squally wind came off the black Point Grey. Someone lost a jib sheet so the group waited. Upon a signal I didn't see, or saw but didn't know so hadn't noticed, the boats lurched into the wind and formed a single file around the first buoy. Then they headed north toward the leafless brown park and melted into the gun-barrel grey mist.

From the mist the boats emerged, or at least they did for a

Photo No. 2 — Well designed stanchion base (through bolted).

moment, then were sucked back into the grey; except for one. It huddled low in the water, its blue flush-deck lay over on its side and skimmed toward the old wood-pier and me.

Then the sailboat became upright; some yellow-men slithered on the deck; a white sail came down and a colored one went up; the

Photo No. 3 — Another well supported stanchion.

TO FIND A HULL

branches of the trees rattled loudly; and the boat lay down almost flat then came up again. As the branches broke she went down violently, and among the cracking wood there was a sudden shrill noise like someone ripping a beer can in half.

Then the sails were in the water, the pretty colored one too, and the yellow men splashed about the rigging and crawled back onto the deck. The naked hull was upright thirty feet away and the wind blew her toward the shore. The deck and the sails dragged behind her.

Then the deck sank and the yellow men scratched toward the hull. It drifted close to the pier. The woman in the galley held the broken top of a thermos bottle in her hand and stared confusedly at the sky. One yellow-man seemed to be tiring. He was close to the shore boat but he was thrashing the water, his right arm only barely rising. His face didn't come up and his arms stopped thrashing. Then he stood up in the knee deep waves. The other yellow-man had reached the shore and sat in the sand. It began to rain.

The woman put the top of the thermos bottle onto the stove, stepped back into the salon, sat down onto the berth, opened up a bright yellow and institution green striped umbrella and held it, slightly tilted, above her head.

The deck had been pop-riveted to the hull. The rivet heads were small; with constant motion between hull and deck the rivet heads bore out the holes in the thin laminates. When the force was too great, the deck popped. The mast had been stepped through to the keel and it too had acted as a lever; so perhaps without this touch, then who knows.

a) Pop rivets are the fastest to install and most-to-be-avoided fasteners. They are sure to work loose in time or at least leak constantly.

b) Screws, if they are large, self-tapping, and used at short intervals in thick fiberglass, are of some value in tiny boats for a tiny time. If small and used in conjunction with thin fiberglass, take a lot of Bibles. Even for a small yacht this method is most treacherous for the drill bit has to be a perfect size. If it is too large the power of the screw gun will tear out the shallow threads the screw has cut in the glass and spin freely and hold nothing. If the bit is too small the screw will tighten prematurely and the heads will snap off. Some companies I've heard of who use this method seldom bother to drill out the broken screw and replace it. Anyway the whole thing is useless.

c) Sheer clamp. If a flange is absent on the hull a sheer clamp of some hardwood may be attached to it with screws and mish mash.

TO FIND A HULL

The deck in turn can be screwed and mish mashed onto this clamp. Since hardwoods hold screws well, this method should be fairly safe for some years. Mahogany would be ideal, for although it does not hold screws as well as oak it is somewhat less prone to rot. If a caprail is installed over the seam embedded well in polysulphide and maintained watertight, the lifetime of the attachment in figure 5 may be prolonged indefinitely. If not, rain water will seep down and the wood will rot; definitely. Replacing it would be a most arduous and money consuming task.

TEAK CAP RAIL

HEAVY POLYSULFIDE BEDDING

DECK

MAHOG. OR OAK SHEER CLAMP

HULL

Figure No. 5 — Wood sheer clamp.

d) Bonding. A small flange may be located on the hull and the deck set in place upon it. Then from below layers of mat and roving are laid over both, building up from narrow to wider strips. If sufficient laminations are used, well fitted, and well squeegeed this method could be excellent, for it will create a leak-proof monolithic

TO FIND A HULL

structure with even stress at every point. If well done this attachment can be the slowest but the strongest of all. If not well done, and there are few things more difficult than bonding upside down with sticky, droopy material, the thing is guaranteed to leak and is virtually impossible to repair. With high bulwarks the method is an impossibility.

One objection I do have to this procedure is that to achieve superlative bonding, the surfaces to be bonded should be "green." That is, the fiberglass should have cured as little as possible. This "green" bonding is very infrequently done on production boats whose assembly system seems to require almost total completion of the interior preceding the placement of the deck-cabin onto the hull. This procedure could be anywhere from two to six weeks, which puts them considerably past the "green" stage.

e) Through-bolts, figure 6. Through-bolting is a somewhat less delicate operation than bonding but undeniably a demanding job if high, narrow bulwarks are encountered. The prerequisites are two extremely strong overlapping flanges. These flanges must be integral; i.e. turned over ends of laminates and not narrow little shelves added later on. If they are added later you might as well sew the things together with pink cotton thread. The turned over laminates must be perfect examples of fiberglassing; e.g. roving with mat and/or cloth, because the strain in these rather sharp angles will be severe.

CAP RAIL

POLYSULPHIDE
BEDDING
COMPOUND

BULWARK

HULL SIDE

Figure No. 6 — Through-bolted decks.

Before the two flanges are laid together a disgustingly huge and shockingly costly amount of polysulphide (either black or white) should be laid onto the lower flange but only after it, as well as the deck flange, have been carefully bathed in acetone to remove dirt and dust. This procedure should eliminate most of the leaks. The holes should again be of perfect diameter for the bolts to hold ideally. The bolts should be fairly large, at least ¼-inch, and stainless steel. They should be flat head so that the tapered cheeks can prevent lateral movement, and they should be countersunk; just. A nice idea if you're doing through-bolting yourself (companies rarely do it for you) is to fill each hole just after drilling with polysulphide and then insert the bolt.

On the lower end a handsome sized stainless steel washer should be popped on, then definitely either a lock washer or a lock nut. The nut should be tightened until it screams. This operation is nerve racking if one must hold a washer, lock washer, and nut between narrow shoulders of high bulwarks. It is definitely a two man operation, for one person has to be outside with a screwdriver while the more unfortunate fellow is down below with nuts, washers, ratchets, etc.

If performed as prescribed above with the bolts spaced no farther than ten to twelve inches, preferably six to eight inches, and covered over again with polysulphide then with a well-sealed cap rail, it should be a good solid method leaving very few things to chance.

Note: For plywood decks with glass overlay consult chapter on deck construction.

5. Mast Step

I include this item under the section on decks because I'm convinced that a deck-stepped mast, *if well done,* is preferable to a keel-stepped mast. Reasons: With aluminum as the most commonly used material for masts, the need for a completely snug footing above which the old wooden mast could indulge in a bit of bending and whipping is mostly eliminated. This theory does not imply that the mast should be footed on ball bearings, but rather it puts forth the idea that the major factor with the stiff aluminum mast is compression. As long as this force is transferred to the keel, the number of stages involved in the process (assuming of course that they are well designed and solidly constructed) will little imperil the integrity of the whole.

For the conservatives who at this point are tearing the book in half, I provide a few basic requirements which should meet with their approval.

First, the deck at the point of stepping should be repeatedly reinforced over an expanded area to spread the load. Four laminated layers of one inch thick plywood twelve inches by twenty-four inches, as in figure 7, I would not consider pessimistic. With fiberglass on the cabin top, any sudden increase in load on a tiny area regardless how brief the span of time involved will cause cracks that can lead to leaks and possibly delamination. A footing of this size will not only help eliminate this occurrence but will also enable the tinkerer to move his mast slightly fore or aft to improve performance, ease, or provide weather helm or just pass the time.

Figure No. 7 — Mast step reinforcement.

Beneath this mast-step, structural bulkheads and deck beams are a necessity. Bulkheads should be installed as previously indicated. The beams will spread the load athwartships and the bulkheads aid nicely in distributing some of the force over the hull as well as the keel on which they are based. To reinforce the deck beams and remove most of the load from the bulkheads, a solid post of steel, teak, oak, or other material of high load bearing capability should be installed directly under the mast step, see figure 8.

This post is no place to exercise frugality. Acquire a post of the most generous dimensions permissible spacially and esthetically, and make certain it fits snugly and evenly between the beams and the cabin sole. If at all possible this beam should be attached to

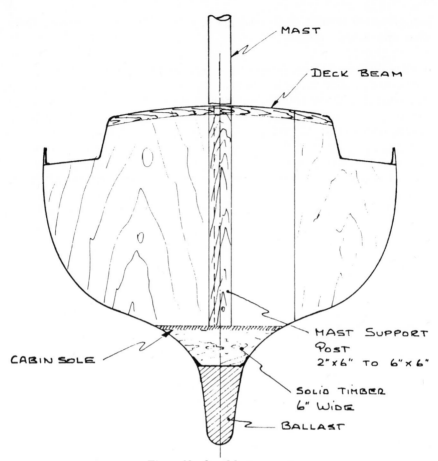

Figure No. 8 — Mast support.

either of the bulkheads to prevent play. The cabin sole should at this point be reinforced with monstrous floor timbers at least as wide as the post. These timbers in turn should be blocked up from the keel. If any of the above steps are excluded, you may as well forget the whole thing and step the stick in a Christmas tree holder.

If you are buying a hull and deck, some of these problems will be of only minor concern to you but you should ascertain the location of the main bulkheads and confirm the potential of completing the above procedure without insurmountable, pre-installed obstacles such as a fiberglass cabin sole with a shower pan directly beneath the mast.

Apart from the foregoing I will recommend very little that will dangerously inhibit your boat buying freedom. But I must stress that the above points are most vital and uneliminatable factors which should not be taken lightly. Unfortunately the industry is so incurably infected by hundreds of quick-buck artists whose intentions are malicious, knowledge non-existent, and ignorance and stupidity totally unbounded, that unless extreme scrutiny is exercised one may belatedly realize that one has purchased a steaming pile of horse manure.

On the other hand many benignant people exist in the industry whose limitless good intentions are unfortunately equalled by their lack of taste and more alarmingly lack of knowledge. Their convictions may sound pure and unquestionable but the material they work with is in its vulnerable infancy and total information on it is non-existent. So I must caution you to employ passionate analytics, ask the most embarrassing and personal questions available, and then if you are convinced that you have found the right boat go somewhere else just to be certain. Have patience . . . the Ark wasn't built in a day.

Design Aspects to Look for in Hull & Deck:

1. Full Bow & Stern
2. Sufficient Beam
3. Long Keel
4. Well Supported Rudder
5. Small Cockpit
6. Bulwarks
7. Wide Cabin
8. Headroom in Forepeak
9. Radius of Deck to Hull Curves
10. Hull to Deck Attachment
11. Room to Sleep in Cockpit
12. Engine Room Access
13. Type of Through Hull Fittings

Construction Aspects to Look for:

1. Hand Lay-up
2. Hull to Deck Attachment
3. Reinforcement
4. Quality of Laminations
5. Laminating Schedule (hull thickness & type of fibers used)
6. Removable Cockpit Sole
7. Thickness of Bulkheads
8. Installation of Ballast

9. Mast — Step Reinforcement
10. Rigidity of Cabin Sole
11. General Care & Attention to Details

General Things to Look for:

1. A Proven Design
2. Proven Construction (sailing history)
3. Manufacturers Ability to follow up with parts, help & advice
4. Potential Marketability in case of resale

Reprinted by permission of SAIL Magazine, copywrited September 1974.

A BOAT FOR DISTANT WATERS
by W.I.B. Crealock, Naval Architect

"A man who goes to sea for pleasure," said Samuel Johnson, "would go to hell for a pastime." And indeed we should devote as much foresight to the embracing of the one as to the avoiding of the other.

Those who wander across oceans in small boats will encounter hardship and discomfort enough, however sturdy their craft or great their expertise, so they should, at least, do what they reasonably can to reduce hardship and possible danger.

I am not discussing the boat intended primarily for local cruises of days or weeks or even months — though she will be well enough suited to that too — or even the boat for a single long passage, at the end of which lies a refit or retirement.

I am dealing with a boat for the increasing number of people who plan to voyage and live aboard for several years, usually on a frayed budget and far from normal facilities for repair and replenishment. These are the sailors who will, I believe, enjoy the greatest experience life has to offer.

It is tempting to be pedantic and to trot out one's own little preference as though it is perfection, but you may often judge the depth of a man's experience at sea by his reluctance to extol a particular type or feature as the ideal. There are simply too many variables in man and boat and sea. Some travel only to arrive, others for the journey itself; some to a time table, others to a whim.

What sort of boat, in broadest terms, are we seeking for these gypsies of the sea? After talking with many in the ports of the world and across my office desk, I believe that the majority want, very simply, a boat in which they can place absolute trust to overcome whatever the sea may offer and which will carry them with reasonable comfort and efficiency.

Most boats will survive 99% of the hazards of the sea — for the boat usually outlasts the man. But, then, if you fall from a tenth floor window you'll be in pretty good shape for 99% of the way; it is that last 1% which may have you worried.

There was a time when "Thou shalt be uncomfortable" seemed to be the unwritten commandment of the salty cruising man, and he was content to travel at the bottom of a damp, dark wooden hole, waging an exhausting no-win war against mildew and weeping seams.

Since fatigue is, I believe, a principal source of danger, we should require a boat with a kindly motion which will steer herself with or without a windvane, a boat which can be handled by a quarter of her crew under most conditions and provide them with dry, comfortable rest.

Though we are not discussing specific interior layouts here, I want to stress that word "dry." One might imagine that a cruising boat would surely have one attribute above all others — watertightness — yet it is, in fact, one of the rarest qualities. Instead you will find fatuous little forehatches depending on a rubber gasket and a Sunday-afternoon fitting and skylights of traditional design which seem almost to beckon a wave below.

Clearly the first question to be settled is that of size. Length overall is an unsatisfactory criterion, although the mean between overall and waterline lengths would be some improvement. Displacement is a more accurate basis on which to judge practicability.

Let's be realistic on this question of displacement. There have been many long passages made by light displacement craft which were no less seaworthy, though unusually more tiring, than their more burdensome sisters. However, one cannot put a camper body on a Ferrari and expect to have a live-aboard sports car.

The cruising sailor wants to carry many months' food and water, extra fuel to make him independent of the substances he may be offered in a distant port, engine spare parts, three or four anchors plus a pile of chain and extra line, tools, perhaps some lumber for emergencies (surprisingly difficult to find in some parts), sail cloth, all the books he can accumulate, etc.

To carry all this without a whimper, his boat should have a displacement of 8,000 to 10,000 lbs. per person; less than 7,000 lbs. would mean some sacrifice and a lack of air space in the tropics, while 20,000 would push building and maintenance costs high and provide a handful for the crew to sail unless the boat were specifically rigged for the job.

Remember, too, that there is a considerable difference between a 25,000-lb. boat designed for 20,000 or less, and a 25,000 pounder intended for that displacement and having suitable proportions and ratios. Displacement is no excuse for poor performance.

While suggesting adequate displacement, we should not be too greatly influenced by the traditional workboats and many world cruisers of the past. The cruising man was often short of funds and bought the heavy cumbersome cruiser because it was older and cost less.

Heavy-timbered workboats have a beauty and fascination of their own, but they were intended for quite a different purpose and their very massiveness was often planned to withstand the rigors of being pinned between laden hulls in port rather than conditions at sea. With, of course, numerous exceptions, they were husky but unrefined in performance and balance, and the faulty impressions which came from them and from the earlier cruisers somehow perpetuated themselves and survive to some extent today.

To convert displacement to length we may use a displacement/length ratio of 360 to over 400, depending on type of construction, tankage required and so on, and since there seems to be considerable interest in boats of somewhat more than 40' in overall length, I am using as an example a 42 footer with a cruising displacement of about 32,000 lbs.

Displacements and measurements by themselves mean little. I recall a friend who used to boast that his girlfriend had the same displacement and leading dimensions as Marilyn Monroe. And no doubt she had, but one had only to see both of them under short canvas to realize that there had been some subtle rearrangement of prismatic and block coefficients.

The choice of coefficients for the underbody need not concern us here, but it should be mentioned that the long-distance cruiser is often shorthanded and seldom involves a large wardrobe of light sails. For this reason and because under power miles-per-gallon is much more important than miles-per-hour, it is unrealistic to provide a high prismatic giving best efficiency at the top of the boat's speed range. Better to have a hull shape that affords good performance over a wide range of speeds.

I suspect that the reverse sheer is the most efficient for a cruiser, providing as it does freeboard and space where it is most useful, in the shoulders rather than the bow. But, then, a female

TO FIND A HULL

weightlifter with a degree in economics would probably make the most efficient wife. Perhaps in some matters one must also let emotion rule and I choose the conventional sheer.

Bow shape offers considerable variety. The straight stem without flam or flare provides a truly comfortable motion, but to remain dry it needs too much freeboard and it provides a poor base for the sail plan. The long overhang is miserably wet, and the bluff bow is, of course, hard to drive to windward and causes a spastic motion in a head sea.

The bow with moderate and carefully matched overhang and flare offers us the best compromise.

In looking at the stern of an offshore cruising boat, think of it as a potential bow. When the weather gods have tired of watching you heave-to and insist on bare poles, it is the stern which must bear the brunt of the seas as you run with warps trailing.

Under such conditions I have seen a following wave strike the helmsman so hard that he bent the heavy bronze spindle of the steering wheel.

The possibility of such forces must be taken into account when considering the wide flat transom which affords maximum boat for the length. Almost as important is the considerable effect that the design of the stern has on the motion of the hull. The blending of these two factors thus contributes to the seakindliness which is a basic requirement.

The long counter and the very wide transom are the sterns which appeal to me least for deep sea work, the former for its slamming potential and the latter because it presents too broad a rump to an impetuous sea. The well tucked-up transom, however, is a good, inexpensive sea-going stern, especially on a boat under 30', but it does little towards easing the motion.

The double ender has gone to sea since the dawn of sail and is the ideal of many. It is simple and strong, and its outboard rudder is easily cared for where tiller steering is feasible. It is at its best in a short, steep following sea which no doubt explains why it is often used on workboats which must cross a bar when reentering port. The steeper run which it produces may disturb a following sea when the boat is running too fast, but this claim is hard to confirm.

This stern is, of course, a compromise as is everything which moves in the sea. The steeper run to the buttocks slightly reduces its upper speed limit and if too fine it may induce hobby-horsing and restrict cockpit space. I prefer the Norwegian to the "lifeboat" version, but either may increase weather helm.

My own choice for a sea-going after end is the canoe stern,

offering as it does a compromise between the seakeeping qualities of the double ender and the efficiency of the short counter. It produces a better run than the former and presents a better face to a following sea than the latter. Moreover, the canoe stern blends well with almost any bow and has good pitch-dampening potential. In wood it is difficult and expensive to build, but in glass it is simple.

Large beam is the attribute most often requested by cruising men. Beam gives not merely space and carrying capacity, but power to stand up to sail in a blow and an indefineable but real feeling of security when the wind is rising. Sailing on one's beam becomes tiring after a few weeks and complicates the routine chores below.

Here again we must control our appetite. The cruising hull does not lend itself to the more efficient wedge shape with its finer entry as readily as does the racing hull, and thus extreme beam brings with it a bluffer bow which takes more driving into a head sea and may cause a mutiny in the forecastle. Too much beam will usually lead to sluggishness in light and moderate airs and in larger boats it may cause too jerky a roll, although I consider this a much exaggerated danger.

In our example, because I considered 13' to be too great a beam for our standard of performance and handling, and 12' to be the minimum for adequate power, 12'8'' was chosen. As a rough guide for cruising boats in this size range, I believe that the ratio of waterline length to overall beam should lie between 2.65 and 2.85 unless there is a strong reason for doing otherwise.

Draft is very much a function of purpose. Too deep a draft will naturally restrict entrance to some of the quieter anchorages. In addition, it may give the boat too much grip on the water and she may be tripped and rolled by a large sea instead of giving a little to leeward. Adlard Coles in his excellent book, *Heavy Weather Sailing*, points out that, when a deck structure is damaged in heavy weather, it is often on the lee side because it has been rolled and hurled against an unyielding bank of water.

Deep draft, on the other hand, does promote steadiness on the helm and gives a boat the ability to tuck its head under its wing and heave to placidly, both absolutely vital attributes of the offshore cruiser.

Too little draft, apart from its effect on ultimate stability, is a serious detriment when you are battling off a lee shore. Remember that in a strong wind the surface water itself is moving quite rapidly to leeward — perhaps at one or two knots. The greater the penetration of the keel through that surface layer, the better the chance of

TO FIND A HULL

clawing off. This explains the particular disadvantage of a small boat under such conditions. For all these reasons I chose a moderate draft of 5'8''.

Distribution of draft is also important. The boat we are considering should have a length of keel close to half its LWL so that it can take the ground safely and promote steadiness and the ability to heave to.

Having considered our hull, how do we propel it? A cruising friend of mine dreamed of banks of comely females at the oars, but Women's Lib has put that power source out of reach and we must be content with a more prosaic rig. Whether the boat should have one mast or two is a question with no certain answer. We have a tendency to choose the rig which has served us well before. I have cruised many thousands of miles under cutter, ketch, and staysail schooner and I doff my hat to each. They will all serve well although I admit a slight personal prejudice towards the ketch rig.

Two masts in a 30 footer provide unnecessary complication though a lot of fun, and a sloop or cutter of 45' will be the upper limit for the average couple to handle. It is generally agreed that a mainsail of 400 to 600 square feet is as large as most couples can handle, depending on their strength and experience.

The cutter offers greater simplicity, lower initial cost, a less cluttered cockpit and increased windward efficiency.

The ketch offers a slight added safety factor if the masts are independently stayed. Smaller individual sails, great flexibility, the occasional convenience of being able to lope along under mizzen and headsails, and the oft referred to, but seldom used, mizzen staysail are the other usually cited advantages of the ketch rig.

I like the assistance in steering one can get from the mizzen and the convenient first reef that lowering the mizzen provides.

The ketch rig, per se, need not be as grossly inefficient as its foes claim. Several ocean racers manage to stagger along successfully under it. However, too often one sees a mizzen being stifled by a mainsail leech a few inches ahead of it. One gains a few extra square feet on paper, but the thrust per square foot is more important. Remember, too, that the average cruiser, frisking round the trade wind belts, will probably spend no more than five percent of its time close hauled. Safety and pleasure demand, however, that it be able to step out to windward when asked to do so.

I am, of course, assuming a marconi rig. It is more efficient with the wind forward of the beam, and it is simpler and cheaper. And yet, somewhere beneath the veneer of civilization, never mentioned without a penitential beating of the breast, I admit to a lingering addiction to the gaff.

If modern and properly proportioned the gaff rig does not fall far behind in efficiency for a cruising hull, and I suspect that for some hull shapes it might even prove superior. While I do not quite go so far as to recommend the gaff, I have to admire its air of elegance, and it is a strong and forgiving rig, easily repaired. It also has two considerable advantages: the mainsail can be lowered under almost any conditions; and the topsail (without which I would not consider the gaff rig) provides an excellent first reef that can be handled by one man without calling the watch below. The gaff rig does, however, have one great drawback, the lack of a permanent backstay.

We are not considering trade wind rigs in detail here, except to say that they form an essential part of the cruiser's wardrobe. On a trade wind passage, one piece of gear may rub on its neighbor 1500 times a day; and the trade wind rig, apart from its benefit to steering, may well pay for itself by eliminating chafe. The most common fault of such a rig is insufficient area, and at least two-thirds of the working sail area should be available in a passage rig.

The layout of the deck will depend in part on the layout below, but a few comments might be made on the center-cockpit arrangement which I happen to have chosen.

I followed three main guidelines. First, those parts of the boat which are used least should occupy the less comfortable sections of the boat. Second, a cruising boat, in keeping with the overriding consideration of simplicity, should be kept as open as possible, for those little cabins which look so snug on paper can be a curse in a warm climate. Third, I consider it the height of luxury to be able to sit in comfort within and gaze at the weather without or watch the activities of a new anchorage over breakfast. This means the boat must have some raised seating even though it entails some compromise.

These considerations become even more important with a center-cockpit. It is tempting to permit the aft cabin to become too spacious at the expense of the main living areas. A main salon with nothing but a dinette for seating does not allow the watch below to spread out, and a gam with a visiting crew resembles a sardine convention.

Accommodation, influenced by a host of minor considerations, must be as much of a compromise as the rest of the boat, for there is no single solution to the boat for distant waters.

A questionnaire sent to over 150 experienced deep-water cruising men some years ago did show a trend towards the ketch of moderate form; but it showed even more strongly a wide diversity of preferences in all aspects of the cruising boat and its gear. That is as it should be, for if you find that your dream ship is the same as she was a few years ago, better add a touch of Cuprinol to your grog — dry rot may be setting in.

THE IDEAL SMALL CRUISING SAILBOAT
by Herb David, Naval Architect

Over a long period of time I have spoken to a lot of people and potential boat owners always asking what their boat might look like and the desired features of their dream boat, making notes about the specifics and generalities. The compressed general characteristics of a close to ideal small offshore cruising sailboat were:

1) The boat should be trailerable! The prices for slips in the marinas and the long waiting lists to rent a slip are keeping many away.
2) The boat should be capable of riding out bad weather and be easily taken out single-handed. It should also be able to stay at sea for some time.
3) The boat should be reasonably priced; not everybody is able to pay fifty thousand for a boat.
4) It should be comfortable below deck, have full headroom, and allow a certain amount of privacy for the crew.
5) It should sail well under all weather conditions and have all basic safety and rescue devices on board.
6) The rig should be safe and simple to operate!

Taking the basic design parameters, the physical dimensions of the boat are immediately evident; length overall 28 foot, beam 8 foot (trailerable boats under 8 foot beam need no special permit on the road), draft 21 inches, draft centerboard down 5 foot 6 inches.

The next consideration is the rig. To make sail handling easy without leaving the cockpit all sails are to be furled. This rig allows extremely fine adjustment on all courses. The boat can sail with optimum balance because the center of effort for all sails can be changed at will and as weather conditions permit. Spinnakers require constant attention and a lot of work on the fore deck; therefore, the double jib has been devised. This sail is boomed out on two poles which attach to the mast. This sail which is actually one piece furls around the roller furler right in front of the mast. Such a functional sailplan requires an absolute minimum of work. A completely new approach is the furling mainsail, so reefing can be done in seconds without even leaving the cockpit.

All sheets and hauling parts from the furling drums run aft to both sides of the sliding hatch where specifically formed trough-shaped holes take all loose ends. From here even a man taking the boat out single-handed can reef and adjust sails in a snap.

The cockpit is almost seven feet long, self-bailing through an oversized cockpit drain which ends above the waterline. This system eliminates the back pressure which always occurs on the cockpit-drains that have a pipe system which exits elsewhere under water; this cockpit drains in seconds. The control panel for the engine is recessed so no clothing or sheet can tangle, and it can still be operated by foot. At the aft end of the cockpit is a six foot long track for the mainsheet-traveller mounted on a sill. A rather ingenious solution is the storage of the life raft. Its permanent location is aft, where it is ready and overboard in a matter of seconds.

The rudder is balanced which makes steering easier over long watches. The silent helmsman shown might not be everybody's cup of tea, but anyone who has gone to sea with one would not want to miss it. Self-steering over long distances is more than just a convenience.

Power is a 15 hp engine with a hydraulic drive system. An outboard engine might be used as alternate solution.

Considering the size of the boat, the interior features have a rather comfortable layout. Forward are two berths which can be made with a wedge shaped cushion in the middle into a large double-sized berth. To starboard is a hanging locker, to port a head with shower and self-contained toilet. The forward stateroom is separated by a door which allows privacy forward. On the port side of the salon is a raised dinette under which the centerboard trunk disappears. A hi-low table makes this dinette into a double berth. To starboard is the galley with sink and two-burner stove. Aft of the galley is the chart table. Navigation is easier and better done on its own table, rather than on coffee tables. The navigator sits facing forward on the quarter berth.

There is ample storage throughout the boat for every purpose and it would go beyond the space available in this article to describe everything.

Basically the boat is laid out for fiberglass construction. With slight modifications, the skilled amateur could also build the boat in plywood with multiple chines, or strip planked over laminated frames, or acquire hull and deck from the builder, several possibilities for owning the boat on a limited budget.

The Hull Form:

The perspective lines drawing reveals very elegant lines, forward are sharp waterlines for windward performance. The boat is practically a double ender under water, reducing resistance and wetted surface in the afterbody. The transom flares out above the waterline to add buoyancy aft and also to make room for a rather large cockpit.

A skeg which starts aft of the small keel will prevent crossflow and provide directional stability. The rudder is balanced which will make the helmsman's job a lot easier. In all, this hull will move without fuss through its element.

A fixed keel version is also planned, with a draft of 3 ft. 9 in.

TO FIND A HULL

DESCRIPTION OF SAIL PLANS (from left to right):

Downwind:
The double jib of 215 sq. ft. total is boomed out; these sails can be left unfurled in most weather conditions.

Light Weather:
With jib, staysail, and mainsail, the sail area totals 358 sq. ft. The main is 147, staysail 72, the jib measures 139 sq. ft.

The Wind Increased:
The jib is furled, the total sail area is now reduced to 215 sq. ft.

Storm:
With the jib already furled, the mainsail and staysail are furled to a total of about 100 sq. ft. and might be further reduced depending upon weather conditions.

TO FIND A HULL

INTERIOR DESCRIPTION BY NUMBERS
(Consists of Perspective, Plan View and Starboard Elevation)

1. Chain Locker, Self Draining
2. Shelves over Berths
3. Berths
4. Storage under Berths
5. Hanging Locker
6. Self-contained Toilet
7. Formica Countertop and Stainless Steel Sink (mirror above)
8. Door to Head
9. Door separates Salon from Forward Stateroom
10. Dinette Storage under
11. Dinette Hi-Lo Table
12. Galley with Sink and Stove, ample storage above and below Camper Refrigerator fits under countertop
13. Chart table top folds up for chart storage below
14. Quarter berth also seat for navigator
15. Especially formed step to allow safe footing when boat is heeled
16. Storage for bottles and glasses
17. 15 hp engine with hydraulic drive
18. Storage under hatches
19. Watertight compartment with overboard drain for gas bottle on starboard
20. Life Raft
21. Centerboard trunk is hidden by dinettes riser of 7 inches
22. Location and route of oversized cockpit drain

TO FIND A HULL 47

PACIFIC CUTTER

— HERB DAVID N.A. —

Specifications:

L O A	28' 0"
L W L	23' 0"
Beam	8' 0"
Draft	21"
Draft (Board down)	5' 6"
Sail Area	573 sq. ft.
Displacement	3800 lbs.
Ballast	1600 lbs.
Headroom	6' 2"

OVERALL DESCRIPTION BY NUMBERS
(Perspective Drawing of Boat Outside)

1. Self steering
2. Balanced rudder
3. Oversized cockpit drain
4. Tiller
5. Life Raft
6. Hatches to storage lockers
7. Recessed control panel for engine
8. Storage on port and starboard for winch handles and small gear
9. Rubrail
10. Sheet winches
11. Mainsheet track
12. Main sheet
13. Main boom aluminum sheet and reefing line run inside
14. Mainsail shown in furled up position
15. Sliding hatch with compass on top
16. Two part doors, upper part vented
17. Recess for loose ends of sheets
18. Recess for loose ends of roller furling lines
19. Mast, aluminum profile
20. Light winches for halyards
21. Mast tabernacle casting
22. Outrigger booms aluminum or wood
23. Staysail shown in furled position
24. Jib shown in furled position
25. Double jib shown in outrigged position
26. Staysail boom
27. Hatch with translucent top
28. Hatch for anchor and chain locker
29. Bow pulpit with bow roller
30. Outrigger boom in position on deck
31. Outrigger downhaul
32. Tinted windows with metal frame around strong enough to stand on
33. Non-skid cover on all walking areas
34. Hydro dynamic shaped centerboard
35. Skeg

DESIGN
IDEAS

Teak deck box.

Fine rigging ware.

TO FIND A HULL

DESIGN IDEAS

Ventilated teak door for refrigeration unit.

Intelligently designed shelf for trnsoceanic.

TO FIND A HULL

Fine stowage for boarding ladder.

Exposed, noise-free cooking stowage. Note wood pegs at tips of tools.

DESIGN IDEAS

Cast iron, solid-fuel burning stove.

Pretty looking, pretty leaking skylight.

Combination dorade-box and navigation-light mount.

Grates look nice anywhere.

Small cabinets are handy over chart table for fog horn, binoculars, flares, etc.

Netting around bowsprit keeps sails and crew out of the water.

Indestructible aluminum submarine hatch. Looks very pretty on trimasted U-boats.

Attractive and practical stowage.

Plexiglas case for stowage.

Flush-fitting pull-ring.

TO FIND A HULL

Space saving pulpit around bow-platform.

Traditionally a star brings good fortune.

TO FIND A HULL

CONSTRUCTION IDEAS

Pusher for large blocks on table saw.

A pretty but futile stanchion base.

Handsome dinghy chocks.

35-gallon/per minute manual bilge pump.

TO FIND A HULL

Vice-grip extension for bending teak decking.

Dove-tailed hatch.

Prefabricated, painted, and wire interior.

Prefabricated, painted, and wired interior with foamed icebox.

CONSTRUCTION IDEAS

Hand layup.

Squeeging resin.

TO FIND A HULL

A stanchion that may hold.

Reaching-pole deck chocks.

TO FIND A HULL

CONSTRUCTION IDEAS

Access plate and cover for chainplate bolts.

Router bits.

Anchor chocks.

TO FIND A HULL

Chapter Three
THE BOATS

This chapter is a list of sailboats built in Canada and the United States available in different stages of completion. I apologize to builders whom I was unable to track down.

THE BOATS

BUTLER 10

E.R. BUTLER & SONS
25 Mugford St., Marblehead, Massachusetts

Specifications:

Bow and Stern .... ½" plywood
Sides and Bottoms .... ¼" plywood
Keels and Chines .... ¾" oak
Fasteners .... Brass Screws
Sealant .... Rubber Base
Length .... 9'10"
Beam .... 50 inches
Weight .... 90 lbs.
Shipping Weight .... 110 lbs.

Builders Comments:

These boats have been built many times by many people with little or no experience at boat building, but with a desire to have a boat of their own. Construction can be as short as two weekends with a few evenings in between. You will need a space at least 11' long by 7' wide for the 8' pram, two feet longer for the 9'10"; a one-car garage is a good space. You can build it completely with hand tools but an electric drill is a great time saver.

We are sure you will enjoy making and using your Butler Pram. However, if for any reason or no reason at all you are not satisfied with the kit after you have seen it and read the simple, easy to follow directions, you may ship it back within ten days and we will immediately refund every cent you have sent us. So there is no risk on your part.

Authors Comments:

The queen of the show. A beautiful little sailing dinghy with fantastic ideas. A spruce mast, stainless steel rigging, copper tipped oars and leather oar handles. The company also sells you sail conversion kit for your own dinghy, as well as oar locks, gudgeons and pintles and other wonderful little gadgets, and best of all the irreplaceable Fuller tapered drill bits and counter sinks. If you can resist buying at least something from them you have a cold, cold heart.

THE BOATS

CHINOOK 37

CHINOOK YACHTS
3260 Edgemont Blvd., Suite 1, N. Vancouver, B.C., Canada
Designed by S.C. Huntingford

Specifications:

Length	37'
Length Waterline	31'11''
Beam	11'8''
Fuel	68 gal.
Draft	5 ft.
Displacement	18,500 lbs.
Ballast (keel)	8,000 lbs.
Water	76 gal.
Ballast Displacement:	
Ratio	42%
Power	77 hp
Construction	G.R.P.

Builder's Comments:

Construction: Hull and deck of hand laminated reinforced fiberglass with Airex foam core. Colors and non-skid surfaces are moulded in. Large self bailing cockpit with stowage under seat hatches, transom door and swim grid. Moulded lockers for propane vented overboard. The pilot house is fully enclosed.

Author's Comments:

Chinook 37 — a very pleasant looking heavy displacement motor sailer, one of the very few that are available in various stages of completion. The underbody is designed with cruising in mind, having a well protected rudder and well protected propeller. The pilot house is pleasing on what looks like a rugged boat. It is a true motor sailer with a 77 horsepower Ford diesel and a giant 21'' propeller. If you are looking for a motor sailer that you can finish yourself, this may be the best thing that you can find.

THE BOATS

DREADNOUGHT 32
"Tahiti Ketch"

DREADNOUGHT BOATWORKS
P.O. Box 221, Carpinteria, California 93013

Specifications:

Length ....32'
Waterline ....28'2"
Beam ....10'
Draft ....4'9"
Displacement ....19,500 lbs.
Ballast ....6,500 lbs.
Sail Area ....550 sq. ft.

Builder's Comments:

Hand laminated in *one* piece by means of a transverse rolling mold rather than the commonly used split molds, giving a strong hull.

Balsa core running the length of the hull from just above the ballast to within 8" of the rail.

Balsa core construction on all flat surfaces of deck.

Removable cockpit for easy engine access.

Flange facing inboard at 90° running fore and aft of hull to allow easy attachment of cap rail, stanchions, and any track or fairleads.

Author's Comments:

Dreadnought 32 — Fiberglass version of the dreadfully slow Tahiti ketch that is advertised to be a faster model. It is excellently constructed with foam core and thick fiberglass hand layups. The deck design has been sadly neglected for what could have been a spacious little boat becomes claustrophobic because the cabin was made too short and too narrow. It is available at any stage of completion and the company in Southern California will custom build the interior for you.

THE BOATS

DURBECK'S D-38
WATER KIT CUTTER or KETCH

DURBECK'S, INC.
4504 28th St. West, Bradenton, Florida 33505

Specifications:

LOA ....41'
LWL ....29'10''
LOD ....37'7''
Beam ....11'4''
Draft ....5'0''
Displacement ....19,200 lbs.
Approximate Tankage:
  Fuel ....50 gal.
  Water ....100 gal.

Builder's Comments:

Hull — Hand layup of mat and roving ½'' at the sheer and increasing to 1'' thick at the keel, with extra reinforcing in structurally critical areas. Standard color is white.

Deck — Hand layup of mat and roving with high density foam (Glasspak) sandwich construction. Molded in non-skid.

Chain Plate Areas — Hull reinforced with additional glass. Locations of chain plates marked on hull.

Ballast — 7,000 lbs. lead, inside hull, glassed over.

Fuel System — Fill and vent on one tank only, with filter, water separator, packless valves. Suction and return lines of 3/8'' copper tubing, temporarily installed to run engines.

Bulkheads — Four (4) plywood bulkheads structurally taped to hull.

Tanks — Fiberglass: 50 gals. fuel, 100 gals. water.

Author's Comments:

Durbeck 38 — An intelligently laid out cruising boat with a long keel, an aft hung rudder and very pleasing lines. It has three very good sea berths, regular size chart table and a settee as main features; and a very well thought out location for heating stove.

THE BOATS

DURBECK D-46
DURBECK'S, INC.
4504 28th St. West, Bradenton, Florida 33505

Specifications:

LOA . . . . 46'9'' (14.19m)
LWL . . . . 35'2''
Beam . . . . 13'8'' (4.16m)
Draft . . . . 4'11''
Sail Area . . . . 1,270 sq. ft.
Ballast . . . . 12,000 lbs. lead & filler
Displacement . . . . 35,000 lbs.
Berths . . . . six
W/Genoa . . . . 117.99 sq. ft.
Main . . . . 351 sq. ft.
Fore Staysail . . . . 204 sq. ft.
Jib Topsail . . . . 292 sq. ft.
Genoa . . . . 535 sq. ft.
Mizzen . . . . 180 sq. ft.
Hull . . . . Hand layup-fiberglass
Headroom . . . . Full throughout
Auxiliary . . . . 60 hp/diesel

Builder's Comments:

A strong hull of hand laid up fiberglass ½'' thick above the waterline and over 1'' thick below the waterline.

A low deck profile that gives added safety in storms encountered during a passage.

A moderate size cockpit located for comfort & safety.

A non-skid deck uncluttered for simplicity of handling.

A full keel with an exceptional amount of ballast.

A moderate draft that enables yachtsmen to enjoy most harbors & cruising areas.

A wide beam that adds to comfort and accommodations below deck.

Author's Comments:

Durbeck 46 — A more cumbersome design with a disorganized main salon. It does have a seemingly perfect galley even though the sink is nowhere near the center line. The engine really does have a room of its own. The company does provide facilities for kit builders as well as providing any amount of factory help that they require after they have taken delivery of the boat.

THE BOATS 77

THE BOATS

HAIDA MK II

PHILLBROOKS SHIPYARD
RR 2, 2234 Harbour Road, Sidney, B.C., Canada

Specifications:

LOA . . . . .25'9"
LWL . . . . .21'
Beam . . . . .8'3"
Ballast (+ -) . . . . .1,800 lbs.
Displacement (+ -) . . . . .4,300 lbs.
Sail Area . . . . .300 sq. ft. (working)

Builder's Comments:

Hull-Deck Construction: Hull of one-piece seamless (FRP) fiberglass construction with color molded in — FRP longitudinal & transverse framing. Teak bulkheads bolted to fiberglass webs — moulded fiberglass hatches . . . all through hull fittings fitted with sea valves . . . deck — FRP with ½" balsa core sandwich construction, non-skid surface molded in . . . entire assembly bolted to the hull flange . . . two cockpit seat lockers . . . large seat drains . . . outboard well in lazarette . . . large cockpit scuppers . . . all exterior & interior trim in Burma teak.

Cockpit: Self-draining, outsize seat lockers, motor well completely enclosed.

Rudder: Deep balanced, advanced design foil form completely outboard for maximum control.

Keel: Iron alloy, hydrodynamically designed foil form, faired into hull. No protruding flange.

Rig: Unique offset masthead design allowing flexibility for draft control. A proven design used on ocean racers. Main sheet arrangement with boom design to allow vertical deflection. Ultimate in convenience for solo or crew sailing.

Author's Comments:

Haida Mark II — A rather mundane exterior of a little cruising racer. I include it here because the engine-galley layout intrigues me, even though you must step into the souffle to gain access to the main cabin. Here you will find 6' headroom and lots of elbow space for a 26' boat. The boat is ideal for local cruising.

THE BOATS

INGRID 38

BLUEWATER BOATS INC.
21920 75th Ave. S.E., Woodinville, Washington 98072

Specifications:

Length on Deck ....37'8"
  (most Ingrids have a bowsprit, bringing the overall length, with
  rudder, to about 48')
Length at Waterline ....32'0"
Beam ....11'4"
Draft ....5'8"
Ketch ....(some Ingrids have been built as cutters.
  The sail area is similar on both versions, and is a matter of
  personal preference.)
True Sail Area ....887 sq. ft. (Genoa not included)
Ketch (Mast Height) ....49'6" on the main mast,
               33'10" on the mizzen. Some Ingrids have shorter masts (43')
               and shorter bowsprits of 5' rather than 8'
Bluewater Boats bring together a six-inch surface on both the hull
and deck. This is through-bolted so that cap rails, bedded in
compound, can be added. Bluewater Boats considers this the most
leak-resistant joint available in glass boats today.

Builder's Comments:

Lay-up: 1½ oz. mat throughout, 7 oz. cloth topsides, 7 layers 24
oz. woven roving throughout . . . double over bottom and center line
of hull. Two extra layers of roving laid waterline and below. 6 extra
layers down stem and stern. Resin-glass ratio held between 50% to
53% overall.

Bulkheads: 1" thick royal marine fir plywood glassed to hull
with 1 mat, 3 layers roving — 12" wide. Bulkheads are held off hull
sides to prevent "hard spots." We recommend a minimum of two
bulkheads, located under mast steps prior to shipping.

Ballast: 6,000 lbs. steel punchings, 2,000 lbs. cement grout
total 8,000 lbs. Poured in keel from bobstay iron position to stern.
Bilge pump located under mizzen mast position.

Author's Comments:

Ingrid 38 — The classic William Atkin design is reproduced and
combined with a very fine craftsmanship. The hull is all hand laid
up, the ballast is nicely spread, providing even comfortable motion.
The deck is thru-bolted onto the hull. All interior finishing is left up
to the owner, but three bulkheads can be installed at the factory.
With its ketch rig, it is some romanticists dream.

LUGER 21' WINDWARD
SEA-WORTHY SLOOP

LUGER INDUSTRIES
3800 W. Highway 13, Burnsville, Minnesota 55337

Specifications:

Length, Gunwale .... 21'0''
Length, Waterline .... 17'6''
Width, Beam (max) .... 84''
Draft .... with centerboard up 12'', down 61'',
with swing keel up 22'', down 61''

THE BOATS

Headroom, in cabin . . . . .51''
Ballast . . . . .with #1489 Centerboard, 240 lbs. (inside)
Hull with #1495 Swing Keel, none
Displacement (weight) . . . . .with Centerboard or Swing Keel
approx. 1,550 lbs. when ballasted as above
Mast Length . . . . .24'6''
Assembly Time . . . . .60 to 85 hrs.
Internal Hull Reinforcing . . . . .Pre-cut fir plywood, solid oak
Fasteners . . . . .All screws, bolts, etc. stainless steel or brass
Thickness of Molded Fiberglass Sections . . . . . .Varies from approx.
3/16'' to approx. 3/8'' as required for strength and sound design
Mast and Boom . . . . . .Anodized aluminum. Boom has roller reefing
Standing Rigging . . . . .Stainless Steel
Hardware . . . . . .Pulleys, bow eye for trailering, stay adjusters, etc.
stainless steel, brass or aluminum
Auxiliary Power . . . . . .Recommend 1½ to 10 hp outboard mounted
on Luger Hi-Lo Motor #10102

Builder's Comments:

Windward's light displacement hull design has considerable beam width in lower sections. This provides a more spacious cabin, more buoyancy and better self-righting characteristics. Hull will automatically right itself if knocked down flat with mast in water. Cockpit is self-bailing and a knowdown cannot flood hull. Windward is ideal for day sailing, points well into the wind and has a "weathering" helm.

Luger's Windward is available (see accessories) with either a ballasted Swing Keel or a retracting Centerboard. The Centerboard and the Swing Keel enable shallow water operation, beaching, trailering and they ride up and over underwater obstructions.

The optional Centerboard retracts fully into hull and thus requires the least water depth when loading and launching from trailer. Centerboard requires a centerboard enclosure inside cabin and uses ballast inside of hull for stability.

The optional Swing Keel retracts under outside of hull for beaching and trailer transporting. Swing Keel requires no enclosure inside hull and has sufficient weight to eliminate use of ballast inside hull. Boat sails well with Swing Keel in raised position.

Author's Comments:

Luger 21 — This little boat looks so simple, practical and so easy to build, (the builder says 60 hours), that I just have to include it. It is also trailerable and it comes with all kits.

GH 31

Scale

0   3   6
        ft.

THE BOATS

GOLDEN HIND 31

TERRY ERSKINE YACHTS
Newport Street, Stonehouse, Plymouth, Devon, England
Designed by Maurice Griffiths, G.M.

Specifications:

LOA .... 31'6"
LWL .... 26'9"
Beam .... 9'0"
Draft .... 3'7"
Headroom .... 6'3"
Working Sail Area .... 370 sq. ft.
Water .... 20 gallons
Fuel .... 20 gallons
Displacement .... 11,600 lbs.
Ballast Keel .... 4,100 lb.s

Builder's Comments:

Construction (all wood version): of double chine construction. For strength and long life only the finest prime hardwoods are used in construction, Burma teak, Keruing and Iroko of the Malayan Teak, Sapele and Utile from Africa planking and decks are of marine plywoods to British Standard 1088.

Construction (glassfibre and wood version): Hulls are a hand laid moulding, to lay-up specifications of Maurice Griffiths. The standard 4,100 pound cast iron keel is moulded internally. The standard hot dipped galvanized steel plate bilge keels will be bolted externally (for extended deep water cruising the bilge keels may be left off). Stiffening —polyurethane foam scantlings are glassed in longitudinally, timber keel floors are bolted to the ballast keel and glassed to hull, backing bilge keel stringers are of solid timber and glassed in for 16 ft. internally.

The standard timber Golden Hind has been proved for performance in all the oceans of the world over the past twelve years and the aim was to produce the mould so that G.R.P. hulls look identical to the standard boat and the designed lines were kept. Decks and coach roof are constructed all in timber, with solid mahogany cabin sides, laminated coach roof beams, hardwood fore deck, stern deck and side deck beams, planked with marine plywood. The whole deck and coach roof then sheathed in 6 oz. scrim with the Epoxy Resin process.

MAIN - 225'

MAIN & JIB
410'

WORK JIB 185'

THE BOATS

RAWSON 30

R. RAWSON INC.
15014 N.E. 90th Street, Redmond, Washington 98052
BEAVER GLASS HULLS LTD.
1242 Bridgeport Road, Richmond, B.C., Canada

Specifications:

Length (hull) ....30'6''
Length (waterline) ....22'
Beam ....9'
Draft ....5'
Headroom ....6'3''
Displacement ....12,000 lbs.
Ballast ....5,000 lbs.
Sail Area (working) ....410 sq. ft.
Fuel ....37 gal.
Water ....40 gal.
Power ....gas or diesel
Designer ....Wm. Garden

Builder's Comments:

Sixteen various kits are available.

Limited blueprints are available.

Rawson, Inc. was founded in 1959 with 8 orders for pre-sold Rawson 30's. We also manufacture commercial and pleasure boats from 32' to 48', designed by Edwin Monk & Son.

Rawson, Inc. is always willing to assist the buyer of our kit boats during its backyard construction.

Author's Comments:

Rawson 30 — A very inexpensive, functional little cruiser. The cockpit is much too large and the galley location is intrusive, but the price is very right. Several of the boats have taken very long, trouble-free cruises. The design is by Edwin Monk and Son. Limited blueprints are available through the company, but factory help and advise is unlimited. Sixteen different stages of kits are offered.

THE BOATS

RELIANCE 44

RELIANCE SAILING CRAFT
P.O. Box 693, St. Laurent (Montreal), P.Q., Canada
Designed by Pierre Meumer

Specifications:

LOA . . . . .44'4''
LWL . . . . .31'5''
Beam . . . . .11'8''
Draft . . . . .6'2''
Displacement . . . . .28,000 lbs.
Ballast . . . . .11,200 lbs.
Sail Area . . . . .905 sq. ft.
Prismatic Coefficient 53

Builder's Comments:

In order to obtain more strength, and keeping the ratio of fibers as high as possible, (up to 45%) no chopper gun is used in our shop. All glass work is hand laid, under strict supervision, and is carried out in a mold shop where temperature and humidity are controlled year round for best possible results.

To obtain high impact strength, rigidity, stiffness, thermal and sound insulation, a full 1'' Balsa core is used in the hull, deck and deckhouse, and provides the best sandwich type construction available today. (Balsa core is approved by Lloyd's.)

The glass laminate is generous and was designed to provide a sailing vessel intended for extended ocean passages.

Author's Comments:

Reliance 44 — A fast, long keeled cruising boat with a well thought out interior and spacious decks. The ballast is all lead. Its location leaves ample room deep in the keel for fuel tanks. It has an owner's cabin with a very thoughtful private companionway directly next to the cockpit. In the owner's cabin are two beautiful sea berths. The galley is ideally laid out, but it does possess a laughable monster of a refrigerator proposed on the drawings. Take a long extension cord. The hull and deck are reasonably priced at $15,000.

SCHEEL 45 DECK HOUSE SLOOP

Box 776, Rockland, Maine 04841

Specifications:

LOA . . . . .45'
LWL . . . . .39'3''
Beam . . . . .13'6''
Draft . . . . .4'8'' Board up;
Board down 8'8'' (6'6'' Keel version)
Sail Area . . . . .900 sq. ft.
Displacement . . . . .About 30,000 lbs.

Builder's Comments:

The Scheel 45 has been especially designed as a spacious, fast cruising yacht, that can be handled easily by a small crew, providing very comfortable cruising and living aboard for extended periods.

Structure: Hull and deck are hand laid-up fiberglass, both mat and woven roving. Deck anti-skid pattern is permanent in nature and can be renewed or extended. Deck to hull connection is through bolted, and set in epoxy resin.

Joinerwork: All strength and joiner bulkheads are marine grade plywood, sheathed in high pressure laminate.

Engine and Propulsion: Lehman Ford diesel of 80 hp. The engine drives a 1½'' diameter shaft through a cutless bearing in the strut. The exhaust riser is water-jacketed and hung on vibration mounts. A shaft lock is installed, providing easy locking for the shaft when sailing.

Steering: Pedestal steering with a 5'' Constellation compass uses chain and sprocket, and wire aft to a quadrant. An emergency tiller steering is provided.

Tankage: Four tanks are installed, two for fuel, 70 gallons each (total 140 gallons), and two for water, 125 gallons each (total 250 gallons) are baffled and vented and have proper shut-offs. Deck plates are clearly marked and grouped.

Ship's Equipment: Handling gear supplied: 2-50' 5/8'' dia. dacron dock lines; 2-35' 5/8'' dia. dacron dock lines; 4-pneumatic fenders and lines; 1-20# H.T. Danforth anchor with stowage; 1-35# CQR anchor; 1-150' 5/8'' nylon rode with 8' 3/8'' chain and shackle for anchor; 1-250' 5/8'' nylon rode with 12' 3/8'' chain and shackle for anchor; 8 approved life jackets; 3-10# dry-chemical fire extinguishers; 10 anchor bell; 1 freon horn; 1 mouth operated horn; 1 set emergency flares; 1 appropriate medical kit; Ensign and staff.

Author's Comments:

Scheel 45 appears to be a very thoughtfully constructed yacht with a provocative little aft cockpit. From it there is a private entrance to the aft stateroom. This extravaganza still leaves vast areas of well utilized space and what designers call "elbow room aplenty."

The main salon on it is traditionally sensible. The navigation station is superbly thought out and the work bench in the passageway is excellent as any cruiser will testify. The aft cabin has its own bathtub and even the electrical panel has its own room. Too bad they can't figure out how to build all this into a handsome 32 footer.

THE BOATS

ENDURANCE 35

WINDBOATS MARINE
Wroxham, Norwich, Norfolk NR12 8RX, England
Designed by Peter Ibold

Specifications:

LOA	39'0"	11.9m
LOA (hull only)	35'4"	10.8m
LWL	26'8"	8.1m
Beam	11'0"	3.3m
Draft	5'4"	1.6m
Displacement	20,600 lbs.	10,500 kg
Ballast	6,200 lbs.	3,150 kg

Builder's Comments:

Seacrete Hull: Hull shell, keel, engine mounting points and mast steps are all one integral unit in SEACRETE high quality marine grade ferro cement, built to LLOYDS approved scantlings and production technique. A ferro cement beam shelf is standard for those 35's fitted with g.r.p. deck, cockpit and superstructure units. It is also an option for 35's built with timber decks.

Deck, Cockpit, Deckhouses: EITHER a custom built g.r.p. one-piece moulding for decks, deckhouse and cockpit, incorporating non-slip finish for the decks, cockpit sole and coachroof top. The moulding is generally the same shape as the timber superstructure OR traditional timber superstructure (deck beams, deckhouse, coachroof, cockpit) and plywood decks, sheathed with teak planking. (Optional extra).

Rudder: Steel spline and flange plates, laminated plywood cheek plates whole assembly glass fibre sheathed. Stock and heel bearing stainless steel.

Twin fuel tanks, outboard of engine, total capacity 410 litres (90 imperial gallons). Mild steel with inspection ports and baffles.

94   **THE BOATS**

ENDURANCE 40

WINDBOATS MARINE
Wroxham, Norwich, Norfolk NR12 8RX, England
Designed by P.A. Ibold

Specifications:
Schooner Sail List

Main	318 sq. ft.	29.54 sq. m.
Fisherman	423 sq. ft.	39.31 sq. m.
Boom Staysail	112 sq. ft.	10.41 sq. m.
Genoa Staysail	256 sq. ft.	23.79 sq. m.
Boom Foresail	108 sq. ft.	10.03 sq. m.
Jib	261 sq. ft.	24.24 sq. m.
Genoa	434 sq. ft.	40.32 sq. m.

Builder's Comments:

SEACRETE Ferro-cement hull built under Lloyds survey. Iroko sole bearers. Fixed portlights, toughened glass in stainless steel frames. Aluminum alloy masts and spars, gold anodised and sound deadened. Coachroof 15 mm plywood (BSS 1088) glass fibre sheathed. 40 mm stainless steel rudder stock. 40 mm stainless steel shaft in bronze stern tube with water lubricated cutless bearings. Teak cap rail. Teak seats in cockpit with lockers underneath. Teak coaming and grating. Diesel burning Perkins Gallipak, supplying cooking pressurized hot water and central heating.

Sole: Laid teak or parquet style.

Head: Formica lined throughout, with prismatic deck lights over.

Windboats Marine Limited are the acknowledged world leaders in ferro-cement construction, and in nearly 20 years they have built around 600 SEACRETE hulls. An ever increasing number of cruising enthusiasts now specify ferro, with its tremendous structural strength, minimal maintenance costs and quick, simple repair procedure. Over three quarters of our hull production is purchased by customers who wish to do all or part of the fitting out work themselves. With all the materials, fittings and equipment required to completion an Endurance hull can be purchased for approximately half the Windboats Marine list price for the completed yacht.

SOVEREL 41

SOVEREL MARINE
2225 Idlewilde Road, North Palm Beach, Florida 33408

Specifications:

LOA . . . . 41'3''
LWL . . . . .34'
Beam . . . . .11'
Draft . . . . .Centerboard Up 4'
Centerboard Down 10'
Displacement . . . . .18,000 lbs.
Lead Ballast . . . . .7,000 lbs. Cast Material
Rated Sail Area, Mainsail . . . . .1,000 sq. ft.
160% fore triangle
Headroom — Main Cabin . . . . .6'5''
Mast Height Above Water . . . . .55'
Sleeps . . . . .7 berths

Builder's Comments:

Hand lay-up fiberglass; hull 10 ply; cabin and deck, 7 ply, with balsa core on horizontal surfaces; molded non-skid deck patterns; six deck scuppers.

Spade rubber of molded fiberglass with 2'' SS Shaft; 2'' rudder stuffing box and bearing; top bearing and deck plate for emergency steering connection.

Molded fiberglass centerboard filled with lead and resin. The deck is fiberglassed to hull with 4-ply tapes the entire length of joint. This hull deck joint is filled with fibrous resin putty. A teak sheer strake is covered with teak cap the entire length to give hull protection and a handsome toe rail.

All structural members, bulkheads, berths, floor timbers, floors & tanks are molded fiberglass bonded to the hull with fiberglass tapes. Exposed surfaces are either gelcoat or wood grain formica.

Inside of hull is ribbed and then covered with teak panelling throughout cabin spaces.

Molded fiberglass headliner with a soft finish throughout the interior.

Engine: Rubber mounted on fiberglass engine mounts. Universal Atomic Four with 2:1 reduction and alternator is standard.

Author's Comments:

Soverel 41 — A giant step forward from the 37 in that it has a fine chart table and an invaluable quarter berth. It seems you can do miracles if you cut your cockpit from 8'6'' to 6'6'' even though you still can't afford to put the skeg back on the rudder.

98   **THE BOATS**

SOVEREL 48 KETCH

SOVEREL MARINE
2225 Idlewilde Road, North Palm Beach, Florida 33408

Specifications:

Length . . . . .48'
Beam . . . . .13'
LWL . . . . .40'
Displacement . . . . .28,000 lbs.
Draft . . . . .5' Bd. Up
Ballast . . . . .8,500 bls. lead, plus 450 gal. fuel/water

Builder's Comments:

With the new ketch we wanted the smallest hull of the shoal draft, keel/centerboard type Soverel Marine has been building but still large enough to accommodate an aft cabin with a full headroom passageway between the aft and main cabins. With our type of shoal draft hull it takes 48 feet if you want to preserve a pleasing profile. The main cabin was to be large enough so that entrance from the companionway would be into the galley and navigation area, not directly into the main salon itself.

The engine room would be a showplace with full headroom, encompassing a floor, an opening port, a hatch to the cockpit, with a workbench and spare parts stowage. Soundproofed, with forced air ventilation, it would appeal to the experienced yachtsman, with its well planned layout, accessibility of main and auxiliary engines and accessories, fuse and circuit breaker panels. A powerful engine would drive the Soverel 48 at hull speed, economically.

Author's Comments:

Soverel 48 — The Soverel Company supplies building plans. There is also unlimited access to factory to observe and gain advice. They also sell all parts needed to complete the boats, i.e. engines, spars, parts, hardware, lumber, etc. at cost plus 10% for handling fee. They project the final completion cost to be $16,000 for the 30' Soverel, $25,000 for the 37' Soverel, and $37,000 for the 41' Soverel. The Soverel 48 is a veritable floating grand hotel.

THE BOATS

SPENCER 31

PHILLBROOKS SHIPYARD
RR 2, 2324 Harbour Road, Sidney, B.C.
Designed by J. Brandlmayr

Specifications:

LOA ....31'
DWL ....23'
Beam ....9'2"
Draft ....4'9"
Displacement ....9,000 lbs.
Ballast ....3,000 lbs.
Sail Area ....440 sq. ft.
Headroom ....6'2"

Kits Available:

Hull only of fiberglass, no rudder.

Hull of fiberglass, two bulkheads and cross bracing, rudder, lead ballast in place, fuel and water tanks molded in.

Deck mounted in place on hull, main bulkheads and floor molded in cabin.

Sloop to include: interior joinerwork complete in mahogany, rough electric wiring, std. windows, mast step, bow plate, chainplates, thru hull fittings, with gate valves, headliner, tiller, molded hatch covers but not including painting, interior installations, bottom painted, tow rail and feature strip painted.

Sloop, as in stage above including interior painted, mahogany varnished, interior installations complete with toilet(s), basin(s), s/s sink and pump in galley, 3 burner stove with oven (gimbaled), carpet or lino, stainless steel standing rigging with bronze turnbuckles, metal spar, boom, interior and running lights, deck hardware, mattresses.

Engine: Universal Atomic Four.

Author's Comments:

Spencer 31 — The smaller less "off shorish" Spencer, with an unsupported galley and cutaway keel. It does have two nice quarter berths but it seems to lack the heart-grabbing romantic quality of the Ingrid 38 or Westsail 32.

SPENCER 35

PHILLBROOKS SHIPYARD
RR 2, 2324 Harbor Road, Sidney, B.C.
Designed by J. Brandlmyr

Specifications:

LOA . . . . .35'
DWL . . . . .25'
Beam (exterior) . . . . .9'6''
Draft . . . . .5'3''
Displacement . . . . .11,414 lbs.
Lead Ballast . . . . .4,000 lbs.
Sail Area . . . . .522 sq. ft.
Headroom . . . . .6'7'', 6'2''

Kits Available:

Hull only of fiberglass, no rudder.

Hull of fiberglass, two bulkheads and cross bracing, rudder, lead ballast in place, fuel and water tanks molded in.

Deck molded in place on hull, main bulkheads and floor molded in cabin.

Sloop to include: interior joinerwork complete in mahogany, rough electric wiring, std. windows, mast step, bow plate, chainplates, thru hull fittings, with gate valves, headliner, tiller, molded hatch covers but not including painting, interior installations, bottom painted, tow rail and feature strip painted.

Sloop, as above including interior painted, mahogany varnished, interior installations complete with toilet(s), hand basin(s), s/s sink and pump in galley, 3 burner stove with oven (gimbaled), carpet or lino, stainless steel standing rigging with bronze turnbuckles, metal spar, boom, interior and running lights, deck hardware, mattresses.

Engine: Universal Atomic Four.

Author's Comments:

Spencer 35 — The Roth's now famous "Whisper" is one of these. It is a totally practical, fast cruising boat, regretfully lacking a chart table. Sloop rig is standard although cutter conversion is possible. The cockpit, again, is a little too large, but it does have a nice quarter berth.

VERITY 30

9775 Fourth Street, #306, Sidney, B.C.
Designed by S.I. Vaguolgyi

Specifications:

LOA . . . . .30'6''
LWL . . . . .26'6''
Beam . . . . .10'3''
Draft . . . . .4'9''
Displacement . . . . .8,000 lbs.
Engine . . . . .4 cyl. Westerbeke

Builder's Comments:

The designer says that "since boats, like beef, are sold by the pound, every effort was made to keep the displacement light. Complimenting this, the whole structural concept was carefully re-examined. Substantial material savings were made through improved engineering and technology. Structurally, the hull and deck shells are designed to Lloyds FRP Yacht Construction standards. The prototype is a one-off FRP sandwich boat; the structure uses both uni- and bi-directional glass reinforcement. Core materials are edge grain balsa and PVC foam."

Author's Comments:

Verity 30 — Now I have seen everything. A 30' aft cabin sloop. Above the waterline the resemblance to a Maserati is undeniable but its underbody is very fine and should provide good tracking characteristics. The standard engine is a Perkins 4-107 which you may think large for a boat of this size, but with the given amount of windage you will probably need it. I still cannot figure out how he got all that accommodation into a 30' hull. He must have studied with a flea circus.

THE BOATS

WESTSAIL 32

WESTSAIL CORPORATION
275 McCormick Ave., P.O. Box 126, Costa Mesa, California 92627
Phone (714) 549-9711
Designed by Colin Archer and W.I.B. Crealock

Specifications:

Length ....32'
Waterline ....27½'
Beam ....11'
Draft ....5'
Displacement ....19,500 lbs.
Ballast ....7,000 lbs.
Sail Area, 100% Fore Triangle ....663 sq. ft.

Builder's Comments:

Joiner Work: All exterior joiner work is teak or suitable hardwood. Corners are rounded to prevent injury to crew. Interior joiner work is teak and mahogany or suitable hardwood.

Fiberglass: Material is of first quality throughout, with polyester resin applied in accordance with manufacturer's recommendations under controlled conditions. The hull laminate consists of a coat of gelcoat, followed by twelve layers of fiberglass material totalling a minimum of 9½ oz. per sq. ft. of fiberglass mat and 120 oz. per sq. ft. of fiberglass woven roving.

Author's Comments:

Westsail 32 — A rather obese Colin Archer design which seems to have instant appeal to every romanticist and every sailor in the world. The blunt bow makes it somewhat less than an ocean racer, but the construction is unquestionable, the interior design reflects the thought that has evolved through a hundred years of experimenting. An enormous chart table and a very sufficient salon, a good pilot berth and an engine room where you can actually move around the engine are the highlights. There have been over 450 of these built to date.

Westsail Comments in General — The factory is steadily expanding its partially completed boat line and has so far sold over 200 partially completed boats as well as 200 complete boats. They will build you a boat anywhere from a bare hull to a complete boat and they have a 400-page construction manual available to back you up for both their products. If you need help, there is a full-time Custom Boat Consultant on duty and an unlimited supply of parts including every last fitting. They also have a walk-in factory store. If it's quality, help and service that you want, the Westsails should be thoughtfully considered.

440

230

176

WESTSAIL 42

WESTSAIL CORPORATION
275 McCormick Ave., P.O. Box 126, Costa Mesa, California 92627
Phone (714) 549-9711
Designed by W.I.B. Crealock

Specifications:
Length . . . . .42'11"
Waterline . . . . .33'4"
Beam . . . . .13'
Draft . . . . .5'8"
Displacement . . . . .31,500 lbs.
Ballast . . . . .11,000 lbs.
Sail Area, 100% fore triangle:
Cutter . . . . .968 sq. ft.
Ketch . . . . .990 sq. ft.

Builder's Comments:
The double ended full length keel sailboat is a seakindly hull form that has a well balanced helm, and is easy for one person to sail. The outboard rudder is a natural for self-steering when the captain wishes some time off. The hull is deep enough for all internal ballast that is bonded in place forever.

Construction of the Westsail hull, as shown in the diagram, is enormously rugged; it is ½" at the rail, ¾" at the bend of the bilge, and over 1" in the keel. For most sailing experiences, the boat is considerably overbuilt. However, this excess material could be valuable if one had an unexpected encounter with a reef.

Westsail's hull to deck attachment is the best possible way to insure safety and watertight integrity. The deck is through bolted and bedded in a flexible polysulfide which cannot crack, and eliminates possible leaks.

All rigging and deck hardware is oversized stainless steel. The exposed chainplates are readily accessible from inside the boat for tightening. They are made of ¼" x 2" stainless steel flat bars. Standing rigging is ¼" 1 x 18. Turnbuckles are ½" with toggles.

Author's Comments:
A very much more modern design than the 32 with an unbelievable amount of volume down below. It comes with two different deck models, center cockpit version and an aft cockpit version with a trunk cabin. The factory has built over 30 complete boats so their experience is very reliable. The 42 can be redesigned to your own liking or you can buy it in many stages from a bare hull to an almost complete boat.

34

Feet
0 1 2 3 4 5 6
0   1   2
Metres

Sheet Winch
P&S

Crockery

Upper Root Berth

Locker

Shelves p&s

Gimbld
Oven
Cooker

Sink

Locker

Ice Box
(under)

Lavac

Berth P&S

Locker

Life
Raft
(under)

Folding
Seat

Table
lowers to seat
level to form
double berth

Sails

Locker

Oilskins

Seat

Chart
Desk

Root
Berth

Hanging
Locker

Root Berth

Books

THE BOATS

RIVAL 34

RIVAL YACHTS LIMITED
Willments Shipyard, Woolston, Southampton SO2 7GB, England
Designed by Peter Brett

Specifications:

LOA	34'0"	. . . . 10.38m
LWL	24'10"	. . . . 7.57m
Beam	9'8"	. . . . 2.94m
Draft	4'8"	. . . . 1.42m
	or 5'10"	. . . . 1.78m
Displacement	10,900 lbs.	. . . . . 4.940 kg.
Engine	. . Bukh DV20M diesel
Sail Area	560 sq. ft.	. . . . 52.0 sq. m.
Berths 6-7

Builder's Comments:

The hull was developed by Peter Brett from earlier Rivals. It reflects up-to-date thinking, with low wetted area fin-and-skeg shape and moderate displacement. The result is an ideal cruising yacht that sails fast at low angles of heel with an easy motion at sea. Two keel depths are available, 4'8" (1.42 m) and 5'10" (1.78 m). The fin-and-skeg shape gives low wetted-area and moderate displacement. The 4'8" draught version is particularly suitable for shallow waters. In the 5'10" version with a lead keel performance to windward is marginally improved, the windspeed required to heel to 28° being about 5 percent higher. The keel is long enough, with its straight base, to allow safe handling ashore or drying out alongside a wall. The skeg-mounted rudder, well aft, gives exceptionally light steering and very positive downwind control. A very desirable feature in a cruising yacht is Rival 34's outstanding ability to hold a course with the helm untended.

Deck and Cockpit: Popular and sensible extras are the stainless steel wire harness jackstays running each side from the cockpit to the bow so that safety harnesses need never be unclipped when working forward of the cockpit.

THE BOATS

YACHTCRAFT 37

ISLANDER YACHTS
1922 Barranca Road, Irvine, California 92705, (714) 549-8526
Designed by Bruce King, N.A.

Specifications:
LOA . . . . 36'9''
LWL . . . . 28'4''
Beam . . . . 10'10''
Draft . . . . 5'8''
Ballast (lead) . . . . 5,000 lbs.
Displacement . . . . 14,000 lbs.
Sail Area (Main + 100% foresail) . . . . 605 sq. ft.

Author's Comments:
A more racy underbody but still with the sober interior and a beloved pilot berth. The same hull is also available as a motorsailer version, something the Northwest sailors will appreciate.

THE BOATS

YACHTCRAFT 41

ISLANDER YACHTS
1922 Barranca Road, Irvine, California 92705, (714) 549-8526

Specifications:

Length Overall . . . . .41'
Length Waterline . . . . .32'6''
Maximum Beam . . . . .13'2''
Maximum Draft . . . . .5'
Displacement . . . . .22,000 lbs.
Keel . . . . .6,000 lbs.

Builder's Comments:

A brand new series offering the ultimate in cruising luxury for the serious yachtsman. The Freeport 41 goes to weather well and has excellent reaching and running capabilities. There's every comfort imaginable for long or short voyages with many new liveaboard features.

Author's Comments:

The Yachtcraft 41 is obese, tradition-oozing, clipper-bowed and aft-cabined. Plenty of room for movement exists inside, but not a sea berth is to be found. It has a very unique athwartships double berth in the aft cabin that should have great appeal to headstand loving yoga experts or nighwatchmen who adore sleeping standing up. They have even installed giant transom windows so you can watch the moonlight dance on the water while you try to figure out where to sleep.

THE BOATS

RIVAL 41

RIVAL YACHTS LIMITED
Willments Shipyard, Woolston, Southampton SO2 7GB, England
Designed by Peter Brett

Specifications:

LOA	41'0"	12.50m
LWL	32'8"	9.98m
Beam	12'3"	3.72m
Draft	5'11'	1.80m
Displacement	22,046 lbs.	10,000 kg.
Sail Area — sloop	879 sq. ft.	81.70 sq. m
— ketch	837 sq. ft.	77.80 sq. m
Diesel engine		Mercedes
Berths		7-9

Builder's Comments:

The G.R.P. hull and deck is a Lloyds approved design, moulded under Lloyds survey. The iron ballast keel is completely encapsulated. The deck is of balsa core sandwich construction for strength and insulation. There is a well for the 60 lb (27 kg) anchor. The aluminium toe-rail is capped with rigid black PVC. The interior is fully lined and insulated.

Rig: The standard rig is the masthead sloop. The alternative sloop rig, with the forestay taken to 90 percent of mast height, makes for easier handling; the genoa is slightly smaller and the extra area in the mainsail can still be handled comfortably by one man. A ketch rig with slightly smaller sail area is also available. This will appeal to those who want the easiest possible sail handling, for example a couple sailing the boat on their own. However, the ketch is more costly, more complicated and offers more windage, and the mizzen is only of real value while reaching. As the yacht handles excellently under one sail alone — mainsail or jib — the mizzen is never necessary for balance.

Engine: Mercedes OM 636 diesel, continuous rating 36 hp fitted with 2:1 reduction gear and heat-exchanger cooling; engine flexibly mounted under cockpit with full sound insulation; 2 fuel tanks with total capacity 120 gallon (545 litre).

10   9   8   7   6   5   4   3   2   1   0

ENGINE
UNDER

CHAIN
LOCKER

C.Q.R

CHART
TABLE

SEAT

FOLDING
TABLE

SHOWER
&TOILET

SAIL BINS

LOCKER

COOKER

LOCKERS

STATION 3
looking aft

SINGLE
BERTH

STATION 5
looking aft

SINKS

STATION 7
looking aft

QTR
BERTH

NAV INST

QTR
BERTH

THE BOATS

VARNE 22

VARNE MARINE LIMITED
263, Church Road, Thundersley, Essex, England
Designed by Varne Marine Ltd.

Specifications:

LOA .... 27'9' 8.45m
LWL .... 21'0" 6.40m
Beam .... 9'0" 2.70m
Draft .... 4'3" 1.30m
Displacement .... 6,200 lbs. ...... 1177 kg.
Sail Area (w/100% genoa) .... 343.8 sq. ft. 31.94m

Builder's Comments:

Bulkheads: B.S. 1088 marine ply is jigbonded into the hull whilst this is still in the mould thus ensuring that no distortion takes place.

Ballast Keel: A lead casting of 2,595 lbs. with the addition of 3% antimony for strength is secured externally by seven No. EN58J stainless steel bolts in accordance with Lloyd's rules.

Glassfibre Mouldings — Woven cloths and chopped strand mat in accordance with Lloyd's recommendations are used, all hand laid up to ensure consistent strength of mouldings.

Chainplates: These are of EN58J stainless steel bolted to reinforcing webs of GRP which are bonded to the hull.

Stemhead: A specially designed and sensible fitting is fabricated of EN58J stainless steel and incorporates, chain and warp rollers, forestay fitting, tack pennant anchorage and pulpit socket. Twin forestays can be provided for a small extra cost.

Windows: Blue tinted perspex secured by EN58J screws with seal between coachroof and window.

**preparations
section 2**

Chapter Four
PLANNING

This topic is difficult to approach, because almost any variation can be supported by what may seem logical arguments. Since everyone's ideal boat is very different from everyone else's, I can only offer ours as an example, giving what may or may not be satisfactory foundations for my reasonings.

I must confess that my predominent motivation is the search for security. I feel uncomfortable in a room that opens directly onto a street, becoming more relaxed and isolated if that room is partitioned off or protected by a hallway. Since this kind of partitioning is most impractical on a small cruising boat, in our boat I placed all the "function" or work areas close to the companionway. In these areas, the purpose is to accomplish or complete a task, not necessarily to relax and turn calmly into oneself.

Apart from emotionality, it is best to keep work areas near an open well-aired companionway. Seasickness occurs with much greater frequency in stuffy, confined catacombs than in well aired spaces. Also, communication is made easy with the helmsman. To be totally practical, I defy anyone to carry a cup of coffee from a galley located near the forepeak and arrive in the cockpit with more than 23 drops.

The salon, because we spend so many waking hours in it, must be the focal point of the boat; therefore its layout shall not be treated lightly. That it must be in the center of the boat, the point of least motion, is obvious. That it must have totally comfortable seats in as many sea conditions as possible is essential, and that it must provide an atmosphere of relaxation and emotional calm is critical.

Beyond the salon, one must make room for a head and also furnish sleeping or storage facilities, or both. The decision is difficult at best, but if one works on a combined assimilation of cruiser-live-aboard, the finalizations come rather easily.

Chart Table

This work area should be next to the companionway to facilitate communication with the helmsman and to prevent carrying a very delicate sextant all the way forward or aft in rolling or choppy seas. In our boat it is next to the galley so that the chart table top can, in port, act as a second preparation area for large meals. The aft section of the boat experiences less motion than areas further forward, thereby making it less difficult to do accurate plotting and calculations.

The surface should be at least 32'' x 25'' to give space for folded Admiralty charts; plus it should allow about 4'' margins on top and on one side where one can place plotting tools while flipping or turning the charts. Chart flipping by means of the old tablecloth-off-the-table trick will simply not work here because you have to slip the tablecloth back under the plotting tools before they hit the table top.

The next decision you face after surface size is whether to make the chart table a sit-down or stand-up variety. I prefer the stand-up because it is easier to brace oneself in a rolling seas using legs and pelvis only, leaving both hands free. The desk type chart table is usually placed, by necessity, next to the curving hull. On an unfavorable heel you will slide on the athwartships seat right to the hull with nothing but your arm and shoulder to maintain your upright position. Plotting with one hand (especially the wrong one) is no fun.

The "stand-up" table also saves storage space underneath the table top, into which you can install a number of chart drawers clear down to the cabin sole, see photo 4. If you don't use them all for charts, they make excellent drawers for small tools, odd screws, and numerous paraphernalia which can be very handy close to the companionway. They can be pigeon holed by building great numbers of dividers, so that the items in the drawer don't avalanche when the boat rolls. The lowest drawer possible should be used for this venture, for down low the boat's movement is minimized and so is the inavoidable racket of what sounds like a million marbles rolling back and forth in a large tin can.

Some advocate that the sit-down table is infinitely superior, for one can get off one's feet while working out sights. True, but there should be numerous other places in the boat to perform this

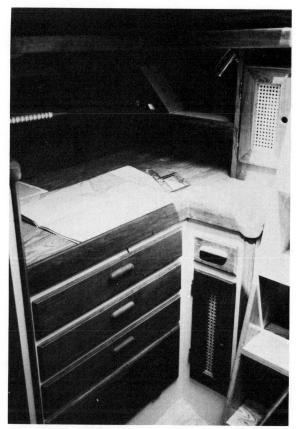

Photo No. 4 — "Stand at" chart table.

function. And to those who want to hide the chart table away from the weather-admitting companionway, I say a little rag can wipe a long way.

Salon

The center table, I think, is an absolute must for a cruising boat. It is usually accompanied by two fore and aft berths which act as daytime settees. The backs should be slanted about 15 degrees to provide comfortable seating, see photo 5. The seats should be about 20-22'' deep to provide luxurious seating, yet to be necessarily snug sea-berths.

We have found that 20-22'' is a perfect compromise. Anything less than this dimension is useless as a berth and not quite comfy enough to slouch back into as a seat. Anything over 23'' is too wide

Photo No. 5 — Sloped settee back.

as a sea-berth, for one is tossed about in rolling seas. As a seat, it will be also too wide, for the edge will cut behind one's knee. I think also that the center table very nicely unites the salon, enabling conversation to flow athwartships from relaxed positions instead of the quarter-neck-twist that one is forced to practice from the straight-backed pews of a cramped dinette.

The back rests do not necessarily require upholstery or padding (photo 6). It is easier to have doors opening to lockers if no upholstery is in the way. If the backs are sloped, they will prove to be comfortable; if they are not quite soft enough, toss cushions can be utilized.

As for the table itself, the number of varieties is endless. Fully supported ones are extremely functional in rough seas, but they act as room dividers otherwise. Pole-less tables create a feeling of open space, but reinforcing them against hurtling bodies is a tremendous task.

One end of our table is attached to a bulkhead structure by means of a large multi-bolted angle iron, as in figure 9. The other end is reinforced with welded steel rod and plate to provide optimum support, see figure 10. We made the table quite short, adequate for the two of us to eat from (in order to keep the unsupported part of the table as short as possible).

PLANNING

Photo No. 6 — Center table with settee.

Figure No. 9 — Attachment of center table to bulkhead.

BRASS TUBING
FOR LEG

WELDED PLATE AND ROD

Figure No. 10 — Reinforcement of table leg.

I have seen numerous collapsible and fold-up tables, but most of them folded up and collapsed at the most inappropriate moments. If you do have a good idea though, try it. At worst, you'll have to build another one.

Design your salon as liberally as you like. You can be quite diversified, see photo 7, but be warned: most people who build their own cruising boats have never cruised before. Being unfamiliar with the reasons for the confined space of a small boat they spread out their settees and berths and end up with a storage-spaceless, grab-supportless barn with uncomfortably narrow outboard settees joined only by air. To imagine the consequences at sea you need only close your eyes and picture a barrel of 11 foot diameter being tossed about on 20 foot waves. You should not forget to picture yourself inside the barrel. Now just sit back and relax.

The Galley

If at all possible, the galley should be U-shaped with adequate body support for either tack, see photo 8. Concentration of sink,

PLANNING

Photo No. 7 — Alternate salon arrangement.

icebox, stove should be maximum. Once you're braced in a seaway, it's a shame and risky to have to let go just to pick up two cloves of cloves. The stove should, of course, be gimbaled with a wooden bar in front of it to prevent you falling all over the burners if the boat lurches, see photo 9. Beware of placing the stove too far amidships with deep cupbard space behind it. Few things are worse than a badly scorched armpit.

Sinks must be near the boat's center line to enable them to drain on either tack. Most people feel strongly that sinks should be as gigantic as possible. For large families, perhaps. But for small ones, it will just invite days' old dirty dishes. A small double sink will function much better than a large single, because the baffle will keep water from gaining splashy momentum. You also have one extra sink in which to drip dry dishes.

PLANNING 129

Photo No. 8 — U-shaped galley.

The greater the depth, of course, the less chance of spillage. But care must be taken that you do not place the bottom of the sink lower than the water line, for you will then have to have a bilge pump to pump it out. This procedure is acceptable, but it does present the new possibility of siphoning in water and flooding the boat if the pump fails.

I think that a fresh water manual pump in the galley is adequate. Pressure or gravity fed water is comfortable, but one tends to use more water than if one has to pump every drop by hand. If you must have self-transporting water, make it gravity fed. It has few moving parts.

Salt water pumps in my opinion, are totally absurd. You drill another hole in your hull and for what? The whole ocean is at your door step. All you need is a bucket. It's more pleasant to wash your dishes on deck if the hot sun is beating down and you can't find enough fresh water to splurge on your dishes. On deck, a bucket functions marvelously well. If the weather outside is adverse, and pouring rain prevents you from exterior dishwashing, then you have more than enough fresh water to fill all of your tanks, wash your dishes, and even paint some miniature watercolors. All you have to do is be ingenious enough to collect it. Collection can be done with awnings, large canvas funnels, and simplest of all, sails.

The icebox should be large enough to carry 50 pounds of ice and still leave at least 2 cubic feet for food. Insulating it is critical. If you can pour about 5" worth of 2-part urethane foam all around, your

Photo No. 9 — Stove safety bar.

two blocks of ice should last you up to three weeks. Pouring this foam takes tact. Although it looks totally harmless as it merrily bubbles away, it does have tremendous power through expansion.

We braced the outside shell as well as the inside fiberglass liner of ours when we performed the task, but the thing still warped and buckled a little. Therefore brace it well and beat the two parts with a drill motor and paint-stirrer (use only half a pint of each at a time). Pour in over a large surface if possible. If you pour the whole thing into a small corner, the outer layer will harden first through contact with air and the lower layers will tend to blow the icebox apart. Wait until the first batch goes off and a tough skin is formed before you pour the second.

Icebox lids are best hinged, see photo 10. The variety that slides does so at the most awkward times. Front opening iceboxes are not recommended because the precious cold air spills out of them when the door is opened. To prevent loss of cold air in top

Photo No. 10 — Hinged icebox lid.

loaders, put a loop in your icebox drain hose. Water will collect here, see figure 11, and prevent the cold air from spilling out into the bilge. Arrange to have your ice water drain into a portable container that you can dump over the side. The smell of spilled milk gone sour in the bilge can foul your boat for days.

All cabinets should be shallow, or as partitioned as possible to avoid the need of lengthy searches. Compartmentalization is most desirable to prevent both spillage and the nerve wracking noise that cans and things make as they roll freely about. I see little need for storing all your pots and pans in cupboards. Copper bottomed stainless steel pans are extremely functional and their either tarnished or polished bottoms are visually pleasing. They can be hung onto a bulkhead (bottoms out) and set into little gallows as

PLANNING

Figure No. 11 — Looped icebox drain hose.

shown in figure 12. They will then become completely rattle-free and can be left exposed without need for a door which would only create a more confined feeling in the galley. If they are hung a few inches above the counter, the space below them can be utilized for food preparation.

Figure No. 12 — Pan gallows.

Berths

I'm not sure if sleep is only a personal problem, but I must have 7 hours of comfortable sleep or I'm a dish rag the following day. Thus berths offering total comfort and safety are an absolute must.

Good sea berths (as mentioned in the "Salon" section) should be no more than 22" nor less than 19". Bunk boards that curve up at both ends are very comfortable in mild seas where they provide some shoulder support and security without the need for leeboards or straps, see photo 11A. Bunk lengths should exceed the person's height by at least 4", especially if the person sleeps on his stomach, thereby extending his toes.

Foot lockers and spaces like those described by Mr. Street and Mr. Hiscock at the foot of a bunk are advisable. They not only create functional storage spaces, but they give the bunk's occupant a feeling of home by allowing him to keep his personal possessions near his berth place.

I do prefer pilot berths for a similar reason, see photo 11B. They are completely private and are not used for any other purpose but sleeping. Thus the occupant need not fear a wet weather geared derriere landing on his face, interrupting his dreams. The confinedness of most pilot berths tend to separate them from the rest of the cabin, creating a secure place that can most often be curtained off to allow undisturbed daytime rest. It can also be easily lee-boarded for a secure foul weather rest. I always found the existence of a separate level in a boat intriguing; for although I may seldom use it, I know the possibility for refuge to "another area" exists if I were ever to need it. Psychological reassurances can be of great help in a small space, especially at sea.

Another sea-berth considered as excellent as the pilot berth is a quarter berth. This berth can be placed well aft, part of it beside or above the diesel. Here the ride is comfortable in all sea conditions, and the berth does not take up otherwise valuable space. Because it is customarily wedged between the hull and the engine room bulkhead, it can be used without any weather boards. The forward end of the berth can, most often, act as a settee for a sit-at chart table if so desired, a commonly exercised procedure in many production boats, see figure 13. The Griffith's "Awanhnee" has a unique quarter berth in that it is accessible from the cockpit and can therefore be used by the second person on watch until the helmsman requires his help.

The quarter berth has two drawbacks: 1) in hot climates it becomes the most stuffy of accommodations and 2) if the engine is

Photo No. 11A — Permanent bunk board.

Photo No. 11B — 20" pilot berth above settee.

PLANNING

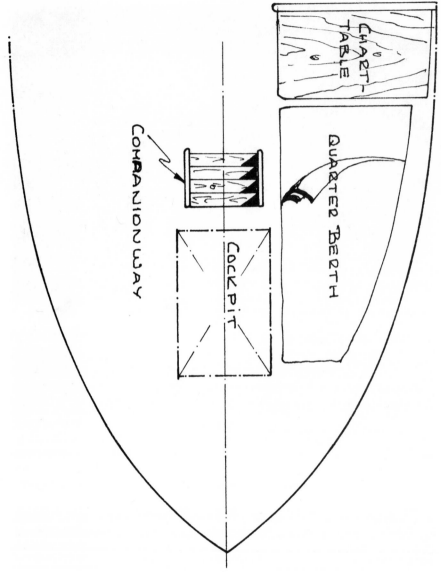

Figure No. 13 — Quarter berth.

being used, sleep is almost impossible. The solution to the first problem could be solved by installing a portlight in the cockpit side, see photo 12, for ventilation. As for the second, don't use your engine.

PLANNING

Photo No. 12 — Portlight in side of cockpit.

Seats and Settees

I find that I cannot build too many seats (in as many separated areas as possible) into a boat. Although Candace and I do get along sufficiently well (we have been together for over four years, almost 24 hours a day), it is comforting for us both to be able to go to another compartment, in this case the forepeak, and be able to sit down and read or write or just sit. Too many people concentrate only on a great number of berths and storage, thereby creating forepeaks in which you can either lie down or hang up your underwear. The inclusion of a settee does create the feeling of a private cabin where one can spend time creatively, productively, privately.

The seats need not be wide or long or enormous. They should be comfortable, and comfort can easily be yielded by a seat 28'' long by 18'' deep, especially if the curvature of the hull is used as the back rest. Light, both natural and artificial, should be generously provided in this area to make the seat more utilitarian.

Personally, I require a desk of my own for whatever writing I may do in the boat. The salon table or the chart table could not serve as acceptable substitutes because I need to sometimes leave notes and reference material undisturbed and uninterrupted by meals and course plottings, etc. This demand was rather selfish in a 32-foot boat, but I managed to talk Candace into surrendering a 3' x 4' storage space (one hanging locker and four drawers) on the condition that we provide some substitutes elsewhere. The miniaturizing of a study into such confines proved quite successful, see photo 13. The seat serves as storage; the desk top lifts up to provide storage space; next to the hull is a bookcase and a small cabinet with shelves.

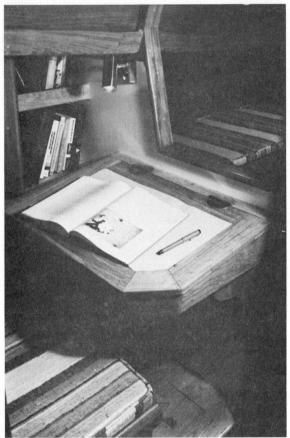

Photo No. 13 — My study.

We had to replace the drawers that normally go in this space, so we built a structure in the forepeak next to the settee, see photo 14. Then we went on to disguise a hanging locker in the salon by putting doors over book shelf space and deleting the top of the bunks back rest, as in figure 14. We now have a ventilated locker that does not

PLANNING

Photo No. 14 — Storage in forepeak.

look like an enormous hanging locker, yet provides ample hanging space. The door in the back rest serves as access to the locker's bottom, where one can store foldable items, shoes, etc.

We worked many hours on the design of the study, adding ¼'' here and ½'' there. The measurements we came up with shown in figure 15 have proved to be very comfortable.

Again I can only reinforce the importance of comfortable seating places dispersed as much as possible in the boat. Remember the boat is small and in time you'll be tired of every cranny. Familiarity breeds ennui; so try to make the layout as exciting initially as your creativity allows.

The Head

Little of importance can be said of the head except that I deem it

Figure No. 14 — Disguised hanging locker.

Figure No. 15 — Plans for the study.

foolish to allow it to take up too much valuable space. I have seen some boats where a very comfortable private cabin could have been installed in the huge space allotted for the head, in which the owners spent about ½ of 1 percent of their total time.

Make the head sink small. You'll waste less water. The head sink can drain into the head to eliminate an additional thru-hull and to help to keep the head clean. Vent the head well, for nothing is less comforting to seasickness than dubious odors. One 6'' diameter port and a 4'' cowl vent are minimum requirements.

It is most helpful to have the head fixture itself face fore and aft, confined between bulkheads, so that you can brace yourself on either tack. If you think the small space is claustrophobic, paint it white.

The Forepeak

Since most of one's life will be spent in port, a comfortable double berth in the forepeak should be available. A width of 48'' should suffice, especially if some additional space for knees (for sleeping on one's side) is provided, see figure 16.

Placement of this berth is most critical. A good 34'' should be available between the surface of the berth and the cabin top so that one can sit up in bed. I do not believe that one's intimate life should suffer just because one is mentally unbalanced enough to live in a sailboat. As I mentioned before, we placed a settee and some storage on the starboard side of our forepeak, but I have seen many boats utilize this space to very good advantage by installing a work bench or complete storage, etc. Discretion is yours. If you intend to have no company and single berths will prove adequate for your tastes, then you can convert the entire forepeak to sail stowage, a dark room, or whatever you need.

Stowage

I placed this section last because I think that it is the most overrated, overdiscussed topic on the boat. It is unquestionable that man can totally congest any volume of space no matter how vast if given enough time (see earth). When I hear people rave about the wonderful amount of available storage space a boat has, I shudder. By the glare in the eyes I can see the caravan of unworthy hoardage ranging from collapsible golf carts to inflatable wading pools meandering into the boat. You do need as much stowage as possible, so plan to leave as much junk behind as possible. You will feel much freer.

Most stowage spaces should be top loading. Not only do top

loading spaces hold more items per equal volume, they prevent their contents from escaping when the boat is heeling or rolling. Front loading spaces require a carefully constructed door, whereas the tops of top loading spaces can be of rough plywood since they are usually covered by cushions.

If you must have front loading storage, make the access hole as small as possible so that the walls surrounding the hole can act as baffles for the stored goods. On the other hand, consider what you will be stowing where and be sure to allow an adequate enough hole to get the gear inside. If you have shelves in any of your storage areas, be sure that they have searails of adequate height (about 2''), or everything is guaranteed to spill in your lap when you open the door on an unfavorable heel.

Most gear in a boat tends to be small. One extra large storage space should be left for awkwardly large items. But apart from that, the many compartments of old traditional boats seem an excellent idea. With this type of storage, one need not rummage through a mountain of goods to get to the tiny item that one is seeking. If you do require special storage for a number of large items, though, be sure to plan it all before you start building. A drawing with a list of compartments that has a fairly good inventory of what each locker contains can save hours of search. Sail lockers, as well as wet lockers for foul weather gear, should be self-draining and well ventilated so that mildew cannot grow.

The Engine Room

This compartment has always been thought of as a greasy, slimy, dingy hole where you should venture only as a last resort. I see no reason for such a situation. A diesel is a simple, clean machine and its room can be kept immaculate with a little fore-thought. Do not try to utilize every square inch above and around the engine for storage. It is a good idea to have spare parts readily accessible, but you will have to get at every part of the engine sooner or later, so it is best to leave open space around it. If possible, leave room above the engine so that you can crawl over it and get to the stuffing box in any seas.

If you have unused areas under tank shelves, put slats across their fronts. You can then store spare parts, common tools, rags, etc. behind the slats and through spaces between them you will be readily able to see what you're looking for. It's good to have all of these items close at hand in the engine room, for once you are peacefully wedged in you will not want to crawl out for any reason.

Plan all your fuel shut-offs and engine intake seacocks so that they are readily accessible when you need them. The finest of seacocks can be of little value if it cannot be got at easily.

All the above planning will be of little use if you can't see anything once you are inside the engine room. If your engine is below the cockpit, install deadlights in the cockpit side or the cockpit sole to bring in the natural light. If your cockpit is small and the sole removable you can consider a heavy piece of plexiglass for your cockpit sole. The plexiglass should be at least 1'' thick to make it rigid enough. This approach is a very expensive proposition, costing approximately $150, but it does make for a beautifully lit engine room that's a pleasure to work in.

You might be able to save on cost by buying some surplus plexiglass that is badly scratched. Don't let the scratches scare you off. You should under no circumstances leave the plexiglass clear, but sand the surface lightly with 220 sandpaper. It will diffuse the sunlight and keep the engine room from becoming an oven. Sunlight is also most detrimental to fuel hoses, which will tend to have a much shorter life and break down sooner if direct sun gets onto them. Teak slats or grates over the plexiglass would be ideal; for even if sanded, plexiglass can become very slippery when wet.

Access to the engine room is also critical. You may have to get in very quickly. I've seen companionways that dismantel into pieces which, of course, fly about with great abandon in a seaways as soon as you remove them. I have even seen an arrangement where the galley sink was hinged upward and had to be flipped up before access to the engine room could be had. I'd feel singularly stupid if my engine stalled as I was roaring into a fuel dock and I had to pause for a moment to wash my dishes before I could remedy the malady.

The best solution is a ladder that hinges up and hooks to the cabin top. In the bulkhead a large hinged door will provide the most rapid, unobstructed access. Be sure to put hooks on the door to hold it in the open as well as the closed position.

Shelves should be so laid out in the engine room that batteries are right next to the entranceway. Since batteries should be checked daily for water level, as little crawling about as possible should be required. Fuel filters should be so laid out that they are also readily available and accessible, as should be the dip stick to check the oil in both the transmission and the engine itself.

Lighting and Ventilation

This topic has been very well covered by Mr. Hiscock and Mr. Street. As it has, I can only emphasize the importance of ample light and moving air below decks. All portlights should be opening and of a good diameter, see photo 15. Plastic portlights are inexpensive but they do have a tendency to warp and break down with heat. If they warp they will inevitably leak. Good solid bronze portlights are most advisable to use, the heavier the better, for then they cannot be warped out of shape and leak. Six inches in diameter is the smallest one should use. Anything smaller, like four inches, will provide very little light or air. Portlights on the forward face of the cabin should be of the deadlight variety, for here one will encounter heavy seaways and can be assured of an opening port leaking. Deadlights, deck-lights, and hatches are well covered in the construction chapters. Therefore, I will only say here that you should try to install as many as you can, but if you do use skylights be sure to get tempered glass. As costly as it is, it will not break easily. Odd sizes of glass are difficult to replace in out of the way harbors; therefore, it might be advisable to take spare pieces with you.

One final note: Personalize your boat as much as you like but if you have some doubts about keeping it forever, try to make it as unoutlandish as possible. Some things that hit you in the middle of the night as incredibly brilliant inventions may prove to be the cause of a lot of smirking and chuckles behind your back and make your boat almost unsellable. A friend who laid out a beautifully open — spaced sitting room type arrangement in his extremely strong very well equipped world cruising boat has had trouble selling it for one year because his personal needs were put ahead of common sensibility and practicality.

Photo No. 15 — Opening portlight.

Figure 16

Chapter Five
MAKE OR BUY

Since most manufacturers offer completed boats, as well as bare hulls and decks, one must decide at what stage to begin work oneself. Finishing aids, such as ballast, cabin sole, pre-cut plywood parts, rudder, etc. can be factory installed or factory bought. They can be either a great help or a monstrous inconvenience, depending on the individual's final goals.

I shall try to evaluate each item for its merits and its disadvantages, discussing the factors such as cost, time involved, machinery or tools necessary. I will purposely exclude the question of ability, for I firmly believe that if one has the inclination and time he can easily eclipse the quality achieved by all manufacturers and most craftsmen. The amount of time to be sacrificed, of course, may be very great. But if time is not a factor, you do possess the interest, and you do want the best possible results, then do it yourself. Otherwise, I hope the following points will aid you in deciding your point of commencement.

Ballast

It's heavy. To lug six or seven thousand pounds of steel or lead up a scaffold is not my idea of self-fulfillment. If you are building an A-frame to install your engine, or if you have your boat under a roof with strong beams, your task will be eased. But the problem of getting the ballast to your boat in the first place still remains. The money saved by ballasting yourself is not a lot. With the mechanized methods of factory installation time is kept to the minimum, and although the hourly rate they charge may bottom out at $15, the total should not amount to more than $300, the price of a good wheelchair. Therefore, unless you have access to scrap lead which you can melt down yourself and you don't cringe at the thought of wearing a truss, by all means proceed. Only then will you be certain of what actually went into your ballast and how.

There are a few reasons for ballasting yourself. Should you subscribe to the alternate religion of your chosen boatbuilder with regards to location (centralized or evenly spread, see figure 17), you

Figure No. 17 — Centralized vs. evenly spread ballast.

have a chance to resolve the conflict. If the builder doesn't supply all cast lead and you are a firm believer in lead as I am beginning to be, you can have it. Undeniably all lead will result in a stiffer boat with more bilge space, and above all it will not rust if gudgeons leak or stray water from inside finds its way down. On the other hand price wise, steel is way ahead, costing as little as 3c a pound. Whereas, lead, even if creatively scrounged, will run 20c a pound minimum. You may also want to relocate some ballast to compensate for changing the location of the engine or tanks (which may in instances be considered as ballast).

MAKE OR BUY

We had our ballast factory installed. Apart from a minor gudgeon seal problem, which they rapidly and promptly corrected, I have had no misgivings or regrets.

Cabin Sole

Most fiberglass boatbuilders offer a fiberglass cabin sole. If you have inbred prejudices for or against one, your life will be simple; otherwise, evaluate.

The cost of a glass sole factory installed, for a 30 to 40 foot boat, is close to $900. If you do your own, using mahogany sole timbers and marine plywood, your cost in materials should not exceed $150.

Even if you are financially independent, you should still consider the following. Most of these soles have raised faces or ridges as shown in figure 18 which (a) give it rigidity and (b) define the location of berths, cabinet faces and other furniture. If you are satisfied with the offered interior layouts, this sole could be a blessing, for you will be able to install your rough interior in very little time. If you plan minor changes only, the fiberglass sole is still acceptable. But if you have drastic divergences in mind, or are uncertain of your final plan, then certainly do a plywood sole

Figure No. 18 — Cabin sole cross-section.

yourself or have the factory install one for you; the ridges will only frustrate and inhibit you.

On the pro side, the fiberglass cabin sole will usually have a non-skid finish of sorts and color that can serve as a final easy-to-maintain surface, if you like that sort of thing. If, however, you're more traditional and want teak, oak, etc. for your sole, then you will have great difficulty engineering your wood over and around the ridges. I must admit, though, that where the cabin sole angles up to follow the curvature of the hull, the fiberglass surface there makes a very very nice bed into which a covering layer of wood can be screwed. Thus you are prevented the annoying problem of having to laminate ribs to the hull to which you finally screw your wood cabin sole.

Apart from the above, the fiberglass sole can actually cut down available floor space, it may be installed in parts and therefore be horribly misaligned, and it will certainly have sloping ridge faces for the furniture (it has to, to facilitate removal from the mold). These surfaces may not offer the best positive methods of attachments.

But, it will not rot, it may have a very handy built-in shower pan, it is practical in heads and galleys where water frequents, and it may have bilge hatch cut-outs with molded seating cleats, which are very strong and very handy. Choose.

If you do decide to get one, make certain that it has a plywood core for rigidity like the one shown in figure 19. Ascertain that this core is at least ½-inch thick; because if not, it will give too much, delaminate, and emit spine scratching noises at every step. If the

Figure No. 19 — Cabin sole construction.

manufacturer does not do so, make sure that you install a goodly number of knees at intervals to keep the thing from behaving like a trampoline.

Rudder

Factories usually charge around $500 for a rudder. High,

MAKE OR BUY

perhaps, but to me it seems a rather complex job to fabricate one (if plugs and molds have to be made). Therefore, if the design offered suits you and the construction appears acceptable, I would strongly encourage factory purchase. It will probably come with fitted pintles, gudgeons, and other items which would require considerable time if attempted on a one-off basis.

The construction here, of course, is very important; one should look for very good fiberglassing and a closed-cell core so that the thing doesn't fill with 300 pounds of water if a leak develops in a seam. If an open-cell foam is used, good construction is self-defeating. Although the foam will provide some rigidity and resilience on rock-banging, it will also act as an insatiable sponge if the glass cover fails. Also, look for a steel plate inside the rudder. If it is foam only, the rudder may be very buoyant, causing a genuine struggle if you are heeled, as it wants constantly to bob up like a fat lady.

If the rudder is outboard, it would be nice to have a straight following edge on it to facilitate a trim-tab installation. Speaking of installation, one should consider having the factory perform this feat; for if your rudder is anything like ours, it will weigh 200 pounds. Aligning it and making gudgeon holes while holding the thing in your other hand is no easy task. Whether you or the factory install it, make sure, even if you have to bribe an employee, that the hull, gudgeons, and the pintles are well bathed with acetone before the polysulphide bedding is applied. The acetone removes mold-resease wax, which is present for the following reason:

When installing a rudder, it is common procedure to drill through the hull, install the bolts in place, then build a dam out of mish-mash or other filler material around the bolts. Installing the bolts first, allows you to drill through two one-inch thick walls rather than a four-inch thick wall. But if the mish-mash goes in after the bolts, mold-release wax or grease must be used on the bolts so that when the mish-mash has set the bolts can be removed. Then the gudgeons are bedded and rebolted. This wax or grease inevitably finds its way onto the hull and gudgeon. Mold-release wax is an excellent product and grease likewise, but if they remain on either of the above surfaces, you may as well throw two unopened tubes of $5 polysulphide into the garbage. It'll save you from getting goo all over your hands. More about gudgeons and pintles under "Rudder Installation."

Engine

To choose a marine engine is a problem at the best of times. I was fortunate because our manufacturer offered only Perkins and

Volvo diesels, therefore facilitating the choice. Of course, one can pick any marine engine and purchase it for any boat. But when a boatyard offers an engine, it usually means that they have a prefabricated engine pan (fiberglass molded pan designed especially for the specific engine mounts, supports, etc.) which besides suiting the engine, fits the hull perfectly in a predestined spot, see photo 16.

Photo No. 16 — Fiberglass engine pan with mounts.

The engine pan usually has a nice bilge of its own to collect oil drips and keep the gooey mess from getting into the boat's own bilge. The pan, above all, is a time-saving device for the buyer. The cost of ours installed (fitted and bonded to the hull) was $240. Other manufacturers charge somewhat close to that. A friend, choosing to install a Faryman for which no pan was available, spent almost a week designing and building a wood platform for the mounts and $90 worth of resin to bond the thing to the hull. So, if (a) you are happy with the type of engine offered, (b) you are satisfied with its location, (c) you can afford it, (d) you don't know anyone who can get you a better deal somewhere else, you may as well buy one of the offered engines. At least have them install the pan, then set and align the engine on it. They can't charge too much for that and it will save you hours of measuring, guessing, and lifting your engine back and forth on its mounts.

In the appendix I will elaborate on marine engines. For now, I

MAKE OR BUY

will mention only that we chose a Volvo MD3B, a diesel, I'm not too familiar with the Isusu block that some manufacturers use. Apart from being difficult to find parts for, they are an automobile conversion (as are Westerbeke and Perkins) and not a thoroughbred marine engine such as Volvo and Farymann. This fact is not in itself a crime, but a single purpose machine gives me more confidence than an egg beater that also mows the lawn and sews on buttons.

With the Volvo, the entire engine can be reworked from the top, i.e. you can change rings, pistons, etc. without having to haul the engine out of the boat. Automotive conversions like the Perkins have to be repaired and disassembled from the bottom.

Of course a diesel is heavier and much more expensive than its gas counterpart. But then it doesn't have an electric ignition system which usually fails when you most need it. And it doesn't have the stray fuel vapors which settle in the bilge, ignite, and blow the cabin and mast across the bay, leaving you seated in the head for all to see.

I must say, I don't know everything about engines. As a matter of fact, I don't know anything about them, but I do know that gasoline vapors explode at the slightest provocation and that diesel vapors don't, unless compressed. I know that blowers work and alarm systems work and sniffing works, but blowers fail and alarm systems die and noses catch cold or get drunk and that's when the cabin and mast go flying across the bay.

Therefore, as long as the company offers a diesel, any diesel, and you're happy with the aforementioned points, have them install it. But definitely don't have them hook it up to tanks, batteries, exhaust, etc. If you are deadly afraid of doing it yourself, hire someone to help you. But be there with him all the time, and watch and help and ask questions. Remember the answers, so that when the emergency arises you will know exactly where to turn, what tool to use, and what procedure to follow.

Some solid arguments exist against getting an engine with the boat. The first one is usually financial. The fact does exist that it is unnecessary to have the engine sit in the boat for a year or two while the carpentry work is being done. It is only gathering dust and it is a large investment sitting there producing nothing. If there is structural work to be done in the engine room, for example the installation of tanks, shelves, etc., the engine could be a hindrance in that it will be in the way in a space which is usually too small in most boats.

The argument that later installation is difficult should not hold true, especially if the engine room is located below a removable cockpit sole. Hiring a crane for a couple of hours to install it should not exceed $30 or $40. Then of course, there is also the argument that while you are building the rest of your boat, you are very likely to discover a lot of facts and information about engines of all sorts which may enable you to make a wiser choice as well as spend a little time hunting around for bargains you may not have considered possible before. Whichever way you go, you should not encounter great difficulties. Whichever way you go, please get a diesel. In the appendix are specifications for the most commonly used marine diesels for 25' to 30' boats.

Tanks

Virtually the identical rule that applied for the fiberglass cabin sole is applicable here. If you are totally happy with the tanks' location, the quantity of them, and the installation method that the company offers, then perhaps purchasing their tanks is a good idea.

If you know a good sheet metal man, preferably one who has worked with stainless, then go to him, because from a few basic measurements supplied by even the chinziest of corporations, he can build you a good tank. And, if you force some tears to your eyes and acclaim in a trembling murmur that the life of your wife and children will depend on the quality of his product, he can maybe build you a jewel of a tank.

If you are somewhat unsure of your final layout, or if you question the location of the tanks even slightly, forget them for now and let them wait until you build some of the interior. Brilliant inspiration may somewhere come upon you.

THINGS TO LOOK FOR
1. Location

Tanks when full can be very heavy. Water weighs almost ten pounds per gallon and diesel fuel is only slightly lighter. To place them as low as possible and as far inboard as possible in the boat is crucial. Some of mine are up high and far outboard, but then I didn't have a book such as this one to guide me.

Not only will this positioning make for a stiffer boat, but the area of least movement in the boat is down low and near the center line. Even in the most disorganized seas, the tanks in this location will have fewer forces working on them, thereby increasing their life expectancy. The argument that you can firmly fasten and secure any tank is admirably academic. Some movement and working will always occur, regardless how miniscule. It will eventually result in great movement, greater working, and earlier fatigue on the tank, its fittings, and fastenings.

To have fuel tanks near the engine is good. The shorter the fuel line, the better. I've had friends whose flexible lines snake through cabinets and lockers only to be continually nicked and crimped by cans of sliced bananas or steel lined heels of undiscardable cowboy boots. The less lines weave about, the lesser the chance of air locks, etc.

With water tanks, the idea of down low installation is still advisable. But it may be nice to have at least a five gallon tank above the galley counter height. This tank could be pumped full from the larger bilge tanks with a secondary bilge pump and provide gravity fed water to the sink. It will not only free one hand (a vital aspect in any seas) but will eliminate the problem of a low-output galley pump that wears out and breaks down with monotonous predictability.

I believe the separation and division of both fuel and water tanks is a must. If one fuel tank is contaminated by water or dirt, it's nice to have a standby. If water goes foul in one tank, it's reassuring to have another that may have escaped calamity. If one set of plumbing lines fouls or breaks, it's good to be able to shut off the by-pass, then use the other.

2. Material

It's almost unquestionable that water tanks should be made of stainless steel and diesel tanks of monel or black iron. Integral tanks are dangerously prone to some sort of salt water seepage. Sealing them, and still being able to gelcoat the interior to avoid the endless fiberglass taste and moisture absorption, is no small task. Some say that seepage is inevitable. Even though fiberglass tanks allow maximum use of given space, I do not favor them. Stainless steel for water is ideal. It's true that some plastic tanks have no flavor, but they may eventually harden, become brittle, and crack. If the hull manufacturer tries to tell you otherwise, don't believe him. Ask a plastic, then a stainless man and draw your own conclusions.

For fuel, I have been told the following by a man who has been supplying the boat manufacturers of Southern California for thirty years. The list goes from most ideal to least:

1. Monel
2. Aluminum
3. Black Iron
4. Stainless

The price of monel is almost double that of stainless or aluminum, making it almost out of the question. Stainless has the advantage of being somewhat easier to weld and solder than aluminum. If your hull man does not supply either of them, have your own built.

3. Construction

Even if you are satisfied with the suggested locations and happy with the material provided, please check the following vital items:

a) Baffles. No section of tank should contain more than thirty gallons without a baffle. If more is allowed, a half-full tank in a violent sea can throw about great amounts of liquid of not little weight, putting unnecessary strain on seams and fastenings. An acquaintance installed a two hundred gallon tank (the size of a decent wading pool) without a single baffle. He insisted that the walls were thick, the welding fine, and the support adequate. Three weeks after launching he owned the world's largest sieve. They don't call him "Old Nutso Anderson" for nothing.

b) Fittings. Fittings should be mounted on top of the tanks. The fitting-to-tank attachment is usually the weak spot. To risk having this attachment or a shut-off valve fail and the contents drain unstopably into the bilge is utter folly.

The fittings on stainless tanks should be brass. Some people, out of thoughtless false economy, install galvanized on diesel tanks. The coating eventually peels and clogs the injectors, which are replaceable at the cost of about $80 each. A brass fitting retails even today at no more than $6.00.

c) Welding. The spot welding on stainless steel should be evenly spread (no more than an inch apart) and shallow enough not to penetrate the steel. The edges should be turned to accommodate soldering. The soldering in turn should deeply penetrate into the seam to make a long soft seal. My friend, the tank man, brought this procedure to my attention, showing me the end of a tank he had to shorten. To demonstrate the quality of his work, he clamped the welded, soldered seam into a vise and assaulted it with a large hammer until I almost went deaf. Then he showed me a piece of coiled and wrapped metal without the tiniest crack in any seam.

The baffles should also be spot welded, with welds occurring as frequently along them as at the ends of the tanks. The ends are sealed with solder and there is reason to assume that the welds on the baffles are at least as vulnerable; therefore, a spot of solder over each weld here should not be considered overkill.

If the hull manufacturer's tanks meet the above somewhat stringent demands then by all means buy them, but install them yourself. In all seriousness your life may one day depend on your

156   **MAKE OR BUY**

tanks (a thorough mention of installation procedure will be made in a later chapter).

Precut Plywood Parts

One of the most time-saving items you can purchase is a precut plywood interior, see photo 17. Most companies offer either full-size paper templates or precut and roughly fitted plywood pieces that are numbered and coded. They are fairly easy to assemble if the routing is at least decent. Most pieces have to be scribed to the hull and perhaps trimmed, but overall the package still saves a tremendous number of hours compared to making and cutting templates, then saber-sawing the actual pieces from four by eight sheets of plywood.

Photo No. 17 — Precut plywood interior.

We bought such a package. I must say I did have a few frustrations when I found some odd looking pieces that seemed to fit nowhere. But in the final analysis things worked out well, even though we modified about 40% of the boat to some degree. The major criteria here is, of course, that you follow the original plans religiously. If you deviate or try to change more than about 20% of the interior, you will lose too many of the original parts to make the precut worth your while.

An interior kit of this sort for a typical 30-35 foot boat can be fit and assembled in about 160 hours at the most. This estimate is providing of course that (a) all the pieces are shipped together and (b) none of the pieces are viciously mis-cut.

The usual labor charge for routing and shipping an interior of this sort is about $400 — really not excessive when you consider how long it would take you to buy, load, unload, pattern, and cut out the pieces. Again, have the manufacturer provide you with an itemized list of pieces (see sample list in figures 20 and 21) and perhaps a set of diagrams, no matter how unpolished, depicting some resemblance of the piece in its final position. These aids will give you a much clearer picture in attempting to guess where a piece that looks something like a cross between an octopus and a chicken should fit.

Figure 20 — Sample List of Precut Plywood Parts.

CHART TABLE PATTERNS — II's

H-1   Chart table top — ½'' fir
H-2   Chart table face — ½'' mahogany plywood
H-3   Chart table face — ½'' mahogany plywood
H-4   Chart table divider — ½'' fir plywood
H-5   Chart table divider — ½'' fir plywood
H-6   Aft hanging locker — aft side — ½'' mahogany plywood
H-7   Aft hanging locker face — ½'' mahogany plywood
H-8   Aft hanging locker — forward side — ½'' mahogany plywood
H-9   Ends for chart table and galley — two of these — ½'' mahogany plywood
H-10   Aft hanging locker top — ½'' fir
H-11   Chart table lid — ½'' fir
H-12   Aft hanging locker bottom shelf inside locker
H-13   Chart table lid — ½'' fir
H-14   Aft hanging locker back — ½'' mahogany plywood
H-15   Chart table cabinet — ½'' mahogany
H-16   Chart table and galley locker face — two of these — ½'' mahogany
H-17   Chart table cabinet shelf — ½'' fir
H-18   Switch panel side — ½'' mahogany plywood
H-19   Switch panel front — ½'' mahogany
H-20   Chart table cabinet — aft face — ½'' fir
H-21   Cabinet corner posts — 1¾'' teak
H-22   Cabinet corner trim — forward — 13/16'' mahogany
H-23   Post above hanging locker — 1¾'' teak
H-24   Sea rail — 1¾'' teak
H-25   Sea rail corner — teak
H-26   Grab rail support — 13/16'' mahogany
H-27   Cabin corner trim — aft — 13/16'' mahogany
H-28   Bulkhead support knee

Figure No. 21 — Main cabin plywood parts.

Again, I'll mention that if you consider buying this kit, be absolutely certain that the bulkheads the manufacturer provides are at least ¾-inch thick and the cabinets at least ½-inch thick. The only place in a fiberglass boat for thinner plywood is on the cabin sides or on the cabin top as a decorative cover.

The grade of plywood provided is, of course, to be seriously considered. I believe no need exists for marine plywood in a fiberglass boat. For the cost, all it really supplies is absolutely perfect pieces with no small voids like you will find in the much less expensive ABX grade ply. ABX is quite acceptable but you should get at least ABX, because it has one perfect side (that's the A), one very good side with no knots (B), and the laminating glue utilized is of exterior grade (X).

Other than the above points, the kit is a worthwhile proposition as long as you won't feel inhibited or restrained from attempting changes, believing that only the gods at the factory can devise the proper design or the proper cut. Hack, cut, and butcher all you like. The world isn't going to fall on your head and you'll wind up with an interior that you like or at least one that you created. If you do plan drastic changes, it may still be wise to buy full-size paper templates from the factory. They usually provide them for approximately $100. And here it's not quite as heartbreaking to throw away a few pieces of paper as it is to throw away a large piece of ½-inch mahogany ply.

Finishing and Trim Kits
1. Metal parts

Most boatyards have stainless fittings custom-made for them in bulk; thus, they get a sizeable discount which they sometime pass on to customers. Even if not, you will spend a tremendous amount of time and money getting a shop to custom make you a few pieces. Therefore, if the parts the boatyard offers are well welded and are guaranteed to be at least the 304 stainless or good bronze, then purchase your hull fittings, stanchions, chainplates, and tangs from the factory. The fittings should be of sufficient thickness to withstand the worse possible weather, even a good number of knockdowns and pitch-polings. Anything that is marginal has no place on a cruising boat. (See table 1)

If you know a machinist who is dying to build your part for the sheer joy, who is trustworthy, and who is willing to do it for little money, by all means don't deprive the man.

2. Wood parts

Often offered are teak or mahogany trim for interior and exterior as well as doors and drawers. These parts are milled,

• **STRAP FORK END**

• **STRAP EYE END**

WIRE ROPE DIAMETER	LENGTH OF STRAP	PIN DIAMETER
1/16	1-1/16	3/16
3/32	1-1/2	3/16
1/8	1-5/8	3/16
5/32	1-15/16	1/4
3/16	2-3/16	5/16

• **BALL & SHANK**

ROPE DIAMETER	BREAK STRENGTH	SHANK DIAMETER AFTER SWAGING	BALL DIAMETER AFTER SWAGING
1/16	480	.112	.190
3/32	920	.143	.253
1/8	2000	.190	.315
5/32	2800	.222	.379
3/16	4200	.255	.442

Table 1 — Fitting Strengths.

MAKE OR BUY
161

bull-nosed, etc. and are very convenient if you are going to follow the standard interior. But even if you think you will be, I would not purchase too many of these items. As you build you will surely find you'd like to change something and no matter how trivial the change may be, the thought of discarding even a few pieces of teak worth the price of gold will surely inhibit you.

I look upon these packages with great negativity for I know from experience that the most enjoyable parts of the boat are those we've conceived and created ourselves. To rob oneself of these tiny joys is being quite masochistic and defeats the main purpose of building a boat yourself, which is to create something to your own needs out of your own dreams and your own design and with your own hands. If you are willing to sacrifice the simple pride and quiet joy arising from this, by all means go ahead. Buy every piece and fit "A" to "B" and "X" to "Y", but next time buy a jig-saw puzzle. They're cheaper and they don't create such an unholy mess in the backyard. Of course, all of the above is my own opinion, and you may have a different idea of boatbuilding entirely.

To be reassuring, I must say that the actual milling of the wood is a very simple operation. You should have a table saw and a router anyway for other uses. With them in your possession, the milling of sea-rails, berth-rails, corner posts, drawer faces, support poles, etc. should be neither difficult nor time consuming. For exact procedure, these things will be itemized in the construction section of this book.

Mast and Rigging

If you are happy with the sail plan, the rigging meets specifications for your size of boat, the swedging seems proper (see rigging installation chapter), and you have the money then factory purchase is advisable. If you have doubts on any aspect, then provide your own. You can buy an extrusion made to your specifications. Tapping holes in aluminum and installing machine screws is no great task. Here, as with all parts of the boat, the more you do yourself, the more you'll learn and the greater confidence you'll have in your craft and yourself.

The rigging will have to be made by a rigger. The turnbuckles you can buy anywhere yourself. If the factory has open-bodied stainless, you could consider buying theirs, but first ascertain that they are machined from solid stock instead of cast. Casting may result in weak air or dirt pockets which are hard to detect or diagnose without x-ray and may result in eventual fatigue and failure. The open body is important (although partially a matter of taste) because you can see how much thread you have left inside the barrel.

Stainless on stainless makes by far the strongest turnbuckle, but it can and sometimes does gall, resulting in an almost unmovable bonding. Stainless and bronze combination is also well proven. Seafast, Navtec, and Merriman have been functioning satisfactorily for years. For the strength they offer please consider table 2.

ALL BRONZE: MERRIMAN

TURN-BUCKLE SIZE	WIRE SIZES	TURNBUCKLE TENSILE STRENGTH	WIDTH OF JAWS	ADD FOR TOGGLE	FIG. 377 LENGTH BETWEEN CENTERS EXTENDED	CLOSED	†LENGTH 2/3 EXTENDED	WEIGHT
¼	⅛	2750 lbs.	¼	1½	11¼	7½	9½	5 oz.
5⁄16	5⁄32	4300 lbs.	5⁄16	1½	11½	7¾	10¾	9 oz.
⅜	3⁄16	6500 lbs.	⅜	1½	12½	8⅜	11½	13 oz.
7⁄16	7⁄32	9000 lbs.	7⁄16	1⅞	13½	9⅛	12¼	1 lb. 2 oz.
½	¼-9⁄32	10300 lbs.	½	1⅞	15	10⅛	13½	1 lb 12 oz.
⅝	5⁄16-⅜	17000 lbs.	⅝	2⅝	18½	12¾	16¾	3 lbs.
¾	7⁄16	29000 lbs.	¾	2⅝	21½	14¾	19¾	4 lbs.
⅞	½	43500 lbs.	⅞	2⅞	25¼	18⅝	23	8 lbs.
1	⅝	56500 lbs.	1	3½	25½	19¾	22	11 lbs.
*1¼	¾	81000 lbs.	1¼	4	36¾	25¼	32	18 lbs.

STAINLESS-BRONZE: SEAFAST

FOR WIRE DIA.		THREAD & PIN DIA.	BREAKING STRENGTH LBS.	MIN. LNG.	MAX. LNG.	PART NO.
⅛"	5⁄32"	¼"	3,800	8"	10¼"	TT-8
5⁄32"	3⁄16"	5⁄16"	5,600	8½"	11"	TT-10
3⁄16"	7⁄32"	⅜"	9,000	9½"	12⅜"	TT-12
¼"	9⁄32"	½"	13,000	13½"	17¼"	TT-16
5⁄16"	⅜"	⅝"	20,000	14¾"	19⅜"	TT-20

Table 2 — Turnbuckle Specifications.

Tracks, tangs, spreader brackets, goosenecks, cleats, chicken heads, and sheaves you will find at good marine stores. Or you can have them made by most mast builders, many of whom will sell you the parts. Aluminum welding is no hobby to begin on your own mast. Leave it to someone who can do it very very well.

Of course if you love wood masts and the manufacturer offers only aluminum, your decision is made. If you do plan to buy the mast offered, however, check (besides the size of tangs, fittings, and turnbuckles) the following:

MAKE OR BUY

1. Mast shape and gauge. See table 3. The table is workable but it is dangerous to generalize, for a mast with thin walls and a great cross-section can be as strong or stronger than a mast with thick walls and a small cross-section. An aerospace engineer acquaintance once worked out a formula for me in about two hours; it escapes me at the moment.

2. Welding. The beads should be clean and even.

3. Fittings should be bedded in good sealant to prevent water from hanging between the fitting and the mast. Constant moisture can and will cause corrosion in the aluminum.

4. Track ends should be bolted if possible, although it is not vital.

5. Cleats for the halyards should be through-bolted. It is vital that you through-bolt them; it will be easy because machine screws are normally used and it's not an earth-shattering feat to reach into the base of a mast while it's down. Install a few lock washers and nuts on the machine screws just to be sure. It's a simple task, yet mast makers neglect it, saying that their method is strong and secure enough. I'd say exactly the same thing if I were building the mast for their boat.

Wiring, Plumbing, and Engine Hook-Up Kits

If the manufacturer's complete boats seem well thought out and well executed; if he supplies you with acceptable schematics; and if his reputation for building quality boats is unmarred and unquestioned, then buy whatever of these kits he suggests and has available. You may eventually end up changing a lot of the original system; but it's so difficult to obtain the exact parts you need when you need them, that it's advisable to buy whatever you can if ever you can so that you'll have it in an emergency even though it won't fit worth a damn. The psychological reassurance its existence provides makes it well worth keeping in the back of some never-to-be-opened drawer.

Apart from the preceding itemizations, it may be well worth it to consider the purchase of hardware, portlights, latches, prop shaft, stuffing box, seacocks, etc. from the manufacturer. I would especially strongly recommend buying them from the manufacturer if you live in an isolated area. I have met a good number of people who have tried building various boats in places like Chico, California, in the depths of New Mexico or Arizona, which resulted in a tremendous amount of frustration. I can certainly feel sympathy for the people although I cannot empathize because I built my boat in Newport Beach, the heart of an area that is innundated by sailboat manufacturers, sailboat suppliers, and various sub-trades that supply the industry. Here, anything I could wish for was no more than an hour's drive away.

I can appreciate the frustrations of those in isolated or non-marine areas and to them I have one recommendation. Hoard everything you possibly can whether it is supplied by the builder,

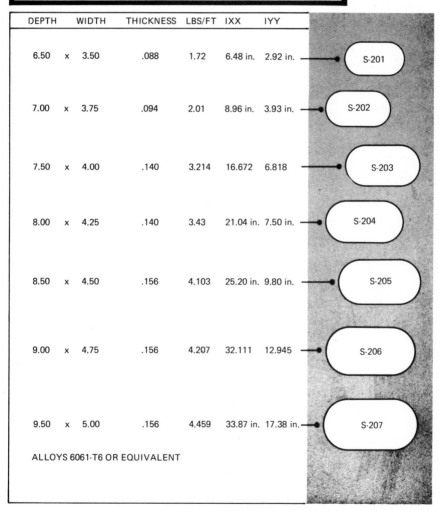

SERIES S-200 MAST SECTIONS

DEPTH		WIDTH	THICKNESS	LBS/FT	IXX	IYY	
6.50	x	3.50	.088	1.72	6.48 in.	2.92 in.	S-201
7.00	x	3.75	.094	2.01	8.96 in.	3.93 in.	S-202
7.50	x	4.00	.140	3.214	16.672	6.818	S-203
8.00	x	4.25	.140	3.43	21.04 in.	7.50 in.	S-204
8.50	x	4.50	.156	4.103	25.20 in.	9.80 in.	S-205
9.00	x	4.75	.156	4.207	32.111	12.945	S-206
9.50	x	5.00	.156	4.459	33.87 in.	17.38 in.	S-207

ALLOYS 6061-T6 OR EQUIVALENT

Table 3 — Mast Sections.

through catalogs, or through your local general store. Nothing is more frustrating than getting halfway into a job you enjoy or want to get done only to realize that you are short two No. 10 inch-and-a-half self-tapping pan heads, or you bought two T's instead of one T and an elbow and cannot complete the task.

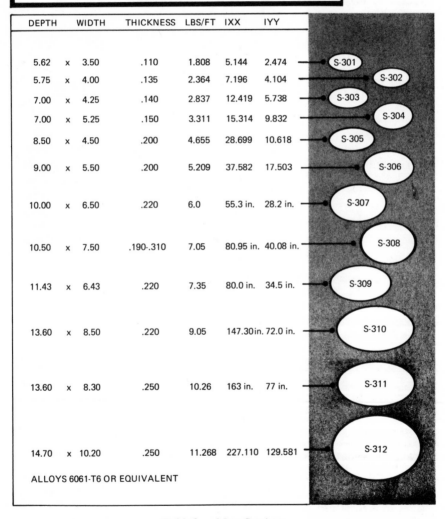

SERIES S-300 MAST SECTIONS

DEPTH		WIDTH	THICKNESS	LBS/FT	IXX	IYY	
5.62	x	3.50	.110	1.808	5.144	2.474	S-301
5.75	x	4.00	.135	2.364	7.196	4.104	S-302
7.00	x	4.25	.140	2.837	12.419	5.738	S-303
7.00	x	5.25	.150	3.311	15.314	9.832	S-304
8.50	x	4.50	.200	4.655	28.699	10.618	S-305
9.00	x	5.50	.200	5.209	37.582	17.503	S-306
10.00	x	6.50	.220	6.0	55.3 in.	28.2 in.	S-307
10.50	x	7.50	.190-.310	7.05	80.95 in.	40.08 in.	S-308
11.43	x	6.43	.220	7.35	80.0 in.	34.5 in.	S-309
13.60	x	8.50	.220	9.05	147.30 in.	72.0 in.	S-310
13.60	x	8.30	.250	10.26	163 in.	77 in.	S-311
14.70	x	10.20	.250	11.268	227.110	129.581	S-312

ALLOYS 6061-T6 OR EQUIVALENT

Table 3 — Mast Sections.

MAKE OR BUY

Chapter Six
PREPARATION FOR ARRIVAL

Location

The greatest determinant of how long you will take to complete your boat is its location during construction. Minor variables like manual dexterity, common sense and other irreparable items aside.

Discussion on this subject may seem banal, but many people are at a loss for the best choice. The ideal situation would be to pack up the kids and dogs or vice versa and move next to the plant where the boat is built. There you will be close to materials, parts, advice. And most important you will be able to run over and see just exactly how part A12 which looks like a kidney fits to B6 which resembles a limp artichoke. Construction manuals are fine (we had a 400 page one) but there is still nothing comparable to looking at the finished product in deducing how it was assembled.

We moved from the northwest to Newport Beach just to build our boat and were more than fortunate with our surroundings. We rented space in a boat storage yard for $16 a month (50c a foot). The lot was perfect. It was paved; it was just below a cliff that was usually covered with blooming desert flowers; it was fenced in with a high cedar fence; and the people who owned it, Bart and Sandy, were the most easy going kindest people we have ever met.

Newport Bay was just across the street. From the deck of our land-locked fiberglass cave we could see the water and hundreds of sailboats. Apart from the romantic aspect this location was most practical; when we needed ideas, clarification, or just a visual change to a finished boat (after awhile one forgets that such a thing exists) we would just run across the street and feast our eyes. The rest of the surroundings were no less enviable. In the next block were two of the largest marine supply stores in Southern California. In between them was a huge hardware store, a marine radio shop, and a bank. Across the street was Minney's, a place that sells everything from antique barometers to nautical underwear. Also across the street were three shipyards, a boat brokerage, and a giant crane for launching. As a final topping, the Westsail plant was only six blocks away and the sun shone 320 days out of the year. Eat your heart out, America.

Other suppliers like mast makers, hardwood lumber yards, tool wholesalers, and stainless steel fabricators were within a radius of two miles. Our experience was one extreme. The other extreme is an enthusiast I've heard of who's building a 44-foot ketch in Nebraska in a gulch.

Even though everything seemed so perfect we still made one critical mistake. We wanted more hills and greenery than Newport Beach could offer, so we rented an old cottage 16 miles away in Laguna Beach — a fatal error. Our only occupation was that of building the boat and if our enthusiasm drooped during the day, we'd fold up and go home. By the time we'd get there we again felt like returning and working; but of course it was too far to drive, so we stayed at home and crossed the day off the calendar.

I do not think abundance of immediate supplies is as critical as having the boat near one's home; the nearer, the better. It is best if the thing is in your driveway with your garage or basement as a well-stacked tool shed and workshop next to it. That way if you have a regular job, the spare hours can be spent working on the boat rather than driving, unpacking, and setting up, etc.

You will more than likely be some distance from suppliers if your boat is near your house, so you'll have to plan more carefully, purchasing everything in large quantities so you won't run out, when you most need things.

Many people have done the contrary. Instead of bringing the boat to their home, they brought their home to the boat. In a boat-yard nearby us is a couple from Virginia (and a gargantuan black labrador) living in a Volkswagen camper below their bowsprit. Not far away lives a man, his wife, and a five-week-old baby who came only to build the boat, from Ontario.

Others even out-extremed them like the one social-psych professor from Michigan whose boat was next to ours. He just pushed the sawdust out of the way in his half-finished boat and moved aboard. I would not recommend this action. There is nothing worse than attempting boat building on any kind of an organized system only to find yourself and your belongings constantly in the way. A boat is a small enough space where merely the tools and the materials you're using are interference enough. Anything like large pillows or chocolate pudding will just be headaches that totally out-weigh the convenience of being near your boat. If you like to rough it, pitch a tent underneath the keel.

If you need criteria other than the above, here are a few basics to be considered:

1. Try to put the boat on pavement or concrete pads. It's likely to spend over a year there and it's good to level it once without danger of it shifting when the rains come. Leveling will facilitate construction by enabling you to use a level for installation of cabinetry and bulkheads instead of attempting to measure and square everything from reference points that are at best, arbitrary and at worst, non-existent. The absence of mud and dirt will make a significant contribution to speeding up construction.

2. Try to leave a space at least three feet wide around the boat so that you can put up a scaffold to work on the exterior items like caprails and decks. It's much easier to work from scaffolding looking up then to hang upside down over the bulwarks. And it's much easier to lay teak decks from a scaffold than to work backwards from a deck, constantly trying to keep out of your own way.

3. Try to stay as far away from neighbors as possible. It's very intimidating to run a drill motor at 11:30 at night when the neighbor's bedroom is only a few feet away.

4. Hide it. At first you will think it's great fun to be the hit of the block but soon you will be out with the molten lead and boiling water when you hear footsteps on the bottom of the scaffold. There is nothing (and I must emphasize nothing) more detrimental to boat construction than visitors, some of whom are interesting, but most of whom are embarrassingly boring and uninformed.

5. Build a roof of some sort over the boat if you can. Even if you are lucky enough to build a boat in Southern California where you will not need to fear rain, it is advisable to have a roof over your head. Dew can keep everything wet until noon and if you're laying teak decks, gluing hatch boards, or spraying gel-coat, this moisture can be disturbing.

6. A tool shed is an almost must. To everything there are exceptions; but it is beautiful to have a shed near you where you can mill your wood, prefabricate things, and above all store the

mountains of junk that you will accumulate. We had a small shed about 12 by 20 feet that we found adequate for band saw, table saw, and routing table, see photo 18. We managed to squeeze a lot of shelfage out of the areas above the tools.

A few prefabricated pieces of scaffolding can also be handy. Avoid building scaffolding at all costs. Wood is expensive and if you look around you'll find old scaffolds everywhere. It's nice to have your ladder removable so that you can chain it to the boat's cradle when you're not there. You'll be amazed at the number of inconsiderates wandering around in cowboy boots on your varnished hatches if you leave the ladder, and therefore the deck, accessible.

Photo No. 18 — A well-equipped though somewhat chaotic tool shed.

Prefabrication

Without being facetious one can safely say that almost every wood part of a fiberglass boat can be prefabricated. That statement really means that you need not initially invest $10,000 in a hull and deck, etc. and then finish it off. But you can actually start with a few dollars worth of tools and some comparatively inexpensive raw wood stock and begin construction. The only awkward possibility could be that by the time you finish the pre-fab, the company that manufactures the hull and deck would have gone out of business.

PREPARATION FOR ARRIVAL

Apart from such an occurrence, you can put a deposit on a hull and begin work on the less expensive items while you save enough to pay for the boat. The degree of completion to which you carry this prefabrication will vary from item to item. But if the manufacturer supplies you with an exhaustive construction manual you can at least mill many of your wood parts and even completely finish and ready some for installation.

Items that you can completely finish including varnishing and oiling:

hatches	belaying pins
sampson posts	teak grates
bowsprit	masts, booms, spreaders
boomkin	ladders
tiller	grabrails
doors	compass boxes
drawers	dorade boxes
tables	

Things you can completely mill and cut to rough lengths:

searails	teak deck covering boards for cockpit trim
corner posts	grabrails
berth rails	bulkhead trim
hatch coamings	deck beams
table legs	cap rails

Things you can mill to size but to random lengths:

cleat stock	plywood seating cleats
small trim slats	tongue and groove covering
teak deck and cabin sole stock	

Other items to keep you busy:

fuel and water tanks (metal)	winch mounts
electrical panel	tangs and fittings

The greatest help will be if you can get full-sized paper templates (available from most factories for about $100) and proceed to precut all your plywood cabinetry. If you are hesitant about finalizing your layout, you can ask the manufacturer to sell you a scale model of an empty hull, see photo 19. You can then mock up, out of balsa or foam, a perfectly to-scale interior. Only then will you actually know whether some of your planned changes can be practicably applied or not.

If a scale model hull is not available, try to secure line drawings. They are more difficult to use than the scale model hull but they are better than nothing. If you are fairly certain that you will adopt the standard construction procedures, arrange to receive the construction manual ahead of time and study the thing from

Photo No. 19 — Model of an empty hull.

cover to cover. Familiarize yourself with pieces, parts, and assembly methods. Ascertain how they are fitted together; thus you won't have a great cold fear when your hull arrives and you're standing in an icy panic not knowing whether to scream or go blind.

PREPARATION FOR ARRIVAL

Chapter Seven
TOOLS

I accept that the finest boats were built with an ax and hand saw. But I have less time and a few half decent improvements have been made in technology during the last century. Tools should not be scrimped on. Buy everything you may need (you won't need very much) and buy the best quality you can; otherwise, the cheapies will give you nothing but trouble and they'll fall apart before the boat is half done. You will find a checklist of recommended tools in the appendix. An analysis of the best ones is given below.

In general, I would say that the best hand tools like hammers, plyers, levels, and squares are made by Stanley. They are costly, but well worth the difference. If you go cruising, most of your hand tools should accompany you. So you may as well get the best, take care of them, and let them help you.

With power tools, you have two choices. You can get the very expensive Milwaukee or Rockwell saws, routers, and drill motors and hope they last forever. They probably will. Or you can buy, fairly reasonably, a good product from department or home-building stores. Most have every tool you can think of and some that you can't think of. Although the quality isn't the ultimate, they are worth the dollars spent. They also have one fabulous advantage. Most of them carry a year's guarantee which means that when something breaks, burns out, etc. you can return the tool to the store and they will immediately replace it with a new one.

In a way, this guarantee is somewhat of an inconvenience because some tools pass away rather predictably. But there is one tremendous advantage to the system. You can burn out a 3/8'' drill motor three or four times during the construction of your boat. Every time you can go in and demand and receive a new one, except the last time when the boat is almost done and the tool dies. Take it back and tell them that you're sick and tired of replacing it and you want your money back. They will oblige. By this time (probably a year later) the price will have gone up and your investment will have paid dividends.

There are a few power tools every boat-owner will want to retain. These should be of the best quality. To play about with cheapo tools, which, although they don't completely die, spark and spit and scream and jerk, would show most improper judgement. If any long distance cruising is to be undertaken, carting decomposing carcasses of wretched junk about would show folly.

The minimal hand-power tool menagerie should include: a reversible drill-motor, with variable speed and a 3/8" chuck, an excellent sabre saw as small and as heavy duty as possible, and the small, indestructible vibrator sander discussed on page 212.

Hand Tools

Give forethought before you buy and get the best.

1. Saws

Probably the only hand saw you will use for wood with great frequency in the boat's construction will be a dovetail, see photo 20. It has a reinforced very heavy blade that will not flex or bend and therefore gives perfectly straight cuts. It's ideal for use with a miter box, see photo 21, during construction of drawers, doors, and trim. A good 12-inch dovetail is an ideal length and weight, although I have heard people exclaim that smaller ones can be used to a greater advantage in short cluttered spaces where a hand has difficulty manipulating.

Photo No. 20 — Dovetail saw.

Photo No. 21 — Miter box with dovetail saw.

Keep the saw very sharp, for if it becomes dull you may tend to force it through hard work, bend the blade, and render it useless. This tool should be kept for cruising; it may be the most important cutting tool you have.

A good hack saw is also a must. The one that can be adjusted to accommodate blades of different lengths, see photo 22, is convenient, even though it tends to be less accurate than the fixed-length ones because it does occasionally wobble about. Buying the most expensive blades is advisable. They last much longer and they are infinitely better than the cheapos which become dull, heat up, and become even duller after only a few uses.

I have seen people build a boat with only a hand cross-cut saw. Construction can of course be done by such means, but power tools can be used to much greater advantage.

2. Hammers

A good claw hammer, see photo 23, is a must. Many people like the lightweight handled rubber equipped ones but I find that they tend to wear out faster because the rubber deteriorates, or the rubber to metal adhesion breaks in which case the hammer comes flying off, hitting you in the forehead. Wooden-handle ones also lose heads but at least they give warning and can be re-wedged.

The claw is necessary for prying and pulling nails. Get one with

TOOLS 175

Photo No. 22 — Adjustable hack saw.

Photo No. 23 — Claw hammer.

not too dramatic a curve or you will have difficulty using the pryer in corners. If the curve is too great the handle will be forced to angle off to one side drastically.

A small machine hammer, see photo 24, with one end rounded is very good to have, although I have not yet found everyday use for the bulby end of it. Take excellent care of hammers. Their heads get easily covered with glue, resin, etc. and any unevenness will cause the hammer to bend nails every which way. Beware of using any old hammer you find. If it was ever used for major construction the flat face may be rounded on the shoulders. The hammer is then prone to either bend nails or glance off and mark the wood.

3. Mallet

A decent mallet with a coiled leather head, see photo 25, is

TOOLS

Photo No. 24 — Machine hammer.

Photo No. 25 — Mallet.

desirable. If you spend $15 for a good chisel with a leather-tipped handle you do not want to bash the leather tip to shreds for want of a $5 mallet.

4. Chisels

You can get by with two or three chisels. Again, get the best quality. The better ones have wood handles with leather tips. If these tips ever wear off, they can be replaced by using a thick cut of hide and making a minor adjustment to the wood handle, see photo 26.

A 1-inch wide chisel will probably prove narrow enough for most jobs yet wide enough to guarantee a straight cut. The ¼-inch chisel is good to have for fine detail work and also to cut radiused curves like the recess for deck fills. Keep a low-quality 1-inch cheapo for brutal usage like scraping dry glue, cutting through fiberglass, and dropping onto the cement floor.

To keep the chisels good and sharp, avoid hitting anything hard like screws and keep the tips covered when not in use by a sheath

Photo No. 26A — Chisels.

Photo No. 26B — Chisels.

arrangement of some sort. A piece of cardboard doubled over and taped is quite sufficient. When working with teak, always have a wetting stone handy and periodically run the chisel over the stone to renew the edge. If you ever suffer any nicks you should grind the edge until it's totally even, then re-sharpen it with a stone.

5. Planes

You should probably own and keep two hand planes. A small 6-inch one is a must, for with it you can shape anything effectively. I prefer this size to the large two hand variety because the little one always leaves the other hand free which is most desirable if you can't use a vise or blocks.

Planes seldom require sharpening, especially if you remember to never store them upright. If you do, the blade dulls a little every time you put it down. Avoid planing hardened glue or resins.

Another shaping tool which I dislike, but Candace and most other people that have used it swear by it, is the "idiot tool." I christened it by that name feeling that it's mostly used by those afraid to use a small hand plane, see photo 27. The idiot tool is more commonly known as a "Sur-Form," see photo 28. It has many teeth, like a rasp, but unlike a rasp, they are flat blades like tiny planes.

Photo No. 27 — Small hand plane.

Photo No. 28 — "Sur-Form."

The Sur-Form is excellent for minor shaping, especially where danger of chipping or over-planing exists. Both the Sur-Form and the hand plane are made by Stanley and Craftsman; however, the one disadvantage the Stanley has is that it is manufactured in

England and this makes replacement of the blades quite difficult for they are often unavailable. The teeth do get rapidly clogged with glue or paint, so take care. When the blades are in stock, get a goodly number of them to last you through the whole boat. Sur-Forms come in two sizes, one requiring two hands, the other only one. The small one seems more functional, because the real advantage of a Sur-Form over a common plane is that the teeth extend clear to the tip of the blade, making work in tight corners possible. And for this type of work, the smaller the tool the better.

6. Levels

I found a 24'' level quite sufficient. Anything larger would be awkward to use inside a small boat. And a much smaller one would react violently to tiny irregularities, thereby give inaccurate readings. It's advisable to get one with vertical readouts at both ends so you won't have to make like a baton twirler 50% of the time.

Making anything completely level is not merely a matter of esthetics. Both unlevel and unsquare assemblies lead to greater problems later when other parts are to be fitted to them. Take your time; level and square things; you'll save yourself cutting hundreds of trapezoids.

7. Squares

Three types of square prove very useful in boat building.

a. Framing square. The large carpenter's steel square, see photo 29, proved necessary on large assemblies of cabinetry, bulkheads, etc. where a smaller one would have given inaccurate lines. It also proves invaluable as a straight edge for marking out plywood and as a cutting edge along which a knife blade can be slid when cutting insulative foam.

b. Small square. This square is used constantly for squaring off ends of smaller pieces like cleat stock, sea-rails, and door frames. The wood portion is much thicker than the metal, see photo 30, thus you will not have to worry about a part of the square "slipping" from the wood's side. Take very good care of this square and don't drop it. If you toss it about or hammer with it, the central bronze pin can work loose and the thing will then be useless.

c. Bevel square. This square is probably the most important tool in boat building, see photo 31. The joint is adjustable with the aid of a wing nut, enabling you to size and duplicate any angle. The steel arm is notched in the center so that it can slide back and forth allowing you to measure in tight corners as well as at open ends. Stanley makes the best of these squares, although many other fine ones exist. With the wing nut type, one should be cautious when

Photo No. 29 — Framing square.

to make sure that in the locked position one wing does not protrude past the outside corner of the square as in figure 22. If it does, measuring inside corners accurately will be impossible. You will find that the handles are notched so that the blade can be recessed when not in use to prevent it from bending when being abused. Always store it in this position.

Photo No. 30 — Small square.

TOOLS   **181**

Photo No. 31 — Bevel square.

8. Rasps and files

The best shaping tool for fine work is the shoe rasp, see photo 32. One side is rounded; the other side is flat and the two halves (longitudinally) have teeth of different coarseness. This tool is an absolute must. It can form, shape, and smooth any joint with great speed and accuracy. Keep it clean with a wire brush. If the teeth get

INTERFERING WING NUT !

Figure No. 22 — Wing nut square.

TOOLS

Photo No. 32 — Shoe rasp.

clogged with glue throw it away and get a new one or you'll waste hours of your life.

Files of other shapes and grades come in handy. For woodwork a 3/8'' or ¼'' diameter round file, see photo 33, is sometimes helpful. And of course for metal work you'll want a good weight bastard file as well as one with some curvature.

Keep a rough square-edged metal file handy. Without a handle (so it fits better) you can do wonders in 90 degree corners working both pieces evenly. This process is the one thing the shoe rasp cannot do.

Photo No. 33 — Small round file.

9. Brushes

a. Acid brushes, see photo 34. This brush is excellent for gluing and throwing away at the end of the day. It only costs a nickle and it is definitely not worth your time and acetone required to clean it. If you made 60c a hour you would probably break even.

b. Resining brushes, see photo 35. The most important consideration here is that the brushes be cheap and have no paint on the handle. They must be cheap because it's impossible to clean them

Photo No. 34 — Acid brush.

after a full day's use. They can't have paint on the handles or the acetone will slowly eat it off and you'll find great chips of paint all over your masterful bonds. You should wash them between uses during the day, but you will find the base full of hardened resin by the day's end.

c. Paint brushes. It is best to get a good batch of different sizes from one inch to 3-inch if you find a deal. You will use them for the strangest things such as dusting, oiling, etc. For varnishing you are well advised to get expensive, well-made brushes. The good ones are about $12 for a 2'' brush but they save the agony of picking out hairs from the varnish every four inches. Wash them diligently with paint thinner and warm soapy water until they squeak, unless you make $60 per hour.

10. Other hand tools

You almost cannot live without a matte knife, see photo 36. This tool comes with removable blades, most of them with two different points. The blades last for a very long time. They are also very sharp and their blades can be set at different depths depending on how thick the material is that you are cutting. They are excellent for whittling, for sharpening pencils, for cutting everything from insulation to cane, and if everything else seems totally gloomy, your wrists.

A new tape measure is good to have. A 12-foot long one is sufficient for most cases. I say "new," for once the tip becomes loose, the accuracy becomes unreliable. With this problem in mind

Photo No. 35 — Resining brush.

TOOLS

Photo No. 36 — Matte knife.

one may be well advised to invest in a folding rule, see photo 37, which cannot lose its accuracy (especially for short pieces) unless you hack one end off with a saw.

As described in "Construction," a good compass with a wing-nut tightener is a must for scribing, making circles, etc.

A hand drill is advisable to have but it will be of greatest use at sea because anything it can do a drill motor can do just as well and a little bit faster. The auger is too large and clumsy a tool for most interior work, but a small wheel type, see photo 38, can be often useful, especially if one has an adjustable drill bit. It can make cutting odd sized holes a possibility although it is the worst possible cutter imaginable.

Two good pairs of plyers come in extremely handy. The adjustable jaw kind, see photo 39, is excellent for substituting as a wrench,

Photo No. 37 — Folding rule.

TOOLS

Photo No. 38 — Hand drill.

Photo No. 39 — Adjustable jaw pliers.

while the heavier fixed jaws have a more accurate tip, perfect for digging out almost buried nails. This type also has cutting jaws, see photo 40, which are very useful for shortening nails and cutting heavy wire. Speaking of wire, you will also need a combination

Photo No. 40 — Fixed jaw pliers.

TOOLS

stripper-crimper, see photo 41, as explained in the "wire connectors" section of "Electrical Installation."

Another handy tool that isn't elaborated on in "Construction" is a pointed awl which is absolutely perfect for splitting plugs in half

Photo No. 41 — Two excellent wire-cutters & crimps.

and pulling or digging them out. You will also have other needs for it.

11. Miscellaneous

    a. Pencils — by the hundreds because they always get lost.

    b. Center punch.

    c. Screwdrivers (all kinds).

    d. Countersink.

    e. C-clamps, see photo 42 — about five with 10-inch opening jaws, 4 with 2 to 3-inch opening jaws, and one tiny one.

    f. Bar clamps (2), see photo 43.

    g. Rat-tail brush.

    h. Wetting stone.

    i. Broom.

Photo No. 42 — C-clamp.

Photo No. 43 — Bar clamp.

Power Tools

It is true that you may have a lot of money tied up in tools if you buy the best or most expensive. But if you are near any kind of working community where other boat builders or builders of any kind live, passing the tools on with very little loss should be no problem. I bought all new tools such as a table saw, band saw, router, etc., and sold them for only 10% less than I paid before I even finished the boat.

1. Table saw

Even if you plan to purchase every piece of wood milled and

precut from the factory, you will still need to fit everything together. Without a good table saw, you'll waste many precious hours. To say that a table saw can do almost any kind of cutting is over-simplification, but it can, with the occasional aid of attachments rip to width, see photo 44, cut to length, see photo 45, miter, rabbet, tongue-and-groove, see photo 46, as well as act as a table disc sander when used with a hard cored sanding disc in place of the blade. It can make the most accurate cuts on even the smallest pieces with the minimum amount of threat to your fingers. To get the very best, you need to spend no more than $300. Very good older saws of the heaviest construction can be bought used from woodworking shops, furniture factories, cabinet makers, or through want ads.

Photo No. 44 — Ripping on table saw.

The older the tool, the more likely it will be that its construction will be heavy, see photo 47. Things like guides, miter arms, and other adjustments will have exceptionally heavy, positive locking settings which will provide the most accurate and safest cuts. The most dangerous thing about any table saw is if it is poorly constructed, such as guides that shift, miter arms that twist, and blades and mounts that quiver and bend unduly.

TOOLS 189

Photo No. 45 — Cutting to length on table saw.

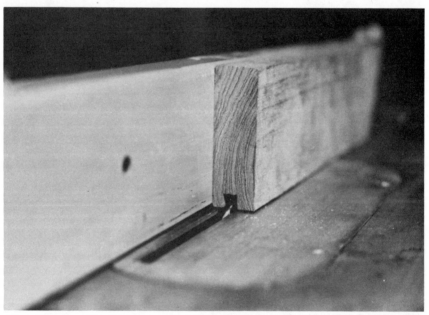

Photo No. 46 — Cutting for tongue-and-groove joint.

190 **TOOLS**

Photo No. 47 — Older behemoth table saw.

Any of the above will cause the saw to ''bind'' and kick a piece of wood back very hard at you. Poor equipment will also cause you to take undue chances and resort to catastrophic maneuvers such as trying to twist a piece of wood so that the wobbly blade cuts straight. Any time you have to use force to push or pull wood through a table saw, you are begging for danger. The saw can bind and kick the wood out, either smashing your fingers or drawing them into the blades.

Good equipment will stand fast, requiring only mental energy to prevent accidents. Again, Rockwell is an excellent source for a good table saw if you are in the market for a new one. Construction is heavy and service dependable. Try to buy at least a 10'' bladed saw. Anything less will not cut through wood thicker than 2½-inches.

For boat building you must secure a carbide-tipped blade, see photo 48. You will most likely be working with woods like teak, ash, oak, and mahogany, none of them very soft and all of them blade-dulling. A carbide-tipped blade will pay for itself by saving sharpening fees, not to mention the number of trips required to visit the saw sharpener. The more teeth the blade has, the finer will be the cut and the longer it will hold the edge. Of course, the more teeth it has the more expensive it will be to purchase and later to sharpen.

Check to be sure that the steel part of the blade is thick and heavy. I once spent $65 for a beautiful 12-inch carbide blade that bent like a cigarette paper upon the first contact with wood. The blade has to be thick and it has to be stiff.

Most good saws have a choice of motors you can use with them. At least a 1½-horsepower motor is necessary or the thing will heat up and the coil burn out when you cut hardwood for any length of time. If you have 220 wiring available, by all means get a 220 motor. Most of them provide more power and will last longer than the smaller 110 ones, which seldom reach more than 1½-horsepower.

Avoid buying the fancy gadgets that some manufacturers install for "safety and convenience." They are usually a hindrance to accurate cutting and will give you false confidence about safety, resulting in mis-cuts and accidents. Get the best built, simplest tool and remember that you are not just a bystander. You have to do all of the cutting. The saw motor only turns the blade. Concentrate and you should never have any problems.

I will refrain from reviewing the multi uses of the table saw, because most handbooks that come with the tools are very elaborate and thorough. Basic things like dado blades are also well documented, so I'll avoid being redundant. A few items that are worth

Photo No. 48 — Carbide-tipped table saw blade.

TOOLS

mentioning follow:

Always use a "pusher," see photo 49. It can be cut from scrap plywood. Cut a goodly bunch. Always have one near the saw and always use it. Never pass your fingers between the blade and the guide; that's making it a little bit too close.

To avoid most accidents, set the blade only high enough to barely cut through the piece of wood. This way, binding is almost eliminated and the chance of drawing your hand through the exposed blade is minimized.

When your saw is not in use, either sink the blade below the

Photo No. 49 — Table saw pusher.

table surface or pull the guard directly next to the blade and lock it there, see photo 50. This way, if you are sitting on the saw and somehow the thing is switched on by mistake the chances of your voice being raised three octaves will be eliminated.

a. Ripping. I found the ripping of random width planks into even-width strips (for decking, cabin sole) one of the most demanding tasks. Working with large planks is in itself awkward. Apart from that, use of the guide is not possible because the edge of the plank is usually too irregular to act as a true edge.

TOOLS

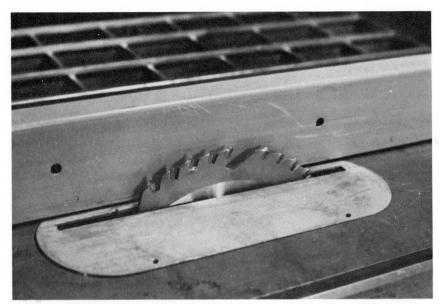

Photo No. 50 — Guarding the blade while not in use.

Therefore you have two choices to guide the plank. If it is horribly bowed or very irregular, use a chalk line, see photo 51, to mark a straight edge. You will now have to hand-guide the plank along this line, but it is not impossible. After this cut you will have a good straight edge with which you can use your guide to rip the rest of the plank.

Photo No. 51 — Chalk line.

TOOLS

If the planks are long, over 6 or 7 feet, it's desirable that you set up rollers behind and in front of the saw. This way you can rest one end of the plank while concentrating on cutting. Be sure to set the rollers at exactly the table level. If you don't, you will find the plank teeter-tottering. As it does so it will make irregular and, in the case of teak, very costly nicks in the wood.

If the bow is not too severe, you can set the guide ½-inch wider than the width you require of the final product as in figure 23. Most guides are 24 inches long so that any small irregularities in the wood will be nicely evened out into long curves. You will find the first cut usably even. You can now reset the guard to your exact desired width and, using your freshly cut edge against it, trim the raw, uneven ½-inch off. The rest of the plank can be cut, using the fresh cut edge as an even enough guide.

Figure No. 23 — Trimming bowed lumber.

b. Mitering. Whether the piece of wood is large or small, the blade has a tendency to push the wood along the miter edge, resulting in more of a curve that a straight edge. To prevent this curve, clamp all the wood to be mitered to the miter arm, see photo 52. Your hand will then be free and distant from the blade. When you are doing 90 degree cuts, using the miter guide is still a must for accurate cuts. Clamping will be unnecessary. Your hand is quite

TOOLS 195

adequate, as it will be for most angles approaching 90 degrees. When you get close to 75 or less, you will need to use clamps.

Keep the table free of glue and dirt. Oil it regularly to avoid rust and to aid in smooth wood movement. Take good care of your table saw; you will find it to be your greatest aid.

2. Band saw

I do not consider this saw the second most important power tool, but it is the second most expensive one. I have many acquaintances who completely by-passed the band saw and managed to complete their boats by substituting saber and table saws. A

Photo No. 52 — Clamping wood to miter arm.

good heavy-duty saber saw can indeed imitate a band saw in many cases. Problems arise only when one needs to cut small pieces. Clamping will then be necessary to keep the small piece from jumping about.

But the angles that the saber saw cuts can in no way be compared to the exactness of a band saw no matter how thick a saber saw blade is. Because it is attached only at one end, it has a tendency to bend and flex, therefore not cutting an accurate angle. Band saw blades on the other hand are guided directly above and below the wood, guaranteeing exact results. If the wood is 1½" or

TOOLS

thicker, even the hardest working saber saw will not be able to do an acceptable finishing cut in less than five minutes.

I loved our band saw. Once we bought one we never used that nerve-wracking, jumping, sliding, bouncy little saber saw for finishing work again. Of course a saber saw is invaluable and irreplaceable for hole-cutting, trimming, or work where a small tool needs to be utilized in a small space. But for quick accuracy in an area which needs little rasping or sanding to fit perfectly, the band saw is unsurpassable.

Again, Rockwell appears to excel in this field. They manufacture a very good 14'' wheel band saw that is almost light enough to move. But it is heavily enough built to last through thousands of board feet of teak and ash. The 2 hp motor it usually comes with will have adequate power to cut through as much as 6'' of teak, but do use prudence. It is not a steam roller.

Always maintain the correct blade tension. If it is too slack the blade will tend to bend and not only execute horribly inaccurate cuts, but also break. To help it somewhat, always set the upper bearings as tight above the piece you are cutting as possible, see photo 53. They will keep the blade from twisting.

The best blade I found was a medium-toothed 3/8'' one. We

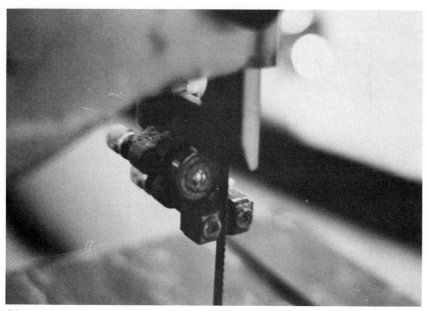

Photo No. 53 — Band saw blade guide.

TOOLS

tried ¼'' wide blades, believing that because of their narrowness they would bend more easily and have less tendency to bind, heat up, and snap. They didn't work out. The narrow blade was proportionately weaker, and the slight difference it offered in lack of surface friction was insignificant. In short, it broke.

Keeping the blades sharp was a great help. No other tool is more sensitive to force and pressure than a band saw. So guide the wood; don't force it through the blade. If you go off the scribe line don't try to twist your wood back onto the path. It is not possible for a blade to cut sideways, but it will break sideways.

Our saw cost $440 new. We used it for 5 months and sold it for $400. Even if I had to give it to an orphanage at the end of the five months it would have been well worth the cost.

3. Router

This tool is the second most important power tool in boat building. Used without a table it can shape cap rails, cut holes, bull-nose deck beams, cut patterns, and even decorate door frames, see figure 24. Used upside down and attached to a routing table, see

'A' = BULL NOSE 'B' = STRAIGHT BIT 'C' = RABBET

Figure No. 24 — Various router bits.

photo 54A and 54B, it becomes a miracle worker bullnozing pre-fab parts, rabbeting doors, and shaping even the smallest piece of wood with little danger to your fingers.

Stanley and Rockwell make fabulous routers, each available with a myriad of assorted bits. The most useful bits we found were

Photo No. 54A — Router upside-down in routing table.

Photo No. 54B — Router.

the 3/8'' bullnose, the straight bit, and the 3/8'' rabbet bits. With that combination you can do anything. For a smaller radius or shallower rabbet you can just lower the bullnose and the rabbet respectively to get your required depth. To do detail, as in figure 25, simply raise the bullnose and you will have a sharply etched line to

TOOLS

199

Figure No. 25 — Detailing with a bullnose.

your liking above the curve of the bullnose. To do shallower work horizontally with any bit, use a guard to control depth, see photo 55. The guard is a piece of wood with the central area cut away to accommodate the router bit. The ends are clamped to the table.

It is an amazing tool, but care should be taken with it. Slip the wood in straight for initial contact, then always proceed with the rotation of the bits. If you go against the rotation you will find chips of your wood splintered out.

A note for your health. Routers turn at fantastic speeds and have very sharp bits (or at least they should have very sharp bits).

Photo No. 55 — Router bit guard.

TOOLS

Therefore when you are changing bits, please unplug the machine. I know you've turned it off but just to be sure, unplug it. It wouldn't hurt. A fast turning router blade might.

4. Disc sander

For fine joiner work this tool is the best to have, see photo 56. You can get one with an adjustable table in order to arrive at exact angles. The sander can take off very small amounts extremely evenly. You will probably save by buying just the disc part with a take-off pulley, scrounging up an old washing machine motor, and building a plywood box. The whole investment should not run over $20. The sandpaper is self-adhesive and comes in all grits. Make the table good and firm so that even with the smallest piece of wood you'll have a perfectly good base.

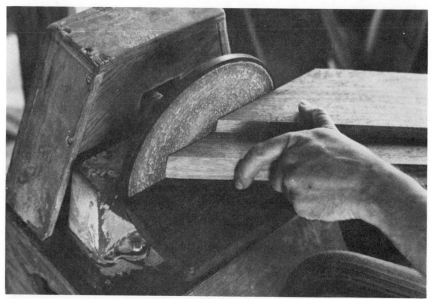

Photo No. 56 — Disc sander.

If you cannot afford the time or the money for a separate disc sander, the next best solution is to set up a jig to hold a belt sander firmly without requiring any manual support, see photo 57 and 58. As you can see, the solution is simple and inexpensive. Make sure you have a clamp at the top of the sander holding it to the box, because when you apply firm pressure to the belt, the machine will have a definite tendency to ''climb up'' your piece of wood then

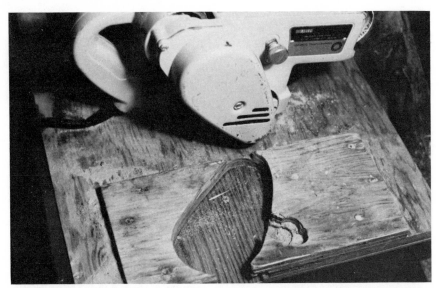

Photo No. 57 — Jig for belt sander.

Photo No. 58 — Belt sander set in jig.

along your arm, etc. Sixty grit sandpaper does much cleaner work than Nair.

The uses you can put the sander to are obvious. Its most important function arises when small pieces of wood that require

TOOLS

two hands to hold need to be shaped and fitted.

5. Drill motors

I begin by mentioning these items in the plural for you do need two. The most rapid way of building a boat is to have two drill motors plugged in beside you, one holding a drill bit and countersink, see photo 60, the other a screw gun bit. The first one, for drilling, can be the least expensive "cheapy" ¼-inch drill motor you can find. I bought mine brand new for $4.95 and it just now (after drilling about 10,000 holes) passed away. This motor needs no reverse or variable speed or anything. As long as it goes off and on almost when you want it, it's perfect.

Photo No. 59 — Drill motor.

A special note concerning the bit and countersink: the combination in photograph 60 is by far the best team. They are made by Fuller. The countersink is a separate tool with a set screw that can be released or tightened by an allen wrench. The set screw enables you to secure the countersink to any point on the drill bit depending on how deep a hole you want to drill.

One tends to use a 3/8'' countersink for most occasions. This size will fit any drill bit between 5/64 and 3/16. A larger countersink is of course available for use with larger bits or even bits of 1/8-inch diameter. It is a wise idea to hoard as many drill bits and countersinks as you can. They do often break or get dull, or even more often they get lost. However, tool sharpening places can sharpen them so don't throw them away when they become frustratingly dull to use.

TOOLS

Photo No. 60 — Drill bit and countersink with allen wrench.

The tapered drill bit has its advantages both with fiberglass and woodworking. Your drilled holes in the wood will seldom be too tight or too loose if you set the bit as shown in figure 26.

The drill motor you substitute for a screw gun has to be slightly more sophisticated than the "cheapy." A reverse gear and variable speed motor will be necessary if the most time is to be saved. Some people frown on a screw gun calling it an overuse of power tools, but I don't particularly consider the hand-tightening of 10,000 screws either a romantic or emotionally rewarding endeavor.

Figure No. 26 — Countersink settings.

TOOLS

Better tools and variable speed drill motors are available for this purpose, namely screw guns. They have a built-in clutch which is activated once the screw is tight. It is a very good tool, for not only does it protect the motor from straining and burning out, but it also keeps the screw heads from being snapped off by a motor whose torque cannot be immediately sensed and counteracted. Drill motors without clutches also have a tendency to keep spinning once the screw is tight, then jump out from the groove of the screw and chip or mark up the surrounding wood. After a few chips and marks, you should, however, be able to feel when a screw is beginning to tighten and back off slightly.

When you are setting screws, there's absolutely no need to pull the trigger back as far as it will go. Putting in screws at low speed with a variable speed drill motor is advisable. You will then run no risk of breaking the screw, breaking the wood, or breaking the screw gun bit.

Screw guns are much more expensive than drill motors. A good Milwaukee costs $90 to $100 and carries the added disadvantage of not being able to be substituted as a drill motor when needed. I do not think that a screw gun is an absolute necessity for building one boat only. If you intend to go on building boats or anything else, it may prove to be a valuable asset.

Another drawback to the "cheapo drill motor"/expensive screw gun combination exists. The cheapy should be ¼-inch with little power. This size will, however, leave you in a dilemma if you need a tool requiring low rpm's for metal drilling, or considerable torque for use with a hole saw, see photo 61.

Photo No. 61 — Hole saws.

To this end, a good ½ hp, 3/8'' chuck variable speed drill motor is needed. If you don't have one, you will suffer because you will miss out on a great variety of uses.

a. Hole sawing. This occupation will recur during the building of your boat for installation of scuppers, conduit, seacocks, cockpit drains, instruments, deck-fills, and hand holes.

Good hole saws that can stand up to repeated use, especially on fiberglass, are expensive. A good one, as in photo 62, has two pins in the arbor to keep the saw from skipping under stress. The hole saw shaft is hollow and is equipped with a set screw so that a drill bit (with one side of the stern flattened off) can be set through the shaft and tightened, leaving whatever amount of protrusion you require. You can simply mark the center of the spot for your hole and proceed. By the time the hole saw hits the material to be cut, a positive, firm guide has been drilled.

Photo No. 62 — Hole saw arbor.

This hole saw is made by Milwaukee and is very expensive. The arbor itself is about $15 and each hole saw costs between $7 and $13 depending on its diameter. Of course they are not adjustable, so for each different size hole you require a new $7 or $13 hole saw. But, their price does reflect their quality. The less expensive items put out by Black and Decker lose their sharpness with uneconomic rapidity, especially through fiberglass.

Some hole saws have solid shafts, leaving no potential for drill bit insertion. Attempting to start a hole with a saw of any diameter usually results in the saw dervishing about, gouging the life out of

TOOLS

the surrounding wood.

Hole sawing should not be treated frivolously because it is dangerous, especially in confined spaces. If you apply too much pressure unevenly the saw will tend to bite and stall (particularly in fiberglass and thick wood). Most people have the frightening habit of pressing the drill motor trigger into a locked position when they are hole sawing, knowing that it will be some time before they penetrate. When they use undue pressure; the saw binds, stops, and immediately the motor begins to spin. If your hand is in an awkward position the torque of the motor can snap your wrist. A friend broke an arm hole sawing, so the above information is dripping with experience.

To recap:

— Do not force a hole saw (or for that matter any saw). Allow the blade to do the cutting.

— If you press, do so very evenly.

— Under no circumstances, lock the trigger in an ''ON'' position.

For the cosmetically inclined, it is worth mentioning that drilling through wood from only one side is a mistake. Some pressure will always be present on the saw as it breaks through the other side, and this pressure is certain to cause the edge of the wood to chip away. It is advisable that you drill through only far enough for the drill bit to come out the other side. The center guide for your hole saw is now made. Then come around the other side and complete the cutting. The possibility of wood chipping will then be eliminated.

A light lubrication oil (like WD40) may be applied to both the inside and outside of the hole saw to lessen friction.

b. Grinding and sanding. Probably the ugliest work that must be done on a fiberglass boat is grinding fiberglass. It's most unpleasant because the tiny glass shrapnel settles into your pores to itch and irritate. But sometimes this process must be done, and the quickest possible way of doing it is with a drill motor and one of the assorted shapes of stone or metal grinding bits.

For shaping wood in hard to reach areas, a drill motor again comes in handy. The same shapes you saw for grinders are available with sandpaper attachments. One or all will be necessary for some use during your boat's construction. The fitted sandpaper pieces are inexpensive so you are well-advised to stock up and have ready a good number for that awkward moment when an impossible piece in an impossible place must be ground.

To save on the cost of the grinding wheel for sharpening tools you can buy a $3 attachment for your drill motor. Set the drill motor in a vise and you will now have the potential of sharpening any knife, any plane blade, or any chisel.

For sanding jobs of major proportions the flat disc sander or the smaller mushroom sander, see photo 63, attachments are ideal. Because of their size they can sand large surfaces fairly evenly and yet, because of their flexibility, they readily adapt to corners and awkward orifices.

Photo No. 63 — Mushroom.

Most disc sanders have the sandpaper changed by a set screw and washer system as in figure 27. On the smaller mushroom sanders, two systems are in practice. One uses an adhesive to secure the sandpaper to the rubber and the other has snap-in plastic cogs. The second is the quicker and cleaner of the two to use; of course it is slightly more expensive.

For the larger disc sanders a buffer is available. This instrument is at best a ring of sheepskin with a drawstring around the edge to tie beneath the disc. At worst, it's a nylon plush rag that will mat and clog upon the first application of rubbing compound.

Wire brushes of different coarseness and diameter can also be used with a drill motor, see photo 64. They are excellent for cleaning and polishing metals. Even more important, when used in conjunction with paint remover, they will take paint off of fiberglass. I mention this function because all too frequently we found ourselves overanxious and began painting somewhat prematurely, only to find that we had neglected to bond something important to the hull. Polyester resin of course will not stick to paint, so the paint had to be removed before further bonding.

TOOLS

TIGHTENING SCREW

RECESS IN RUBBER DISC. FOR WASHER & SCREW

Figure No. 27 — Changing sandpaper.

On cloth or over resined mat, paint removal is an easy task because the surface is smooth. A judicious layer of paint remover followed by scraping with a putty knife will clean off all the unwanted paint. On a more textured roving, you will find paint remaining in the dimples. To remove it you will need a wire brush. The higher the rpm of the drill motor the better. Do beware of the erosive potential of wire. If you maintain rotation over one area, you may find you have quickly worn through numerous layers of fiberglass. Grind with a back and forth motion. When the paint is gone move to another spot.

    c. Plug cutters. Plug cutting can be performed by the purchase of a $4 plug cutter, see photo 65, and a small drill press adapter for the drill motor, see photo 66. Plug cutting without aid of the drill press is not advisable, for most of your plugs will end up badly

Photo No. 64 — Wire brush.

TOOLS

chewed or slightly eliptical or both. The adapter can be bought at Sears for about $12, well worth the price. Apart from being used for plugs, it will help with the cutting of holes that need precise accuracy in wood or in metal.

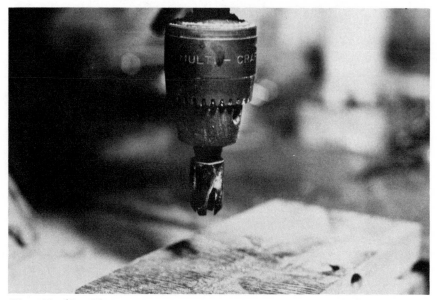

Photo No. 65 — Plug cutter.

d. Paint or foam stirrer. A very inexpensive attachment is a paint stirrer. We used it not only to homogenize paint but also to mix, or rather "whip," the two-part polyurethane foam we used for insulation of the icebox, engine pan, and dinghy flotation. You may find this attachment impossible to clean once the foam has catalyzed, so buy or beg a goodly number when available.

6. Belt sander

This device is probably the most valuable "butcher" tool for boat building. It can remove enormous amounts of surface very rapidly and because of the size of the belts, very evenly. A great number of them are available, the most common being 3" x 21" and 4" x 21" or 24" belt users.

Consensus has it that the 3" x 21" is to be preferred not only for its lower price but because of its smaller size which makes it lighter and a more flexible tool. Apart from its previously discussed

Photo No. 66 — Drill motor in drill press.

use as a small wood shaper, it is ideal for sanding large surfaces such as decks, cabin tops, counter tops, and cabin soles. It is very suitable for primary dressing of any wood.

Care must be used however, for like the wire brush it is a very potent eroder. If not moved about constantly and with even pressure, irreparable gouges may be inflicted in the wood, especially if one tends to press the forward or the aft rotating barrels tenaciously. One should hold the sander parallel to the surface and seldom press. The tool's weight is more than adequate to enforce the paper's friction. Stanley, Rockwell, and Sears all make very acceptable belt sanders at various prices. It is difficult to pick one over the other.

Two points of caution. A spring-like steel leaf is located on the underbody of the belt-sander. One end is attached, the other free-floating to act as a spring. This leaf is a very thin piece to begin with. After a few hours of use its edge, particularly the free-standing trailing edge, becomes as sharp as a razor blade. Do take care when you are changing belts to avoid deep painful cuts.

The next point may seem obvious, but it happened to me on two separate occasions. Therefore I feel its mention worthwhile. I used a belt-sander while building a floating house. The house was under construction on the water so power tools and materials were strewn everywhere. One impatient afternoon while belt sanding an outside patio area, the extension cord got hung up on something. When I jerked the sander to try and free the cord, I jerked out the sander's plug.

I laid the sander down on the deck, went back, freed the cord and plugged in the sander. With the power back on and the trigger in lock-on position, the sander scooted off across the deck like a little electric Sherman tank. I dove for it and barely managed to grab a piece of the extension cord just in time to hear the splash and get the salt spray in my face. I saw a few sparks and waved goodbye to $58.46 plus tax.

7. Vibrating Sander

The customary vibrator which has fore and aft motion has proved to be a little less than useless. It adequately massages one's plam and nothing else.

The Rockwell rotary vibrator, see photo 67, on the other hand, is almost invaluable for finishing sanding. It is designed to be held in one hand and is built to last through hundreds of hours of non-stop sanding. It cannot, however, act as a shaper of any consequence unless it's being used to put a round of small radius onto the edge of a piece of wood. It is perfect for fine sanding and ideal for use with 60 grit or higher sandpaper, ideal for preparing gelcoat for respray or bottom paint, and irreplaceable for that refined touch between coats of varnish. Regular sheets of sandpaper cut into quarters fit exactly onto the sander and the change is accomplished rapidly with two spring clamps attached to either end. The process can even be speeded up by attaching 5 or 6 layers at one time and simply ripping off the layers one at a time as they wear out.

The rotation is even, therefore it will not gouge the wood and the only need for caution arises when one is sanding next to a perpendicular surface. If one comes too close (and it's very easily done) the vibrating clamps have a tendency to nick the vertical piece. Come only within ¼-of-an-inch and finish the last bit by hand.

Photo No. 67 — Rockwell rotary vibrating sander.

8. Saber saw

As violently frustrating as a saber saw can be, it does perform services without which a boat could hardly be built. Whatever you do, you must get one. But, whatever you do, do get a good one. The cheapy smaller ones lack power and weight. The consequence is the blade chews instead of smoothly cutting and the body begins to madly vibrate, jerking the tool off a given line and shaking the fillings out of your teeth. Some cheap ones have bevel adjustments that are tightened with a set screw. The set screw holds reliably only until the saw begins to vibrate, which is the second the blade touches the wood or fiberglass.

Again, Rockwell makes very dependable ones that utilize heavy wide-bodied blades for wood, metal, or fiberglass cutting, see photo 68. The bevel adjustment is done by a hefty positive locking nut removing fear of loss of accuracy. The motor and body are heavy-

TOOLS 213

Photo No. 68 — Rockwell saber saw.

duty and long lasting, but I did find one frustrating point. The part of the blade that receives any support from the mount is very small. The small set screw that holds the blade tight seems inadequate because it allows the blade to angle backwards when pressed. I realize that one is not supposed to "push" saws. But when one is cutting the first of 12 portlight holes in 3/8" thick fiberglass and one has gone only an inch in a minute, one tends to get impatient and begins to "push." When the blade slips and angles backwards, its cutting becomes less efficient; one pushes harder; and the blade heats up and breaks. If you find a good heavy tool with what looks like a more ideal blade securement method, by all means buy it.

Check the construction of the bevel plate carefully, see figure 28. It tends often to be flimsy and can bend if stressed or dropped. If it does bend, you will find it impossible to cut accurate angles.

One completely useless attachment that is on the market is a small lightweight metal table offered by some hobby tool manufacturers. Ideally this table is utilized to mount the saber saw onto it upside down. This assembly does eliminate some of the vibration from the saw but the blade is still unsupported at one end, making accuracy very dubious. Besides, what is the advantage of having to control a jumping table instead of a jumping saw? Methods for using the saber saw are dwelled upon in more detail in the "Construction" section.

BEVEL PLATE

Figure No. 28 — Adjustable saber saw base.

9. Other electrical tools

a. By far the most important unit is a good hard sucking vacuum cleaner. Painting, varnishing, and bonding become almost futile if you haven't previously gotten rid of dust and dirt.

b. Again, I don't know if you would consider it an electrical tool, but it's nice to have a small electric heater which can be safely set close to certain bonds that you require to catalyze rapidly. It also helps to dry paint, set caulking compound, etc.

c. A small soldering gun becomes useful during wiring. Soldering does make for a most corrosion resistant joint.

d. A portable tape recorder may prove invaluable at hand. It can be readily flipped on when you begin screaming at your wife and it can adequately record the sound of smashing objects and falling bodies. You can then go home at night and listen in amazement at what a fool you are and just exactly how much fun building your own boat really is.

e. I'm uncertain whether lights are commonly alluded to as tools, but they are vital. Even if you have portlights and the boat is in the open air under a merciless sun, some areas of the interior will still be underlit. To provide even light in all weather, six or eight 100 watt light bulbs should be constantly on. They can be attached to a bar of wood and screwed to the ceiling, cabin top, or wherever they'll be the most out of the way.

An additional work lamp, see photo 69, on an extension cord is most useful for hard to light areas, like interior cupboard corners. For this purpose, be sure to use only a lamp with a wire cage around it. The most dangerous thing you can do is to have bare bulbs lying about in unsupported sockets.

I once placed an unlit light bulb onto our beautifully finished teak decks and went below to work. Somewhere during the day I

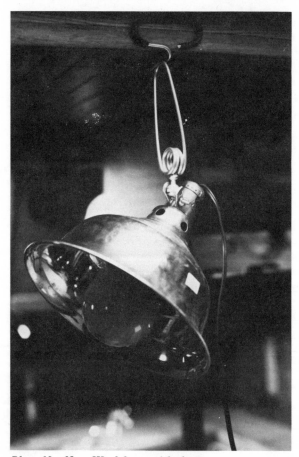

Photo No. 69 — Work lamp with clamp.

TOOLS

mistakenly plugged in that lamp and kept working. Only an hour later did I come running from the cabin trying to locate where the smell of burning teak and burning polysulphide was coming from. I found it. On the aft deck was the light bulb lying on the wood and around it in a four-inch radius was a piece of smoking charcoal that had once been our deck. It was the saddest, most depressing moment during the building of our boat.

We were fortunate, if one can call it that, in that the bulb was directly next to a deck fill. It is due to this mistake that you see such an elaborate little pad around our two fuel intakes. A good habit we got into was to use only well protected or well secured light bulbs. Even thus, we unplugged the main incoming wire and rolled up the extension cord before going home each night. You can only have so many deck fills with elaborate deck pads around them on a 32-foot boat.

10. Electric fan

A very vital accessory that's indispensible during bonding, sanding, and painting is an electric fan. A good-sized one that will completely cover a hatch will help tremendously. Keep a good safety screen over it so clothing and hair will remain safe.

Chapter Eight
HOARDING & SCROUNGING

Once you have selected the layout you will build and are awaiting delivery of your boat, you can begin the most fun part of boat building: hoarding and scrounging. This effort will take a lot of time and a sizable amount of money; but if you couple a little inventiveness with the former, the latter can be kept to a minimum.

Used Material

Nowhere is the saying, "One man's garbage another man's jewel" truer than in boat building. I have known people who have, after buying a new hull, finished the entire boat from used and salvaged materials. One friend who finished off a Spencer 35 hull kept his final expense under $10,000 plus the hull. And I must admit his was one of the best equipped boats I have seen set to sea. I helped him gather some of his supplies and here's what I learned:

Plywood for deck and cabinets can be had at ½ the customary price if one goes to the factory and gets damaged sheets. They seldom have exactly what you want and it helps to have a friend who drives a forklift at the plant. He can arrange to slam his forklift (gently) into a designated bunch of plywood, nicking the edge of every sheet on the pile ever so slightly. You will have to cut around the nicks, but that's no problem. The pile of plywood is damaged and it will be cheap. If it's 5/8'' instead of ½'', so what?

Teak was cheap at one time in the old days. It was customarily used in very great quantities on all yachts and old luxury liners. You can go to any large marine salvage place (San Diego, Long Beach, Seattle, New York, etc.) and find mountains of the greyed wood. All you have to do is pry it from its original bedding. Most doors on old boats are solid teak or solid mahogany. A 2'' thick cabin door can yield an awful lot of trim. Berth rails, cabinets, etc. can also be salvaged and used either as is or cut up for lumber. If you don't mind tearing everything out yourself, you'll find prices like 10c per board foot very common.

For samson posts, bowsprits, and boomkins the best material to use is oak. Most of it checks badly, but if you go through a large enough pile you are bound to find some good stock. These large piles can be found in the backs of boatyards where abandoned boat cradles are stored. Most of the older cradles are, because of its great strength, built of oak and most of the older ones are free for the taking. You will have problems cutting the steel-hard wood, but free is a good enough price to warrant the extra labor.

Engines

One of the best engines for any use is a 4-cylinder Mercedes diesel, which can be found in newspaper ads and junk yards. You will have to put a marine conversion on it and perhaps rebuild it; but all in all you can come away with a total expenditure of $700 for an almost new engine. Mercedes are somewhat delicate engines because the aluminum head can warp when subjected to great heat, but if you are cautious and watch your oil level you should have no problems.

If you have a boat over 40' you may consider the old Buda diesels the Navy used until recent years. They put out over 100 horsepower and are extremely reliable. They do weigh over 900 pounds and parts are sometimes scarce, but they can be bought for $200 to $400 each. If you can make one good one out of two bad ones, you will still be ahead and you will have learned a lot about diesels.

If you don't live near large cities you still have a chance. Old tractors use (a lot still do) fairly small 4-cylinder Ford diesels. If you write to Ford they will be happy to provide you with pamphlets on how to convert these engines to marine use. Any small Nissen diesel, which is commonly used world-wide in taxis and small trucks, can also be used as a starting base for marine diesels.

Ballast

SCOOP: Large hospitals receive radioactive materials in lead cases. These cases can be bought very cheaply, especially if you know the hospital's buyer (10c per pound instead of the customary 30c). If you can't find lead, railroad track is second best; when it is surrounded snugly by steel machine punchings the results are very satisfactory. Be sure to pour in generous amounts of resin.

Spars

Used wood spars are the easiest things to buy. They come off salvaged boats or older racing boats whose new owners have decided to go to aluminum for less upkeep and added performance. If any bad spots of rot or knot or fastener holes have to be contended with, cutting out the problem with a chisel and then scarfing in a new piece using resorcinal glue is no problem.

Do beware of almost new spars from the far east. I was offered a near new 50' mast with booms, spreaders, and hardware for $560. The offer was tempting but I had no money at the time so all I could do was sit back and hope no one else bought it. They didn't. I ran back three weeks later with the money and found the thing had delaminated in four spots and popped out three good sized knots. I was then told by the shipyard owner who was storing the mast that it was from a Taiwan boat. Many others he had seen were at least as bad. That was five months ago. No one has yet jumped up to grab the bargain.

Aluminum bargains are less frequent. An old aluminum mast is hard to convert to your specific needs, for its stainless screws can be very tightly corroded and their removal is almost impossible. Even if you could remove them, how could you plug up the holes in an aluminum mast?

Take care if you are buying new surplus aluminum extrusions. Some may have a small, almost undetectable dimple which will lead to a buckled mast upon the first opportunity.

Hardware

Bronze portlights are not extremely expensive. Only two major outlets exist for new ones: Perko and a small church bell manufacturer in Milford, Connecticut. Rostand, the church bell people, do beautiful work and will do almost any custom portlight you desire if you can wait long enough. They're never in a hurry and never on time. If you call on the phone in an expeditiary attempt they will tell you that, "Al is not in right now but he knows what the score is and he will get in touch as soon as he gets back" or that "Al is out but he left a message that the portlights should arrive tomorrow, for they were shipped over a week ago."

The portlights did of course arrive, but it wasn't tomorrow, as a matter of fact it was almost 4½ months later. I'm now convinced that "Al" is a myth and attempted communication with him is completely futile. So order your portlights in advance and if they still don't come on time, phone them up and tell them that "Al" is standing beside you but he can't come to the phone because his mouth is full of a pastrami sandwich, but he says to ship the portlights today or else. Punctual or not they are very kind people and do beautiful work but you should order ahead.

Used portlights are everywhere if you know where to look. Old boat salvage yards have all sizes hidden by coats of paint. If you don't mind the elbow grease and the smell of paint remover, you can usually buy them at less than half-price. The rubber sealer probably died years ago, but you can scrape it out and buy a new one in lengths, cut it to size, and put it in yourself.

Salvaged and abandoned ships that you board at night are the greatest source for old marine hardware. I bought ten 6'' opening portlights for $125, which is about 200% under list price. Old ships and salvage yards also have huge collections of miscellaneous hardware like brass hinges, beautiful double jointed hooks, see photo 70, giant bronze Herreshoff cleats, ladder hardware, door handles, drawer handles, and incredible, unidentifiable but irresistable items. I night-skulked the one from a dying freighter (along with a beautiful dove-tailed teak box) and used it for years as an incense burner. Only lately did I discover that it's a depth sounding device whose two holes in the sides scoop up bottom samples, thus an invaluable aid to anchoring. Therefore, if you see anything interesting, take it and store it.

The best cowl vents I've ever seen were old ones of either soft brass or aluminum, only found in salvage places.

It seems that bronze deadlights are almost unheard of in modern new marine supply stores. Thus old ones have to be bought and usually repaired because the glass is either broken or pitted or both. I have no concept of how a deadlight gets pitted. But it does, so you will have to take out the old glass and replace it.

The glass is usually held in place with a brass ring which is most likely brittle from age and will snap if you try to force it out of place. To prevent its breaking, you will have to do something that at first glance seems most illogical, but I vouch that it does work. Take a small propane torch and heat the whole ring until it's almost red hot. If the glass breaks, no matter, for that's what you're trying to replace anyway. When the ring is very hot, drop it into a bucket of cold water. Believe it or not it will soften the brass. You will have no trouble removing the glass and springing the ring back into place. Recaulk all the new glass with silicone sealer or polysulphide for best results.

Beware

Many items are available that should not be bought used,

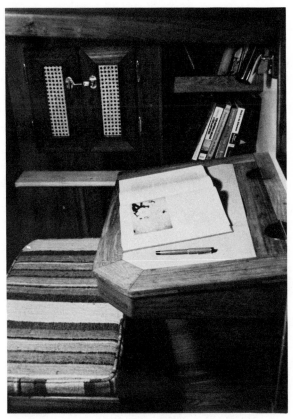
Photo No. 70 — Double-jointed brass hinges.

because testing them is difficult. And even if they don't fail immediately they may fail the next time.

Turnbuckles and fittings could fatigue at any moment if they are old, especially if they are bronze. The same holds true for old seacocks and bronze chainplates. Old mechanical things like heads and bilge pumps should not even be brought close to a new boat because their reliability is almost nil. Even if you replace all the packing there is a good possibility that the cylinder walls are scarred, rendering the whole thing less than perfectly safe.

Apart from being a money-saver, scrounging is great fun and your total boat building bill could come out something like my friend's did:

Hull $5,000

Plywood for deck and interior 600

Fiberglassing materials for deck and interior 380
  (scrap ends)
Portlights 139
Used teak 200
Tanks (integral) 140
Engine (Mercedes) rebuilt . . . . total 870
Prop, shaft and wheel 210
Used oak . . . . free
Anchors (2 Navy, 1 Danforth) . . . . 140 plus a sack
                                        of avocadoes
Interior hardware (liberated from old ship) for gas 2.85
Galley stove (alcohol) 85
Marine head . . . . free for asking
Used wood mast 220
Galvanized rigging 120
Used chain (3/8" - 200') . . . . plus bicycle 25
Re-galvanizing 30
Sails (from an old 6 meter, resewn himself) 200
Winches (used) (2 sheet, 2 halyard) 150
Windlass (new, single action) 180
Line (halyards & sheets,
  new drum — 600'-7/16") 95
Plumbing (new hose & fittings) 130
Bilge pumps (1 new, 1 rebuilt) 110
Wiring (surplus, new breakers & batteries) 180
Used compasses (4) 175
Scrap lead & steel ballast 500

                                               $9,881.85

A few more thousand dollars were spent on miscellaneous blocks, stanchions, kerosene lamps, lifebelts, spare engine parts, sinks, battery charger, chronometer, sail cover material, mainsheet traveler, etc.; but, all in all not a bad new cruising boat for under $15,000.

New Materials

To save on new hardware, one needs first a piece of information and second some gall. The information is that a lot of marine hardware stores operate at 100% mark-up. This margin is partially acceptable because they must have in inventory huge quantities of dissimilar and very costly items. I can sympathize with their position but I refuse to pay their prices.

Now, the gall. You have to convince the owner-manager to sell you everything for less. First try honestly and tell him that you are building a boat and will be spending a few thousand dollars on hardware, fasteners, electronics, etc. within the next year. Tell him that you'll give him all of your business if he'll agree to open an account for you and constantly apply a healthy discount, say between 25% and 50%. Tell him that if he won't do it you'll go somewhere else.

If he says no, connive to get a resale number. Get a license to operate a small marine supply store. You will then be able to buy everything wholesale. The license costs about $55 in most municipalities. If they want an address for your shop, give them the address of your aunt Muriel.

If you can't get a license then band together with other boat builders and start a co-op. You'll be able to buy things cheaply if you buy them in great quantities. This approach is only inconvenient because it forces you to plan ahead and order things like screws, line, wire, etc. when it's most convenient to everyone else.

If you are greedy you can actually start a small marine hardware outlet. Don't buy anything unless people order it and put a small deposit on it. You can then run around, pick up the materials, and pass them on with say a 10% profit. And then of course buy all of your materials at wholesale for your own boat. This kind of business you can operate from your basement, or your attic with very little or no overhead. Whichever way you choose, do not pay retail unless you absolutely must. This advice goes for everything including lumber, diesels, and portlights. Go to the vendor and smile or shout or throw yourself on the floor and kick your feet or beg or flatter or whatever needs to be done. If nothing works, breaks both his arms.

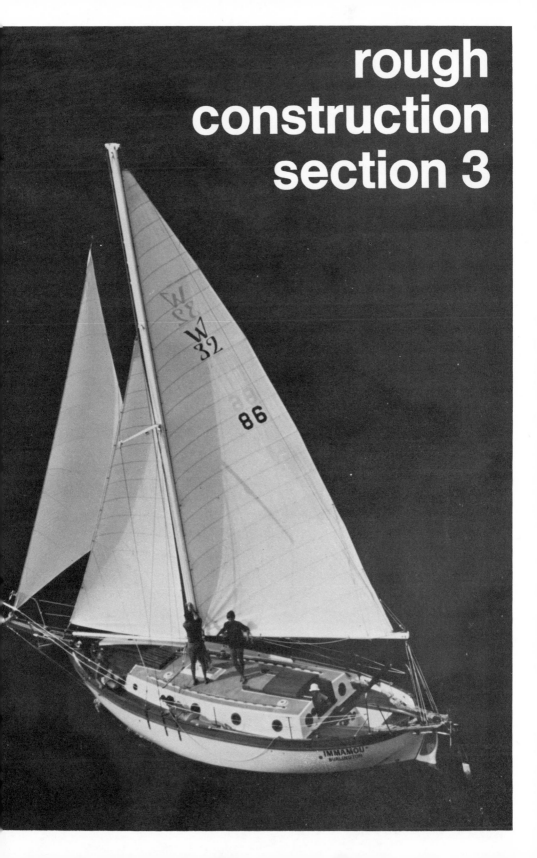

rough construction
section 3

Chapter Nine
BALLASTING

Abruptly one morning a painful realization will hit you in the face: You can't stall any longer. You've prepared until there's nothing left to prepare, you've set up a shop with all your tools in all their places. Now you've got to get your hands dirty and get glue all over that leather apron.

If you insist on ballasting the boat yourself, here are some hints on installing various kinds of ballast:

Steel Punchings or Lead Shot

Probably the least expensive ballast (except for cement) is steel boiler punchings. Perforated metal fabricators will be happy to ship punchings to you in discouragingly heavy 55-gallon drums. Upon receipt, immediately punch 15 good-Christian-sized holes at the bottom of each barrel. You will find oil, usually a lot of oil, coming out through these holes. Machinists use oil on the tools that punch the punchings to keep them lubricated and cool. This oil, if not drained off, will eventually seep to the lowest part of the boat where it will build and build to the lower gudgeon holes, dissolve any bedding or sealing compound, and then seep out into the water. When the oil stops seeping out into the water, the water will start seeping into the ballast. Whether this seepage is critical or not, I'm not entirely certain, but it is an unnerving thought so you may as well drain the punchings and perhaps pour in a gallon of acetone or other solvent to expedite matters.

Meanwhile, to keep the punchings away from the extreme stern of the hull and the gudgeon bolts, one should install a dam as shown in figure 29. A piece of ¾" plywood loosely fitted and bonded over

Figure No. 29 — Punchings dam.

3/4 fir Plywood

MISH MASH

7"

4"

6"

8"

KEEL

℄. OF SHAFT

First Layer 30 oz. Mat. 24 oz. Roving

Second Layer " " " "

Third Layer " " " " "

BALLASTING

extremely cautiously should suffice. In most hulls this operation is difficult, for the keel in this area is probably no wider than 5 inches. But it can be done and should be done with great care, even if you must lie on your stomach on a piece of board and stretch your arm into the abyss a foot farther than you ever thought you could. You should use two layers of mat-cloth combination. To use roving here would be rather daring, for you may miss one row of heavy weaving and leave an air tunnel. The oil will find it. The overlaps onto the sides of the hull should be a generous 10 inches and similar at the base of the dam. This bonding point is critical, where continuous and widening layers would be a commendable idea. Because of the tightness of the hull and the two sharp corners, you will most likely make a mistake here and leave a void. Don't.

Wet out the paired layers well, see "Bonding," (the section after "Rough Interior Installation"), and when you've laid them in place, punch every square centimeter with a coarse bristle-type paint brush well soaked in resin. You can attach a piece of wood as an extension to the brush to help you fabricate the bottom. The bonds against the sides of the hull are a problem, for you may not be able to hit them with the brush end-on. I found the best tool to use here is your hand. The idea of having sticky resin all over one's fingers can be rather frightening at first, but a good acetone bath will remove even the odor. Once all the bonds have gone off you can proceed to fill the space aft of the dam. This procedure you should do with a mixture of resin thickened to a still-pourable pulp with some sort of fibers. Asbestos is satisfactory and inexpensive, but mill fiber (finely chopped glass strands) will provide a less brittle result.

If you are enterprising you can pick up mountains of mat, cloth, and roving scraps from a local boatyard, fiberglass shop or the like and stir the mixture into the resin, then pour the concoction behind the dam. Use a stick, much like the vibrator in cement work, to ascertain that all corners are well filled.

Do not over-catalyze, for a great amount of heat will be given off which may warm the hull which will expand the dam which will crack the bond that will sink the ship that Jack built. As long as you put in a goodly amount of catalyst, see appendix, the witch's brew will eventually go off. It may take a day or so, but it will go off. To ensure that catalyzation is homogenous, pour the catalyst into the clear resin first, stir well, and then mix the fibers.

If you do over-catalyze and the dam gets hot, put a wet cloth over it. Keep changing it. Once the dam has set, put a mat-cloth bond over the top of it so that stray oil or water can't seep down.

Draw in lines which will indicate where the ballast level should finalize. The boat builder or designer should be able to supply you with measurements.

Once the dam has been installed and the lines drawn, the rest is all up hill, literally; for a few thousand pounds of punchings have somehow to get from the ground up to the hull and into the keel. The simplest method is bucketing. The next simplest is to have a friend with a forklift put the barrels onto a very very strong scaffold.

If you want to build a simple A-frame like the one shown in figure 30, and if you have a friend to help you, you can save a lot of time. The person at the bottom fills the empty bucket and the one on the scaffold dumps it into a plywood shoot. While the man at the bottom rests, "Dumper" can level the mounds of punchings in the hull with a rake. Ideally, after a three-inch layer of punchings (or lead shot) has been dumped in, the entire thing should be saturated with resin. Here it is all right to over-catalyze, for the metal will absorb a lot of the heat and the resin will be slow in going off.

Rent a cement vibrator for this occasion. Not only will it mix the resin and punchings better, but you will be able to get the punchings to settle densely, thus lower down, resulting in a stiffer boat by lowering the center of gravity. If you do use one, don't be shocked when, after installing the given weight of ballast, you end up two or three inches lower than the boat builder's ballast line. He doesn't vibrate, usually.

Even off the top of the ballast as much as possible, then top off with resin. When the resin has gone off, put two layers of mat and roving over the whole thing (overlapping onto the hull by a good foot on either side). If everything else fails these two layers will keep the ballast from falling on you if you ever turn upside down.

I have heard of people substituting cement for resin with the punchings (or shot). This material would make mixing child's play, because you could use a small cement mixer, but I've also heard of cement cracking and the ballast beginning to move. Using punchings only, without any bonding agent would be short-changing yourself. The loose shot would be able to move about and settle and then move more at the spacious top, all the while slowly grinding away the sides of the hull.

Cast Lead

The manufacturer usually offers lead in the form of cast fish. It will be expensive (lead costs 30c per pound) but if it is all-lead you want, a fish may be ideal. You may as well have them drop the fish into place, see photo 71. To assure that it won't move about or slip

Ⓐ A-FRAME
Ⓑ SCAFFOLD
Ⓒ BARREL OF PUNCHINGS
         OR SHOT
Ⓓ BLOCK - SEE DETAIL
  (COULD BE FUTURE
            MAINSHEET)
Ⓔ TRACK (FUTURE MAINSHEET)
    -THRU- BOLTED TO FRAME
Ⓕ PLYWOOD CHUTE

DETAIL OF BLOCK

SELF-CLEATING
FIDDLE BLOCK WITH
         BECKET

BALLASTING   **233**

Figure No. 30 — Ballast A-frame.

Photo No. 71 — Lead castings for ballast.

out of place, ram a thick mixture of fibers, scrap, and resin between the hull and the fish. If you have large voids to fill (one or two cubic feet in an open area), pouring in two-part urethane foam, which boils and bubbles and expands and hardens, is a fast and functional method. When the foam is all done, bond over it extra well. At least two layers of mat-roving should be used.

If you want to cast your own lead it can be done, and it might be economical if you have access to scrap lead. You may as well melt it down to get the most from its density. You can get a good idea of the shape it will take by using the above mentioned two-part urethane foam. Line the hull with heavy polyurethane sheets, then pour the foam over it. The plastic sheets will enable you to easily ''pull the plug'' once it is set. From the foam plug, you can make some inexpensive tin molds into which you can pour the molten lead. Use gas to melt it down. The location of such semi-roughly made ballast castings is critical. You may put the boat out of trim, so think it out first, consult the architect, and after you're absolutely certain as to its position, make sure you leave lots of room for trim ballast.

I could elaborate on how to build the tin mold but then I may as well tell you how to smelt the tin, then how to build the furnace to smelt the tin, and then how to make the bricks to make the furnace.

BALLASTING

Chapter Ten
RUDDER INSTALLATION

There are no great mysteries clouding rudder installation. If you have the old-fashioned gudgeon-pintle set-up, see photo 72, then dry fit the factory supplied pintles onto the rudder. You should have the whole unit assembled at this point (gudgeons, pintles,

Photo No. 72 — Old-fashion gudgeon & pintle.

washers, pins, etc.). If you have a rudder as heavy as ours, just struggle and strain and block it until you get it to align with the hull.

It is wise practice to elevate the rudder's base about two inches above the keel so that if you ever ground the boat, the rudder will not be the one to take the punishment.

Once aligned, simply drill through the gudgeon holes. Using a pilot bit a good ¼-inch smaller than the final one may be advisable, for sometimes it's difficult to hit a hole through 3 or 4 inches of fiberglass. Once the gudgeon holes are drilled, remove all of the hardware, wash it and the hull with judicious amounts of acetone, then polysulphide everything in sight. Then reassemble. The rudder installation is no place to save on caulking. If you are using stainless steel hardware, be sure to install some sacrificial zinc anodes to take the brunt of the electrolitic onslaught set up with the bronze wheel and bronze thru-hulls.

If your boat has a single gudgeon arrangement into which the rudder shaft fits, see photo 73, you simply place a small worm-gear jack under the gudgeon with the rudder in it and jack it into place. When you can feel that the gudgeon is snug on the hull, yet the rudder swings freely, drill your pilot holes.

Photo No. 73 — Single gudgeon at rudder base.

Chapter Eleven
LEVELING THE HULL

Up to this point, eyeball leveling the hull upon setting it into the cradle was sufficient. Since the next operations such as cabin sole installation, bulkhead installation, etc. need to be precise to facilitate rapid completion, it is necessary at this point to level the hull fore, aft, and athwartships. Two common methods make leveling rapid; one is less expensive than the other.

String Level

For the less expensive of the two methods, leveling a bare hull athwartships requires a piece of slight string, pulled taut from bulwark to bulwark with a string-level set in center. Buy a cheap one because you'll probably never use one again. A small rented hydraulic jack will suffice for adjustment. If a trunk cabin is already installed, raise the bulwarks' height by attaching the string to the tops of two equal-lengths sticks. This procedure requires either two people or two C-clamps, so that you will have freedom to move into the center and read the level. Leveling fore and aft requires one more step since the bow of a boat is customarily higher than the stern. Therefore, you must compensate by setting the stern end of the string the desired measure higher than the bow and then begin the leveling. After fore and aft leveling is done, recheck the athwartship level to make sure it has not been altered drastically.

Waterline and Tubing

Most fiberglass hulls have a scribe line etched into them to facilitate painting of waterline or boot stripe. By using (a) the knowledge that this line is level right around the hull and (b) about

70 feet of fairly costly transparent tubing, you can level the hull by a second method. Tape the tubing (old garden hoses work as well although it's harder to see the bubbles through their crusty walls) along the bottom of the keel running it from a few inches above the waterline in the bow to a few inches above the waterline in the stern. Run another piece of hose from similar height above the waterline amidships down under the keel and up past the line on the other side. Now fill the tubing with water until it is close to the waterline in both hoses; whether above or below is of little consequence because we're looking for equal distances and not exact fittings. Now you can jack and shim the cradle until the water level is equidistant from the waterline in both ends of each hose.

This method is preferred over the string and level because it may be left on the hull indefinitely without getting in the way as the string-level system will. One danger here is that if the tape used to hold the tubing is left on for over a few weeks in a hot climate, it may be impossible to remove it without peeling off substantial swatches of gelcoat. It is advisable to retape in different locations at different times.

LEVELING THE HULL

Chapter Twelve
INSTALLING THE CABIN SOLE

Fiberglass Cabin Sole

If you choose to install a molded fiberglass sole provided by the manufacturer, your task is relatively simple. Now that the hull is level, you can simply lower the sole into place, level it, then bond the usually un-gelcoated edge onto the hull, see photo 74. The ends of the sole will have to be screwed into the floor timbers mounted on your bulkheads.

Photo No. 74 — Bonding in cabin sole.

Use a good bedding compound between the timber and the fiberglass so that moisture won't have a chance to come and stay. Again, make certain that you wash everything with acetone before bonding, then follow regular bonding procedures. Once the bonds have gone off, find a heavy friend or two and ask them aboard. Then ask them to walk about. You will spot areas, hopefully not too many, where the glass sole flexes under their weight. If the flexing is over an eighth-of-an-inch, mark the location, for here reinforcement will be required.

If this location is outboard of a hatch-opening in the sole, then a number of knees must be installed. They need not be elaborate; ¾-inch plywood is sufficient. Exact fitting can be bypassed because the strength will come from bonding the plywood to the hull. It is a good idea to dry fit the pieces of mat and cloth that will be required, for working away loose ends smoothly in tight corners is a very difficult operation. It may be simpler to wet these pieces out in place. Be sure to bond the knees to both the hull and the bottom of the cabin sole. Here, double bonding two layers of mat and cloth is a good idea, see figure 31.

Figure No. 31 — Double bonding.

In inaccessible areas where you cannot double-joint your arms to bond both sides of the knees, a sole timber should be installed as in figure 32. This timber can be fir, mahogany, or oak 2 x 4 with the edges tapered to fit the hull. I recommend a loose fit, about ¼-inch on either end, for if you sledgehammer it into place,

240   INSTALLING THE CABIN SOLE

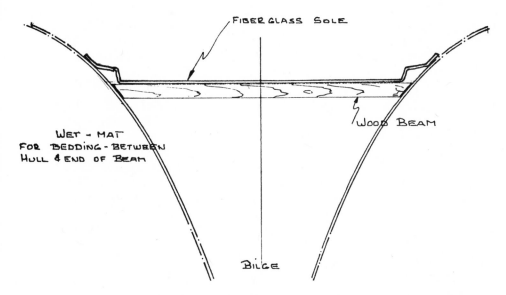

Figure No. 32 — Installing sole timber.

you may have a sharp point adjoining the hull. Because a sharp edge puts great stress on a very small area, it can cause the glass to flex around it and graze the gelcoat, as well as prematurely graze the glass.

Once it has been loosely fitted, remove the timber and brush healthy amounts of Cuprinol or a similar wood preservative on all surfaces but the last four inches on either end. Then take some mat, about five times longer than the angled end of the timber, wet it out, fold it five times, then slip it onto the hull where the timber ends will be. Let the resin go off, only enough so that it won't move but is still soft and tacky, then slip the timber into place over the mat. After dry fitting some mat and cloth over both ends, bond the timber into place. Don't walk on the cabin sole above it for awhile. If you find after the bonds set that the timber has settled heavily, leaving a gap between it and the sole, slip a long preservative-treated slat of a wedge between them. Do not try to place a wedge between the timber and the hull. You will create hard spots.

Plywood Sole

This type of sole requires the laying of floor timbers similar to those mentioned above, about every twelve inches with a pair of longitudinal members which must be let into the ones running athwartships as shown in figure 33.

Figure No. 33 — Letting floor timbers.

MAIN BULKHEAD

CARRIAGE BOLTS

NOTCH HALF + HALF

CARRIAGE BOLTS

242   **INSTALLING THE CABIN SOLE**

The critical point here is that all timbers running athwartships, especially the ones that will adjoin bulkheads, must be absolutely square with the center line. This alignment can be done by running a string fore and aft at sole level and using a large carpenter square to adjust the timbers. The timber joints should be clamped and glued (resorcinal glue may be advisable here), then bonded to the hull. Make sure that no bonding material comes any higher than the top of the timbers, for it will interfere with fitting the plywood sole over them. When the bonds have gone off, treat all exposed areas with the aforementioned Cuprinol or other wood preservative. Do not treat the tops against which the plywood sole will be laid, for the sole will have to be glued and glue does not adhere to the oily Cuprinol.

It may be necessary to make templates for the plywood unless the manufacturer supplies you with patterns. For this purpose, one can use inexpensive 1/8-inch veneer and staples. The next step is to cut the plywood into narrow slats (two inches wide is plenty), then cut them to about one and a half foot lengths and lay them on top of the floor timbers as close to the hull as possible. Overlap the pieces slightly, then staple the overlaps to each other. Staple some extra braces athwartships, so that you can handle the templates without changing their shape, then simply place the rigidified *or* reinforced template on a sheet of plywood and trace.

It may be just as easy to substitute measuring for the templates. If one end of the sole timbers is square, then you can simply measure points across each timber and place a mark at the opposite appropriate distance from the plywood square end, see figure 34. Then join the points and you will have your outline. If the resulting fit is within ½-inch of the hull (it can be left too small but not too big) do not worry, for you will glue and screw the plywood to the timbers, then bond the plywood to the hull. If the rest of your boat is built as solidly as this cabin sole, it will last forever.

If at all possible, crawl into the bilge and treat the underside of the plywood. You may have a demanding task, but it is well worth the effort because fresh water from sinks, glasses, or rains will easily find its way down here and cause dry rot.

It is also good practice to build the sole in sections, that is from bulkhead to bulkhead, then install the bulkhead, then go on with laying timbers for the next section. In this way you'll be able to have the bulkhead come down past the timbers enabling gluing and through-bolting, giving a very positive, lasting joint.

INSTALLING THE CABIN SOLE   243

PROCEDURE:

A) MEASURE EACH TIMBER'S LENGTH (STATION 0 TROUGH 6)

B) MEASURE DISTANCE BETWEEN TIMBERS "X"

C) RECONSTRUCT EXACT POSITIONS OF ALL POINTS @ "X" AND "Y" ON PLYWOOD SHEET THEN JOIN ALL POINTS AND CUT OUT OUTLINE.

Figure No. 34 — Measuring for cabin sole outline.

INSTALLING THE CABIN SOLE

Chapter Thirteen
MAST STEP SUPPORT

If you are stepping your mast on deck, you'll need to transfer the compression load from its base to the keel, or at least to the ballast. A support post should be wedged between the cabin top and the sole. This post in turn must be supported by a large block of wood at least six inches wide between the sole and the keel. If the block of wood is laminated from a number of pieces so much the better, for then it won't be as prone to crack or warp. The block should be fitted very snugly, as should the post above it. Then bond it into place, then treat it well or paint it. Working in these areas may be difficult because of the usually limited space but the extra effort will pay good dividends.

If design allows, the mast support post should be attached to the edge of a structural bulkhead to tie the structural posts tightly together.

Chapter Fourteen
BULKHEAD INSTALLATION

As mentioned before, this operation can and should go hand in hand with installing the floor timbers. You will get the most accurate results by installing them at the same time. If you choose, however, you may install either the entire cabin sole (leaving plywood spacers between timbers where the bulkheads are to go) or the bulkheads first.

Bare Hull Bulkheads

If the boat is not decked, your task will be easier, because you will have ample room to move larger pieces of plywood about, see photo 75.

First mark the distance your bulkhead will be from either stern or bow, (whichever is closer) on your bulwarks. Make sure the points on each side are indeed equidistant from the bow or stern; i.e. square to the center line, as shown in figure 35. Temporarily attach, with either clamps or bolts, the least warped piece of 2 x 4 or even better 2 x 6 that you can find, from one bulwark to the other. This bolted or clamped attachment has to be a firm one, not only so that the piece of stiffener won't move fore and aft, but also to prevent the hull from losing its shape when you are standing in it.

If you have a prefab deck to be installed later, it is advisable to measure its width in the bulkhead areas at this time and adjust the hull accordingly using the cross-piece as a stiffener. Later adjustment will be extremely difficult once the bulkheads are bonded in. If you have your floor timbers installed, your task will be simpler; for you can now install a true 2 x 4 vertically, attaching its bottom to the

Photo No. 75 — Undecked hull.

floor timber and its top to the temporary cross-member. This vertical 2 x 4 should be located at the point where the most inboard edge of your bulkhead will be. It, of course, must be perfectly level.

From this point on you will have two choices: (a) make up the template for the bulkhead out of 1/8-inch plywood strap or (b) measure across from the vertical member at given level points, see figure 36. The latter method is considerably more practicable because you won't have a giant template to move about. When using the measuring method, add an extra inch to your measurement and try to unite the outboard points with curves instead of straight lines. When cut, you will find the curve sitting fairly well to the hull with, of course, the bulkhead being one inch too wide.

Now, using an ordinary compass and a pencil set to a one inch gap, run the metal arm of the compass along the hull as shown in figure 37. This procedure will leave a pencil line on your bulkhead which will be a true reproduction of the hull's curvature. In addition to trimming the bulkhead to fit snugly, you should somewhat overtrim, depending on what sort of spacer you intend to use between the bulkhead and the hull. One inch urethane foam (acetone or resin will not dissolve it) cut on 45 degree angles on either side of the plywood (see "To Find a Hull") is commonly used.

BULKHEAD INSTALLATION

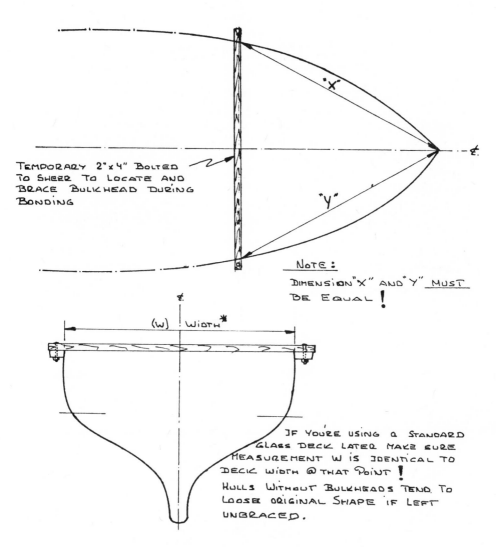

TEMPORARY 2"x 4" BOLTED
TO SHEER TO LOCATE AND
BRACE BULKHEAD DURING
BONDING

NOTE :

DIMENSION "X" AND "Y" MUST
BE EQUAL !

(W) WIDTH

IF YOU'RE USING a STANDARD
GLASS DECK LATER MAKE SURE
MEASUREMENT W IS IDENTICAL TO
DECK WIDTH @ THAT POINT !
HULLS WITHOUT BULKHEADS TEND TO
LOOSE ORIGINAL SHAPE IF LEFT
UNBRACED.

Figure No. 35 — Marking bulwark points for bulkhead location.

We used urethane foam. It was simple and fast, but some argue
that with constant work the bulkheads and hull undergo at sea, the
foam will eventually wear away to dust. If so you will still have a
very nicely curved bond over either side of the bulkhead. Therefore I
don't think this argument is completely valid; but if you do dislike
this method, you have the alternative of placing a run of fiberglass
rope of generous diameter between the hull and the bulkhead. The

BULKHEAD INSTALLATION   **249**

rope is more expensive and will not give you as gentle a curve as the foam unless you get enormous line at enormous expense, but it will surely last forever and remain an ideal movement absorber.

You may think it a fatuous point, but make certain that you leave enough plywood on the upper end of the bulkhead to reach the top of the cabin and deck when it is installed. A good friend totally forgot that he wasn't building a flush-deck and chopped the upper end of his bulkheads off. ¾-inch ABX mahogany can run about $35.00 a sheet, and tearing out already bonded bulkheads is no fun.

Also remember to cut off the lower end of the bulkhead that protrudes past the bottom edge of the sole timber. Water may be passing through here; this protrusion may catch flotsam and jetsum, absorb moisture, and rot. Therefore, cut it off and treat the bottom with a preservative.

Now that the bulkhead fits everywhere, temporarily clamp and screw it to the sole timber vertical member and the horizontal

Figure No. 36 — Measuring for bulkhead outline.

BULKHEAD INSTALLATION

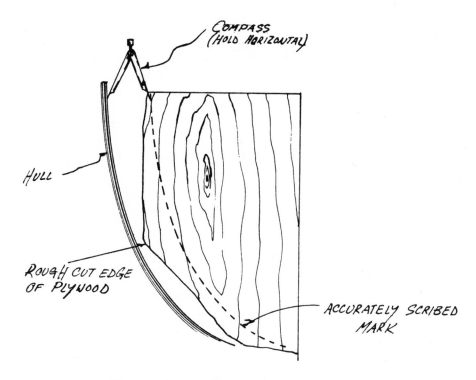

Figure No. 37 — Scribing final curvature onto bulkhead.

members so that it is as immobilized as possible. Bond it into place. For smaller bulkheads such as the chain locker bulkhead, engine room, and lazarette bulkhead with no passageway through their centers and no floor timbers to meet them, clamp only the top horizontal member and use a plumb line or level. These bulkheads should be fairly small and easy to handle, so that making templates is advantageous over measuring for them.

Deck and Cabin Top Installed

If you have bought a boat with deck installed, you will be more limited in your maneuvering, but you can do a good final job the first time you fit your bulkheads. Instead of attempting installation of a horizontal top member, screw some pads into the cabin top, making sure you don't come through the outside of the deck. Now measure the vertical distance from the cabin top to the lower edge of the floor timber at the spot where the most inboard edge of the plywood bulk-head will go. If the deck has a crown, make a small template for it, and scribe it onto the plywood. You can then add in the angle of the cabin side-slant, if any, with a bevel square as in figure 38.

After you determine the distance from the cabin side's bottom to the hull, you may use either the template method or the level-measure method. Whichever you use, do it fairly accurately because it takes a lot of effort and patience to repeatedly trim and try-fit a bulky piece in a tight place. I guess that's why they call them bulkheads. Go ahead and bond the bulkhead to the hull but do not bond it to the fiberglass deck or cabin top, especially if it's a main bulkhead adjoining the mast support. I'll explain why later.

Figure No. 38 — Measuring for bulkhead with deck installed.

Chapter Fifteen
DECK INSTALLATION

Fiberglass Deck

Leave on the temporary 2 x 4 cross members that you put atop the bulwarks and put the deck in place. Play around with the deck and make sure it fits everywhere; if not, this is the time to cut or modify. Then wipe off both hull and deck flange with acetone, cover the hull flange with great amounts of polysulphide, and fasten down the bow or stern then work amidships, pulling out the temporary cross-members as you go. This is not the time to through-bolt, for it's a slow two-man operation. Use hefty No. 14 sheet metal screws. They will be more than sufficient to hold the hull and deck together while all of the fittings is done. You can then pull them out and replace them with bolts. When so doing, don't be afraid to shoot a blob of polysulphide into each hole before you slip the bolt into place. It will be messy for the man putting on the nuts and the washers, but it will stop leaks.

If you have bulwarks, and you should for safety, the fitting will be easier because you can cut plywood U-clamps, see photo 76. Using these plywood clamps in conjunction with a pair of bar clamps, you will get a perfect match throughout.

For through-bolting, use at least ¼-inch flat head stainless steel machine screws. You will have to countersink them so that you can cover the heads with filler or caprail or whatever. Be careful not to countersink too deep, for you'll go right through the glass and lose any grip of the bolt's head. On the inside you will require a flat washer, a lock washer, and a nut. You can substitute a nylon insert lock nut for the lock washer and nut to save you handling an extra

Photo No. 76 — U-clamp spacers for deck installation.

piece, but they are expensive and harder to turn than the ordinary nut, which you can usually just spin on until it hits the washer. Pull the nuts tight. You may not have a chance to get at them again.

Wood Deck

I will not elaborate on wood deck and cabin construction. There are many excellent books (for example Chappelle) that are extremely thorough and their authors are much more knowledgeable than I on this topic. I will, however, mention those items which are relevant to fiberglass hulls only.

1. Hull to deck joint

The best hull to deck joint in this instance is achieved by usage of a sheer clamp. The clamp should be a clear (no knots) length, a full 2½ x 3 inch mahogany or oak or fir. If your hull is as beamy as ours and a double ender to boot, you may have to laminate the clamp from four pieces of ¾-inch stock, placing one on the hull after another, using resorcinal glue in between each. You should screw the pieces together, for if you use clamps you'll have to wait until the glue goes off on the first joint before you are able to proceed. As for choice of wood, oak holds screws the best but it also rots. Fir is easy to get and easy to work with, so perhaps it is the best wood to use. Mahogany is also relatively inexpensive and comes in long clear pieces that might be a very good choice also.

DECK INSTALLATION

Bed the sheer clamp in polysulphide and through bolt it. If you have to laminate, just screw the first layer to the hull (screw head on the outside of the hull) about every six inches. You can pull out the screws later and substitute bolts. The location of the sheer clamp from the top of the hull is, of course, vital. Predetermine how thick your laminated deck beams will be; add to that number the thickness of the two layers of plywood or whatever you will use as decking. Using this total, measure down from your sheer. This total will give you the location of the top of your sheer clamp, see figure 39.

Figure No. 39 — Location of sheer clamp.

When you are laminating be sure to wipe the glue that squeezes out, immediately. If you don't, it will take you twenty times longer to chisel off the hard brittle little mounds later on. Through bolt the sheer clamp every six inches, then place the deck beams atop it on twelve inch centers. Through bolt and glue the deck beams to the sheer clamp, using one 5/16 or 3/8 inch bolt. Stainless would be nice here to use, but galvanized costs about 1/8th the amount, so I will let your own discretion and pocketbook determine the selection. Fill the space between the beams atop the sheer clamp with blocks. You can screw these blocks to the hull again from the outside. This extra work is a bit of a luxury, for it will cause more labor in filling over the screw heads and gelcoating unless you're planning on drooping caprails to cover them.

DECK INSTALLATION 255

2. Sheeting

Now comes the rapid, rewarding part — sheeting the deck. If you prefer a nautical interior you can use a layer of tongue-and-groove directly over the beams. The type of wood you use is not important, but I would advise against cedar. Pretty and rot-proof as it is, it does not glue well and soft as it is, it's not the finest nail holder in the world. Glue each tongue and groove onto each beam and nail it. Bronze ring nails are much less expensive than stainless steel screws. They hold at least as well and are fun to put in because they go fast.

The spacing of the tongue-and-groove is vital and must be planned for future changes in the wood. If you are certain that your wood is very dry, then don't squeeze the pieces perfectly tight. Once in the water, the wood will swell and the strips buckle. If you think your wood is at all green, hammer your tongue-and-groove as tightly as you can; otherwise as it drys it will shrink and open unsightly gaps between. It's advisable to lay the center piece of the tongue-and-groove in first, for then you will get a true line to work from. When pounding the tongue-and-groove into place, use a block of soft wood. Tongues and grooves as well are very delicate beasts. It doesn't take much to break them off. Apart from looking bad because of chips or dents, they become almost impossible to fit together.

The laying of plywood is a somewhat similar procedure. It's cheaper even though you may suffer more loss through scrap than with the narrow tongue-and-groove. It may be a good idea to use plywood with tongue-and-groove edges, a material which is commonly used in decking for house construction. If you can't find a high enough grade manufactured thusly, then run your plywood through a table saw and rabbet the edges. It's not as firm a joint as the tongue-and-groove but it's infinitely better than butting the sheets together.

Two layers of ½-inch plywood laminated with the seams well staggered (or the second layer put on a diagonal as you would over tongue-and-groove strips) is preferred over a single sheet of one inch plywood. Where the first layer had to be nailed into the beams and the blocks above the sheer clamp, the second layer can be nailed anywhere into the first. When laying the second sheeting, mix only enough glue to see you through one sheet of plywood, for it may get tacky and be worthless. The best tool for spreading the glue evenly and not too thinly over a large surface is a serrated metal trowel that tile layers use. After the second layer is on, fill all of the cracks and flaws with a resin and mill-fiber combination (the nail heads should have been sunk just below the surface and filled as well), then sand the entire deck. After the deck to hull seam has been filled and sanded, you are ready to lay the fiberglass.

3. Laying the fiberglass

To get a well-sealed bond between hull and deck, the fiberglass layers covering the plywood deck sheeting should hang well over the side of the hull and be bonded to the hull. Before this bonding can be done, the gelcoat has to be ground off the top twelve inches of the hull with coarse sandpaper, then of course washed very carefully with acetone. The first layer of mat and cloth should overhang the deck by six inches, the second by ten inches. At the same time, remember to let the cloth overhang the layer of mat beneath it by about two inches. In this way you will get a gradually even layer which will be easier to fill and feather than one obese seam.

4. Fairing out the bond

The filler to use for fairing out the bond is a mixture of resin and micro-balloons. "Micro-balloons," the red foamish-looking powder, makes a very fine putty that, although not possessing the inherent strength of mill-fiber or scrap fibers, is incomparably easier to sand and shape. Once the final shaping has been done, decrease the grit of sandpaper to 120 and finally 240, then do the gelcoating.

5. Gelcoating

For spraying gelcoat over the bond use a fine-tipped nozzle and do thin layers, constantly moving the gun to prevent runs. Be sure to tell the man at the place where you are renting the compressor (it costs only about $10.00 a day) what you will be doing and what kind of nozzle you will require. He will be happy to help you.

Catalyze the gelcoat only after it is in the sprayer; use it all up. If you have any left over, dump it and immediately half fill the gun with acetone. Spray it through to clean the nozzle. If you let the gelcoat go off, either in the can or in the nozzle, the job of cleaning will be monstrous*.

6. Finishing the deck surface

For the deck use something other than gelcoat. A good marine epoxy paint will do the job. After sanding the deck with 220, wipe it with acetone (I know this procedure is redundant, but you should never forget it). Then using a roller apply the epoxy paint. While the

*Spray a green APB over the gelcoat. APB seals it from air and helps in catalyzing.

paint is still wet, sprinkle on either silicone or ground walnut shells using a fine salt shaker. Either silicone or the walnut makes a perfect non-skid surface. When the first coat has dried, paint on a second one. Don't sprinkle it with anything.

Chapter Sixteen
ROUGH INTERIOR INSTALLATION

Whether you have bought the precut plywood interior or not, you will find installing the rough interior one of the quickest and visually most rewarding operations. The basic question is where to start or which piece to install first. Since the only immediate requirement is to have a flat place for assembly, I suggest you build a work bench. I don't mean to do extra work and fabricate a bench; I mean assemble that piece of cabinetry which will best substitute for one. A lower settee berth in the salon is ideal. It is wide enough, long enough and has a lot of elbow room around it.

Before I get into actual construction, I would like to give a list of tools, materials required, and preparatory procedures to follow.

Tools

If you are short on money, you can delay a large expenditure for a band saw, for it will not be of any great use here. A table saw would be of some help, but if you have access to one for half a day, that should be enough. Then you will need a saber saw to cut the plywood and cut out door holes, etc. You'll need a bevel square to measure angles, a small builder's square and perhaps a large one, a short one-handable level, two drill motors, three screw gun bits, three tapered drill bits with three No. 7 countersinks, ten pounds of Weldwood plastic glue (resin glue that mixes with water). You'll also need about 1,000 stainless steel No. 10 pan head self tapping sheet metal screws one inch long and about 500 No. 10 screws ¾'' long; 300 feet of ¾'' x ¾'' mahogany cleat stock (in six or eight foot lengths); 50 acid brushes; 50 disposable cups; and a lot of rags. The above will enable you to permanently assemble the entire interior and set it temporarily in place, ready for bonding to the hull.

Since the construction of templates has been touched upon in the section of bulkhead installation, I will go on immediately to patterning and cutting.

Layout and Cutting

It is vital, whether you oil, varnish, or paint the plywood surface that the grain goes the same way on all of the pieces. If it does not, the boat will be an eye-disturbing frenzy of lines which may show through even four coats of paint. Therefore, make sure you have grain either all horizontal or all vertical.

When marking out door and drawer holes make certain that if a series exists in the same face, you cut the holes exactly the same size. It's well worth checking, for I've found it much easier to build and fit three identical drawers than to plane, sand, and gouge three dissimilar ones to fit three dissimilar holes. This tip may seem trivial, but do try to make doors in different areas to an identical measurement if possible. I'm not advocating making twenty identical doors in a boat. But if one door is 9'' and the other 8'' why not compromise; sometimes it makes life a little bit easier.

For cutting, always use a sharp medium (7 teeth per inch) blade in your saber saw. Anything rougher than 7 teeth, or duller than very sharp, will have a disgusting tendency to chip irreplaceable chunks out of the plywood.

Cutting openings that will be filled with drop boards (tops of settees, berths, etc.) requires special attention, for the piece that you cut out should be used as the cover for the same hole. Therefore, you cannot use a drill to start a point of insert for the saber saw blade. You'll have to place the blade above the line, resting the frame of the saw on the wood for a pivot, see photo 77. Then start the motor, tilt it down slowly and gently so that the blade has time to penetrate evenly.

For a lid, it's also good practice to mark the corners with a compass or a quarter so that you can execute its extraction with one uninterrupted cut. Not only will rounding the corner enable you to escape making four "tilt penetration" cuts; it will also give you well rounded corners on the lid that will not break off nor penetrate your big toe when dropped.

The edges of the lids should be lightly bull-nosed (¼''). Cut the finger holes to 7/8'' diameter, a dimension which seems to fit an average finger, whatever that is. The underside of the finger hole

Photo No. 77 — Inserting saber saw blade.

should be generously bull-nosed with a 3/8" bit for an easier fit of the finger and thus an easier lift. Once the lid has been cut off, seating cleats will have to be installed around the perimeter of the hole as shown in figure 40, to keep the lid from disappearing in the abyss. Two inch or 1½" stock cut from ½" plywood scraps is ideal here. A 3/8" lip is more than enough to support the lid. Make sure that you round and sand the corners of the seating cleat or slivers may befall you. Painting the bottoms of these surfaces before installation is a commendable idea, much easier at this time than trying to work around the corner hanging upside down in a dark hole later on.

Figure No. 40 — Seating cleats.

Assembly

The assembly process falls into two major sections. One is plywood to plywood, the other is plywood to fiberglass (hull).

1. Wood to wood

The simplest way of attaching two pieces of plywood that come together at an angle is to use cleat stock made of mahogany, oak, or other wood that will hold screws well and will not split. To this cleat stock both pieces of plywood will be glued and screwed. A good size to use is ¾-inch square, for then you can rip it from ¾-inch by random width, random length stock, as shown in figure 41. If an angle joined other than 90 degrees is to be made, simply rip your cleat at the required angle.

Figure No. 41 — Cleat stock.

Once the pieces of plywood have been dry-fitted, wipe one piece where the cleat goes and the side of the cleat to be glued with a wet cloth. Not only will the cloth clean both surfaces of dust and bits and pieces, but it will also wet them so that the glue won't be too rapidly absorbed. Measure and cut cleat stock to length, but make certain that you leave the last four inches of plywood which

adjoin the hull uncleated. You will be able to make a much cleaner and better finished fiberglass bond if you leave the corners clean, see photo 78. Now:
— apply glue to ply and cleat with acid brush
— clamp cleat to plywood
— drill and countersink at ten inch intervals going from plywood to cleat
— countersink should penetrate one-half way into wood
— insert screws
— remove clamps.

It is important that you go from plywood to cleat with your screws because you prevent the possibility of the screw coming

Photo No. 78 — Plywood adjoining hull is uncleated.

through the veneer or the cleat stock splitting if the screw is set too tightly.

Once the wood is assembled, all excess glue should be removed immediately and the wood wiped clean with a damp cloth. Nothing is more unsightly or harder to remove than a long brown dribble of hardened glue.

When joining two, what are to be finished surfaces at a corner, the simplest method is to use a corner post, as shown in figure 42. The post should be milled out of hardwood, preferably of the kind to

ROUGH INTERIOR INSTALLATION

match the rest of your trim since it will remain exposed. Screws will be applied from the exterior faces of the plywood pieces, only slightly staggered so that they will not run into each other, forcing a new hole to be drilled. The diagram below depicts a standard corner post for joining two ½" plywood pieces.

Figure No. 42 — Corner post.

2. Bonding to hull

The installation of cabinetry should be treated as seriously as the installation of bulkheads. In a fiberglass boat, every piece of plywood, whether longitudinal or lateral, will act as a structural component. The degree of importance of each cabinet will vary with its location and size but I don't believe any piece should be neglected.

Once the piece has been dry fitted to the hull (using a foam spacer may be time consuming, but it does isolate a potential hard edge from the glass) attach it temporarily into place by screwing into bulkheads or cabin sole or even temporary blocks. Make sure both horizontal and vertical surfaces are level; it will be much easier to fit

ROUGH INTERIOR INSTALLATION

adjoining pieces and trim. If something is out of square or level now is your last chance to correct it. After you have bonded it into place, changes will be time consuming and very tiresome.

It is advisable to leave off the face or top from the piece of furniture to be installed to facilitate bonding. If you are using teak veneer surface plywood you should grind the teak veneer off the area where the bond will lay (6'' adjoining the hull). Teak has great amounts of natural oil which will not allow it to bond with any reliability.

Grind all paint and rough burrs from the area to be bonded. Resin will not adhere to paint, and burrs will become an impossible nuisance to work around because they will act as a tent pole, creating a lofty air pocket between the surface and the bond. When grinding, cover eyes with goggles and wear long-sleeved shirts and gloves or you will suffer insufferable itching caused by glass specks lodging in your pores. It's advisable to tape the gloves to the shirt and tape the shirt sleeve shut tight to keep out the varmints.

Once everything is sufficiently secured so that it won't move out of plumb even if knocked or leaned upon, and both surfaces to be bonded have been well washed with acetone, you are ready to bond.

Bonding

Bonding is a simple operation that is best left until the whole interior has been assembled and reasonably well secured.

1. Preparation

Since preparing for bonding is a rather complex proposition, I believe it to be much more practical to entirely clean the whole boat *once* of dust, scrap, dirt, and moisture; then all the cabinets can be bonded in with one or two full days of labor. If you try to do it over a number of days, at different stages of assembly, you'll waste tremendous time repeatedly cleaning up your boat, and much material for each bonding operation. You will have to use a new brush, new gloves, and a new container every time. Therefore, once the foregoing preparations have been done, gather up your bonding materials.

To bond cabinetry to the hull, it is common practice to use a layer of mat co,vererd by an overlapping layer of cloth. You should use rolls of six inch wide mat and eight inch wide cloth. They are both strong but the cloth gives a more pleasing and easily manageable finish. The average 35-foot boat will require about 100 yards of each.

2. Dry fitting

Cut and dry fit the pieces to their designated positions. If long areas are to be bonded, use length no greater than two feet at a time. Once the mat and cloth are wetted with resin they will hang, droop, and cling all over you like a coquettish cobra. Overlaps are not a moral crime, so cut the pieces shorter than two feet and save a lot of agony.

When bonding a curved surface to a hull it is stylish to cut "V's" into the mat every ten or so inches, depending on the radius of the curve, so that the unstretchable mat will not bunch up and form a ghastly mound over which the cloth will not adhere acceptably. There is, however, no real need to cut V's into the cloth. It stretches and conforms and if you do get an unsmoothable bubble in a curve, just cut it in half with scissors and mat it down with a resin-wet brush. Clean your scissors with acetone as soon as possible or they will never shear again.

3. Wetting out

Once you have a few pieces dry fit (have a good batch done at one time so that you can wet out uninterruptedly for awhile) get a piece of cardboard that will be larger than your largest piece of cloth. You will use it to wet out the mat-cloth. "Wetting out" means simply saturating the fiberglass with resin.

But first, have a good sized large-bladed fan over one of your hatches. The fan should be in operation at all times when bonding, because the resin emits highly intoxicating fumes which can result in brain damage. If you are working in very closed airless areas, place the fan as close to you as possible, blowing as much fresh air towards you as it can. It is important that the fan blow air into the boat rather than draw out the fumes. Blowing fresh air in prevents the possibility of the fumes and fan motor combining to start a fire.

Wear a disposable paper mask to keep floating bits of fiber out of your lungs. I suggest the disposable variety, for you will be incessantly touching the mask with your resin covered hands and an expensive mask would just become unusable after awhile.

Wear gloves. We found the cheap (10c each) surgical type rubber gloves the best kind. You might use up a dollar's worth a day but at least you are always working with clean supple gloves. If you try and use a good pair over and over, it will be covered with hardened resin and stray fibers which set like porcupine quills. They catch and gnarl every piece of fiberglass cloth at every opportunity. Don't try to wash them with acetone. The thin rubber will break down and come apart like rotting onions.

Use disposable brushes with unpainted handles (the paint gets dissolved by acetone and flakes off in annoying little crusts). Cheap ones, about 39c each, can be had at surplus stores. To wash them when you take breaks during the day is fine, but by the day's end they will have a mountain of insoluably hardened resin at their base. Throw them away. The acetone you waste trying to clean them will cost you a lot more than the brush.

The best containers we found for mixing resin and catalyst were the plastic gallon or quart milk jugs. You can cut them away, see photo 79, leaving a large opening and a very useful handle. Drink lots of milk. It's good for you and it will save a lot of problems, because once the resin has set in the jug it is impossible to clean it completely. Hardened lumps will constantly turn up in the next batch, ruining your otherwise pristine work. If you must reuse a jug, allow the resin to harden; then jiggle, shake it, and smash it against a wall. The very pliable jug will flex and the rigid resin will gallantly fall away.

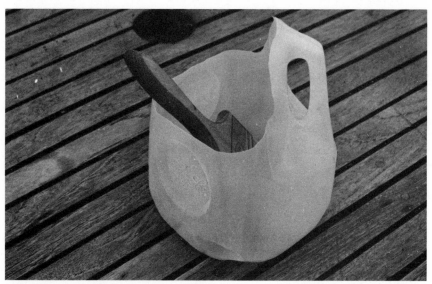

Photo No. 79 — Milk jug mixing container.

4. Catalyzing

MEK peroxide is the only commonly used catalyst. It must be thoroughly mixed with resin at a proportion of between 10 cc. and 70 cc. per gallon depending on the temperature and gel time required. At an ambient temperature of 77 degrees Fahrenheit, one percent MEK will gel in 26 minutes (one percent equals 10 cc. per

U.S. quart).

Accelerators such as DMA can be used if necessary, but only if mixed independently into the resin. If catalyst and accelerator are mixed together a nice explosion will likely occur.

I found it practical to use only a pint of resin at a time. This practice assured me of not wasting any resin through premature catalyzing in case uncalculated interruptions occurred. They always did too, because either the mat wouldn't fit or the power went off or something.

When all is ready, mix in the catalyst and stir thoroughly. Lay the mat and the cloth on the cardboard; then pour resin over them. Spread it evenly with a brush soaking the mat-cloth with quick jabs, making certain that saturation is complete; that is, no white fibers remaining. Then peel the gooey mess from the cardboard (it will come away easily). After applying a good layer of resin on areas of the plywood and the hull that the bond is to cover, put it in place. Lay at least half the width of the tape onto the plywood, for resin won't adhere to plywood as well as it does to fiberglass. If a choice must be made on or near a curve, put the wider half onto the wood; then, while holding with one hand, punch the mat-cloth with short punches of the resin-wet brush.

Do every square centimeter and get every air bubble, see photo 80. Any loose strands or protruding edges can and must be worked completely smooth at this time. Letting them go, only to have to grind at a later time, is absolute lunacy. You'll have itchy irritating glass in your eyes, your clothes, and your nose. Work fast or your expensive resin will gel in the jug. Work off all the excess resin with a brush and go onto the next piece.

It's very rewarding to have two people perform this operation. While one is wetting out on the cardboard, the other can be putting a piece in place. It is most difficult to have to do both operations yourself, especially if you have to crawl to the depths of some locker with each new piece. As mentioned, be sure to get the fan very close to you in these confined areas. You'll need every grasp of fresh air you can get. If you get to feel like you'd like to lie down and go to sleep; get out of there before you do, for a long time. If the resin starts to gel badly before you finish the piece, tear it out and acetone what remains on the hull. It can become so bad that you'll end up with a hard irremovable clump. On the opposite end, if after a few hours the resin still hasn't gone off, then place a small electric heater close to the bond to help it set.

You will find the inside corners most difficult to bond. If you

ROUGH INTERIOR INSTALLATION

Photo No. 80 — Thoroughly wetted out surface.

followed advice and did not put cleat stock on the last few inches, your task will be easier. The best bonding method is to run the two straight pieces as close to the corner as possible, leaving only a small crack. Then take a square piece of mat-cloth (about 8 by 8) and cut inch and a half V's in all four sides, see figure 43. Wet out and work into place. It should be easy.

If possible, double bond both sides of plywood. In spite of other advice I would bond each cabinet so as to isolate it from all others. Not only will this practice localize leaks to keep water from spoiling goods in other lockers, but it will also help you find the source of the water in much less time.

After the bonds have all gone off, check for flaws or missed corners and, worst of all, lumps and cowlicks. These protrusions must be ground or you will have dangerous weapons in your cabinetry that will tear not only clothes and wrappings but also skin. Nothing can penetrate quicker or more painfully than a hardened strand of needle sharp fiberglass.

Bonding fiberglass to fiberglass (hull to deck) requires the same procedure. Upside down bonding, however, does present problems that you will be able to solve only after a giant piece of goo has draped all over your head. Use as small pieces as practicable. As you can see, bonding requires no great amount of practice. The steps are basic and the results predictable. If you miss cleaning or pre-resining a surface, don't go to the river. It's important that you do the ritual but exactly why I'm not certain. Once, while bonding, I threw a running shoe into a sawdust filled locker. When I retrieved it an hour later, only half of it was willing to come away from the hull. The whole upper body remained solidly bonded where some resin had been spilled . . . and I hadn't even carefully washed my sneakers with acetone for quite some time.

FIBER GLASS MAT TAPE

Figure No. 43 — Cutting mat to fit curves.

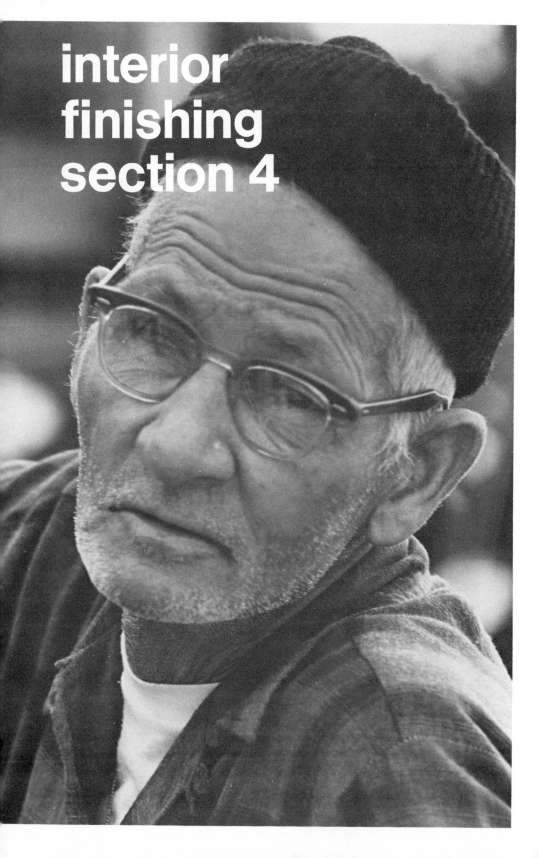

interior
finishing
section 4

Chapter Seventeen
INSULATION

One common complaint of all fiberglass boat owners is that their hulls "sweat." This condition is more aggravated in colder climates where condensation is more frequent, due to the great temperature difference between the heated interior and the very cold exterior.

Many excellent thermal insulators are available to boat builders and each has its own very valuable place in a boat.

Styrofoam

This material is a very good insulator. A half-inch of styrofoam has the "K Factor" (insulative quality) of two inches of common house insulating glass wool. It is easy to cut with a sharp "exacto" knife and a metal straight edge. It's very light, quite inexpensive (about 20c a square foot), and very uncomplicated to attach. Any common tile cement applied to a few critical spots will hold it in place until a hard covering of wood liner is laid over. It is perfect to lay onto a hull, cabin side, or cabin top where tongue-and-groove or plywood can be used to cover and protect it. It is most impractical inside cabinets or in a place where no protection over it is planned, because even a paternal tap with a can of anchovies will cause a rivulet of cascading foam chips. Such an accident is messy and affects the life span of the foam quite adversely.

To cover over styrofoam with either plywood or strips requires some ribbing to which one can fasten the covering wood. Two methods can be used for ribbing, one a little more expensive, the other quite dumb because it consumes a tremendous number of hours.

1. The dumb way

— rip ¾'' plywood into 1½'' wide strips
— cut to 24 inch lengths
— run it through a table saw with the blade set so high that it will cut all but the last two layers of veneer.
— slit in this fashion at about one inch intervals, see photo 81.
— mix up a batch of mish-mash and using a putty knife squeeze it into the cracks, leave a judicious layer over the rest of it.
— acetone hull where rib is to fit, then fit it into place. It should bend easily. Now the only problem is holding it there. Brace it, however, with whatever you can until the mish-mash goes off.

Photo No. 81 — Slit plywood strips for ribs.

When using mish-mash the catalyst must be stirred into the resin first, then add the asbestos or whatever. It is advisable to practice on a small quantity until you ascertain the amounts of catalyst you require.

Once the mish-mash has gone off, put at least a bond of mat tape over the rib just to be sure. You can nail or screw into the ribs as well as slip ½-inch sheets of styrofoam in between them. The centers need not be more than 18 inches if you are using 3/8''

274   **INSULATION**

plywood or tongue-and-groove. If you are butting slats without any tongue-and-groove or other overlap, use twelve inch centers.

Decks and cabin tops usually have a plywood core for stiffness; thus the ribs can be fastened with screws while the mish-mash is going off so that awkward bracing won't be required.

2. The more expensive way

In the same fashion that you scribed plywood to fit the hull, scribe ribs out of 1¾" stock of fir, mahogany, or other easily workable wood. Ribs may have to be cut from as wide as six inch stock if the hull's curvature is drastic. Because once cut out these ribs have no tension forcing them straight, mish-mashing and bracing can be bypassed. A single layer of mat will bond them to the hull quite securely. You can fabricate your ribs to the thickness of syrofoam you wish to use.

Needless to say, I did our ceiling the dumb way. That's why I know it so well.

Rigid Urethane Foam

To insulate the rest of the hull, inside the cabinets, etc. is a grueling two day job but it may save mildewed clothes and soaked underwear. I at first thought it a simple matter, believing it feasible, economical, and rapid to simply spray the whole empty hull with urethane foam and then glass over it. You can rent a sprayer and the bonding should be easy in an open area.

This method has two giant failings: a) if you insulate before you install the cabinetry you will have to bond the insulation to the thin covering of glass. Since the foam has no structural strength, the exercise would be similar to putting wallpaper over a layer of air, then trying to nail a picture hanger into it; b) it's impossible to spray on a smooth even coat of urethane, even for the most experienced craftsman. The result, at best, would be wartish to the extent where a solid week is required to bring the surface to a condition smooth enough for bonding over. The week would be spent at planing, curving, and grinding the foam, a dusty, itchy, miserably unrewarding task. Avoid it.

The remaining alternative is fitting and installing solid urethane foam sheets into cabinets after they have been bonded to the hull. This procedure is no dream job since you'll have to crawl into spaces you've previously considered too small for a dog and work often in very dim light with very little air. The foam can be cut with a knife. If the surface is large and curved, the foam should be filletted to allow small straight pieces to form the required arch. A few spots of tile cement will suffice to hold the pieces in place until bonding.

Since bonding over the foam is necessary to protect it, one must use urethane. Like styrofoam, urethane comes in sheets of varying thickness and, although it is more expensive than styrofoam, it has two advantages. First, it is a 30 percent better insulator. Second, it will not melt when used in conjunction with polyester resin. It is usually green or tan in color, is very brittle, and is much itchier than styrene but you have to use it.

Because it is almost impossible to measure and cut large accurate pieces of mat to fit over the odd curves and angles of a cabinet's belly, I used six inch mat tape (the same that I used for bonding plywood to hull). A single layer of ounce and a half mat (with edges overlapped an inch) proved sufficient after numerous stress tests. The tests were quite basic, involving little more than dropping a quite ordinary hammer from assorted heights. If you can devise more profound testing, proceed.

One noteworthy point. When you are putting in the foam, leave a two inch gap between its upper edge and whatever plywood surface you have above it. When you bond over the foam, finish off the bond only onto the hull and not onto the plywood as shown in figure 44. We had made the mistake of doing the opposite. When water found its way onto the horizontal plywood surface, it ran behind the bond and into the sealed pocket formed by the lower bond. We didn't discover this mistake until installing a transducer. I was drilling from outside of the hull, waiting to see light, only to be showered by brown stale water. We ended up tearing a part of the insulation out and rebonding the whole cabinet. So beware.

Perhaps a few inconspicuous drain holes through the bottom of the bond would not be overcautious, but try to be sure that you don't drill through your hull. Again, as in bonding cabinetry, do as clean a job as possible, leaving no hard strands or upturned ends.

Once bonded, paint over all surfaces, first with a coat of undercoat (Z-Spar 105 or equivalent) then with one or two coats of easy-to-clean gloss or semigloss enamel. It's best to get mildew-proof paint. Although manufacturers of marine paints insist that their product exceeds all others in quality and wonderfulness, I have been reassured by those who know that paint is paint is paint. So use almost any exterior mildew-proof oil base. The cheaper the better.

Soft Urethane Foam

Some people advocate the use of soft urethane foam (like cushion) with a vinyl contact-cemented to the hull. I think that it is quite satisfactory under a wood cover, but I cannot see how a clean

HULL

PLYWOOD CABINET PIECE

MAT. BONDING

OVER

URETHANE FOAM

Figure No. 44 — Bonding over insulation.

tidy fit can be achieved inside cabinets, for the shapes created by compound curves are almost unimaginable. Apart from esthetics, if heavy objects such as cans and tools are to be stored, the soft foam will collapse to such an insignificant thickness that its insulative qualities will be measurably decimated.

I do, however, believe that neoprene foam (preferably the non-flammable type) is ideal for soundproofing the engine room. This material represents an expensive venture, but diesels are annoyingly noisy; therefore it may be worthwhile. Thickness of up to 1½'' may be required to be effective. Applied to the engine room bulkheads and around the cockpit sides it should provide very comfortable passage.

Chapter Eighteen
SURFACE COVERS

Once the rough interior is in, insulated, and painted the next item should be installation of cabinet surfaces.

Formica

This surface is inexpensive, easy to work with, and stands up fairly well to abuse; but it has its failings. If something hot is placed upon it by accident it will buckle and lift. To repair without tearing the whole thing off is impossible. If chipped or cracked or burnt, the same situation will exist. If you leave any kind of space, no matter how tiny, between the formica and the plywood, water may find its way in and rot the plywood beneath. If you still insist on using it, in spite of all these reasons, here are a few pointers I learned while applying it (not on our boat):

It can be rough cut to size with a skill saw. Overcut by at least 1/16th of an inch. To rough cut, lay the formica onto a scrap sheet of plywood and set the saw blade so that only enough protrudes to barely cut through the formica. You'll have to flip up the guard and hold it, so you had better get a good two-handed grip on the saw. You'll need to grip well anyway because the formica is extremely slippery. Any little inattentiveness can result in wasting the whole $20 sheet. Once dry fit, cover the plywood top and the formica with contact cement. Don't miss any spots. I have heard of people using epoxy cement. I don't know how well it works; therefore I'll just mention the contact cement.

Once the glue has set sufficiently so that it is not tacky, cover the counter top with sheets of newspaper. Over the paper lay the formica in place as accurately as possible, then lift up one edge and pull out the piece of paper nearest the edge still resting on the plywood surface. Let the back few inches down and pound that area evenly but hard. Your fist will be the best tool to be used here. Now pull out the next piece of paper and repeat. In this way you'll be sure to get out all of the air bubbles. When adhered, rough grind the outer edge with a good coarse sander or trim with a small hand plane. If you chip the edge somewhat, don't worry, for a sea-rail will cover it.

Holes for drop boards will have to be treated differently. First of all, you have to cut them out with a saber saw. Begin by drilling to make room for the blade. To try the angle immersion method will only result in chipped formica or broken blades. Use a sharp hacksaw type blade with very fine teeth for a very smooth cut. Once the formica has adhered to the surface, file the overhangs into the hole with a good metal file (bastard file). When close to the plywood edge either apply a vertical formica edge or angle-file so that no sharp formica lip will stick out to crack and chip. If you use the vertical piece, file calmly and evenly until a 45 degree joint is achieved as shown in figure 45. I have seen a lot of people cover both sides of their drop boards as well as the edges with formica to prevent warpage. This practice is probably very good, because a drop board of any size, even if no longer than twenty inches, will in time absorb moisture unevenly, dry unevenly, and warp badly.

Figure No. 45 — Formica edge.

SURFACE COVERS

Wood Surfacing

A more preferable surfacing material is wood. It will not lift if heated; and if chipped, burnt, or scratched it can be sanded, filled, or just left. It will still look quite acceptable, and I think that teak or maple or oak looks an awful lot warmer and more emotionally stimulating than black formica with gold marbly cracks and silver specs to boot. I admit that wood is more expensive and its fabrication is a lot more time demanding, but to me the results well justify the extra effort, see photo 82.

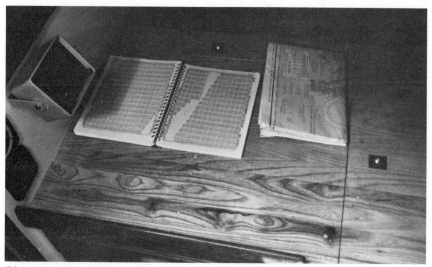

Photo No. 82 — Wood surface.

Wood selection is not critical. Teak is oily and will not rot, so that it can probably be used without any varnish or urethane protection. Oak and maple are very hard and stand beating well, but they are prone to rot, therefore they have to be coated with varnish or urethane. Oak is rather dark, offering little contrast to teak searails.

To make a long story end, we used ash. It too is prone to rot and has to be sealed, but it has nice grain and an occasional beautiful knot. Even when it's varnished or oiled it remains sufficiently light to contrast ideally with teak or mahogany sea-rails. I must admit, it is an extremely hard wood, thus very difficult to work and fabricate. Ripping it requires patience and an exceptionally sharp carbide-tipped blade. Cutting to length on a band saw again demands an unhurried attitude or the blade will heat up and break. On the band saw you must not force the wood to cut curves. If your curves are of drastically minute radius, get a very narrow blade (¼") and feed your wood through with little, even force. Also, be familiar with your band saw; lower the blade-backing bearings as much as possible to offer maximum protection to the blade.

The width of planking used is a matter of personal preference. The narrower they are, the less loss in scraps. But of course the narrower they are the more labor required to fit and fasten them. At any rate, width can be left a choice. But thickness, I must emphasize, should not exceed 3/8". I recommend this dimension because a) wood is expensive (about $1 a board foot for ash, at printing); b) it adds substantial weight to the boat; and c) a thinner piece is infinitely easier to sand or trim, when you are working with end grain. To this end I propose either having a mill rip some one inch stock in half for you or doing it yourself. I did ours myself without a joiner, ending up spending a considerable number of hours grinding the uneven thicknesses to some semblance of smoothness.

Once your stock is ready, clean off the plywood surface completely. Even the slightest sliver or drop of old glue (which should have been wiped up when still wet) can cause a most frustrating teeter-tottering. At this point the decision to use glue or bedding compound between the plywood and wood is to be made.

1. Bedding compound

Since you use and waste a lot of it, even the least expensive one like acrylic sealant, bedding compound is expensive (about 60c per tube). It is also terribly messy to work with because to achieve proper sealing you must put a bead of caulking on the edge of each piece as well as the bottom of it to seal all cracks. Consequently, when two pieces are butted together, a great gush of caulking will surge upward onto your hands, screws, drill bits, and ears. In spite of all this, I think that bedding compound is preferable in areas where water may frequent such as the galley counters, cabin sole, and head sink counter.

The compound should be spread evenly, especially on the edges, to allow a tight fit. Clamps may be used in certain instances but I find them quite awkward. Therefore the most feasible, although slow, alternative is blocking and wedging each piece. This practice requires screwing a block (a piece of 1" x two or three inch ash is fine) into the plywood at whatever intervals you feel intense pressure will be necessary. The distance should be no more than two inches away from the piece to be wedged. If it is greater, the pressure may cause the wedge and the piece to tent up. Now drive a wedge between the block and the piece to be fitted. Tap it only until the butt-fit is made. Any further wedging is superfluous and may even cause the screw in the block to bend. Should it bend, extraction is very tiresome and the screw will have to be discarded. Just think of throwing 5c into a lake each time you ruin a screw. Once butted, drill and countersink every six to nine inches. A single screw per piece is sufficient up to 2½-inches in width. If your plank exceeds that dimension, I would use two screws side by side to make sure that the edges won't lift if any warping occurs.

If you are using the suggested 3/8'' stock, your countersinking skills will be put to the test, for you will have to penetrate deep enough to leave space for a secure plug (at least 3/16''), yet shallow enough to allow the screw's shoulder to have a goodly thickness of wood to rest on (at least 3/16''). So you can see your room for error is nil. To aid in this direction you should use flat head screws (No. 8's are heavy enough). Their heads are spacially less demanding than the pan heads. However, the heads also have a wedge-shaped bottom, as mentioned before, which may split the ash in half if not cautiously tightened. Therefore don't lean on your drill motor when screwing, but tighten it down so that all surfaces will be flush and all underbodies will be sealed.

When fitting the surfacing hardwood for drop boards, the most accurate method is to cut one piece to length at a time. Fasten down a piece leading to the edge of a hole; then using a continuation of the same piece to match the grain, cut a piece which will cover the drop board. Butt this piece tight to the first piece. Now, butt up the last section of the same piece and screw it into place. This way you'll have a tight fitting lid which will need trimming, for it's almost impossible to set each end up along the same line. The other alternative is to leave your hole cutting for last, but then installing the seating cleat will be a horrible job.

2. Gluing

On areas not likely to get wet often (I'm not sure such a thing exists on a boat), using resin glue instead of bedding compound is quite acceptable. It is also quicker and easier to wipe clean. You may save on screws here, because the screws act only as a clamp until the glue hardens. I think it quite safe to remove all screws once the glue is hard and use them elsewhere. If taken to extremes it may be possible to build a whole boat with 27 reusable screws.

One last reassurance — complex as these operations may sound through my verbosity, I assure you that in practice they are not particularly mentally or manually taxing. Common sense will see you through most of your problems. If you think things through thoroughly, you will discover your own procedure sequences, such as wiping all glue and bedding compound off immediately before it hardens or gets tacky. If you don't think such a thing through, and you leave it set slightly, then try sanding it; you will find that most bedding compounds are soft enough to clog up every pore of an 89c belt in 23 seconds.

After sanding, seal the wood with varnish or urethane. It may be a good idea to use either of the two sealers to insert your plugs. If you use glue you will have great difficulty extracting them if the need ever arises.

Lining Fiberglass

As mentioned before, hulls, cabin sides, etc. may be lined with either tongue-and-groove, solid wood, or plywood. The plywood is quicker if two people are doing the operation, because they will have no difficulty in shifting and holding large pieces into place. Plywood is also cheaper; yet, it will result in considerably more waste. We used tongue-and-groove teak in our entire boat and I swear I lost only a little more than twenty lineal feet of 2¼'' teak stock. Plywood may also be applied directly to fiberglass cabin sides or tops, whereas to tongue-and-groove here without ribs would be folly. No matter how cautious the tooling was on your deck mold flaws and lumps still remain which your tongue-and-groove cannot follow or if it does follow it will only emphasize the problem through its harsh seamed lines.

1. Installing plywood liner

Plywood can be applied to ribs (install ribs as per the section on ribbing for insulation). I would also put glue on each rib before screwing the plywood onto it.

If you choose not to use ribs, you will have a lesser task. After you have dry fit your plywood pieces, simply apply a thick layer of mish-mash, stick the piece in place, and screw it tight. Before applying the mish-mash, set your countersink right at the top of the drill bit and drill a few 1/8'' deep pot marks (about 6 to 10 per square foot). The holes will give the mish-mash a better grip on the plywood, see photo 83.

If you are installing the plywood liner where no plywood core is beneath it, for example on the cabin side, it may be a good idea to do so without using screws. Even the most skilled of us will have difficulty screwing and drilling into ¼'' fiberglass just deep enough for the screw to hold and just shallow enough so that the thing

Photo No. 83 — Pot marks in plywood for mish-mash adhesion.

doesn't stick out the other side.

The alternative is simple if the cabin sides are being lined, because portlights will be eventually fitted here (the sooner the better for they will provide ventilation and much needed light). Find the location of your portlights. Somewhere within the circle (or oval or whatever) they are to occupy, drill a 3/8'' hole. When you dry fit the plywood piece that is to line this area, continue that hole through the plywood.

Now, after pot marking the underside of the plywood, cover it with mish-mash and stick it into place. Slip a bolt through the hole (using large plywood washers to distribute the pressure) and tighten the nut onto it, see photo 84. I hope that you decide to put in a lot of portlights because then you will have a lot of holes to slip a lot of bolts through for good adhesion. If, however, you have large areas where no holes can be drilled, use braces wherever you can. As nice as it is to put portlights in early, it may be advisable to leave this procedure until at least some of your cabinetry is in place so that the cabinets can be used to brace against. Try to leave braces and bolts overnight to make sure that the mish-mash has completely catalyzed.

In areas of great curvature, use as thin a plywood as possible (¼'' is enough) or you will be attempting an impossible fit.

When installing ribs on the hull the procedure is simple if you are using tongue-and-groove. But it is impossible if you are using plywood, because the curvature will necessitate using ¼'' ply at its thickest and I defy anyone to put a screw into this thickness and plug it. If you don't mind screw heads or nail heads showing you'll have no problem.

SURFACE COVERS 285

Photo No. 84 — Installing plywood cabin side liner in upside-down deck.

2. Tongue-and-groove

If you are having your wood milled, make sure that they put a 1/8'' bull-nose on both edges. Then if the pieces shrink and open (ours did) the consequent gap won't look as out of place as it would on a theoretically unseamed surface. Tongue-and-groove is easy to apply over ribs. Once you tap the tongue into place, the piece will stay there in all but the worst curves until you stick a screw or nail into it. Don't forget to glue each piece. We used bronze ring nails to fasten our tongue-and-groove. They have very salty looking unevenly cast heads which I do not find offensive to look at. Obviously nailing is much easier and cheaper than screwing and plugging. Take your pick.

In areas of compound curvature (bow), it is advisable to have some friends present. It took three of us in some instances to force one seven foot long piece into place. Here the tongue-and-groove is definitely a nuisance, for you're fighting compound curves which require a twist of the wood while bending. Then you have to fit the almost invisible tongue into an almost invisible groove. Good luck.

SURFACE COVERS

Chapter Nineteen
ELECTRICAL INSTALLATION

This phase is most frightening if you haven't dealt with it before, but in actuality it is almost boringly undemanding. Most manufacturers will supply you with wiring diagrams which you can either follow or throw out. In most cases you can lead wire anywhere, place your lights anywhere, and put your switch panel almost anywhere. How to wire instruments is either self-explanatory or at least elaborately clarified on supplied instructions; however, I will touch upon a few generalities.

Primarily I feel obligated to press the aspect I consider most important: the best way to have a trouble-free electrical system is not to have one in the first place. If you must have one, keep it as basic and simple as possible so that it can't break down or, if it does, you can repair it with minimum effort and no parts. If you rely on parts, you're dead unless you never leave the U.S. coast, because there is nothing more certain than as soon as you are out of sight of land, everything mechanical will cease to function as if on a given signal. The gravity of malfunction will increase geometrically the further you go and will reach its apex when you reach Tahiti, where, when you beg for a No. 10 butt-connector your cab driver will promptly locate for you a lady of the night.

That you will never find parts to fit your Acme deep-freezer, your Sear Roebuck generator or your Warner Brothers micro-wave oven is axiomatic, so think about it hard. If you can do without, here are some points.

Batteries

Regardless of the size of your alternator you must have two

batteries with a selector switch that enables you to draw off one or the other or both. One battery should be used strictly for starting the engine and nothing else. A blinding sign over this battery switch designating it as "Engine" would not be a bad idea.

About 100 amp hr. heavy-duty recreational home or truck batteries will suffice. Place them in a plastic case, see photo 85, so spillage won't corrode everything in sight, but make sure the top of the box is ventilated so the very explosive hydrogen gas can dissipate. You can make your own battery cables. Since distances vary with each installation you may as well make your own. All you'll require is a given length of battery wire and four terminal couplings for the battery.

Photo No. 85 — Plastic battery case.

A Selector Switch

One four position switch will be required. The positions are Off, Battery 1, Battery 2, and All. Buy a reliable switch for this purpose like a Perko or equivalent. Perko also makes an attachment for a large 60 amp fuse and it should be the only fuse on the boat. All other protection should be breaker type, because fuses are hard to replace in remote areas.

ELECTRICAL INSTALLATION

Needless to say, the fuse should be installed as close to your switch panel as possible, both of them being placed well out of weather, see photo 86.

Photo No. 86 — Switch panel beside companionway.

Breakers

To simplify matters, the best breaker system is the one which combines a toggle switch with a breaker in one unit, thereby halfing the moving parts, see photo 87. It is quite true that you may wear out the breaker by constant use of it as an on/off switch. But practice has shown that these units last for very long periods without failure. Of course they are expensive, but I think well worth the cost.

A sampling of a typical panel and system of fuses used is shown in photo 86. As you can see, the navigation lights have one common

Photo No. 87 — Breaker with toggle.

breaker servicing five breakerless toggle switches that control the mast head, anchor, red over green, and navigation and stern pulpit lights respectively. Their total draw does not exceed 20 amps, so the one breaker for all of them is sufficient.

Wire

Sixteen gauge wire color coded for easy servicing will be sufficient for most 12 volt installations, including cabin lights and navigation lights. A 12 gauge wire should handle spreader lights, whereas 16 gauge will suffice for running lights. A No. 10 black can be used for a common ground to which all mast lights can be hooked.

I hear from experts that solid wire should be avoided in favor of the multi-strand cores. The multi-strand are more flexible and less prone to break in half if stressed or drastically bent.

Terminal Blocks

It is unwise to make unaccessible, unsealed splices in a boat. They will, in time, corrode. If the wire is hidden the corrosion may lead to problems. To make a group of wires more accessible all at once a terminal block should be used where a number of wires are being spliced at one point (for example, at the mast base where the wires coming from the panel join the ones coming down the mast), see photo 88. The terminal block, in conjunction with end fittings, makes for a secure joint which can be inspected, cleaned, and serviced.

The same principal is applicable to the area around the chart table where wires from instruments meet the power supply lines.

ELECTRICAL INSTALLATION

Photo No. 88 — Mast terminal block.

Blocks can be bought with different numbers of terminals on them. If the smallest block has too many terminals for you, cut it with a hack saw and use it wherever you can. On a multi-terminal block, save the fuss of connecting one return for each terminal by using a buss-bar, see photo 89. To the buss-bar you can connect one return wire and get a good job done inexpensively and accessibly. If you don't have the brass stock to make the buss-bar, a 10 gauge solid copper wire bent to interconnect the terminals will substitute nicely.

Photo No. 89 — Buss bar.

ELECTRICAL INSTALLATION

Conduit

All wires running through cabinetry or elsewhere in the boat should be run through a conduit. Here they will be out of harm's way instead of being cut or pinched or flying about madly chafing against each other. Inexpensive PVC of about 1'' diameter will hold a lot of small gauge wires and it costs about 5c a foot. If wires turn sharp corners, it would be wise to use PVC elbows; the sharp edge of the pipe is prone to chafe through the wire casing.

To look slightly ahead and install two or three spare wires may be very advisable. Then should some uncorrectable failure befall a wire it could simply be bypassed and one of the spares used in its place.

When terminating a conduit and running the wire on further, file the rough burrs off the end of the pipe. Then, as an added precaution, pull the wires out 3 extra inches, wrap a few generous layers of electrician's tape over the last protruding 6 inch length, and stick three inches back in the tube. The use of electrician's tape will help in potentially dangerous areas as well, for you will find places where the wires twist and turn over a short distance making conduiting impossible. In these areas, wrap all the wires over with electrician's tape and don't scrimp, see photo 90.

Photo No. 90 — Wrapping wire with electrician's tape.

ELECTRICAL INSTALLATION

Stripping

Be sure to use a good wire stripping tool with different gauges legibly indicated, see photo 91. There is nothing worse than having a beautifully laid out and executed system with wires that are half cut through because someone insisted on using cheapo adjustable strippers, or pliers, or an old bowie knife.

Photo No. 91 — Two excellent wire-cutters & crimps.

Tye Wraps

These items are very inexpensive and they can save a lot of chafing and unsightly wires, see photo 92. Tye wraps usually have an eye in which you can insert screws and fasten the mess out of harm's way. Make sure you put the wrap where you finally want it and make sure you don't have to run more wires through it later. Once it's pulled tight, the only way it can be removed is by cutting. This operation usually results in cut wires, or at least split wire casings.

Wire Connectors

Although inhumanly expensive for what they are, wire connectors are fast to use and they do work. They come in different gauges and colors to fit all wires. When crimping, use only the appropriate tools (usually the same tool that you use for stripping will have a crimp on it) and press very firmly. Make sure you strip off only the amount of insulation necessary or you will have great lengths of

Photo No. 92 — Tye wraps.

unprotected wire dangling from the connector. Once crimped, you cannot hurt anything by applying a well spread dab of silicone sealer to either end of the connector to keep all the moisture possible out of there.

Lamps

Many will disagree, but I find the flat, diffused, relatively dim light given by dome lamps undramatic and boring. I much prefer a high intensity 12 volt light (same bulb as used in the powerful reading lamps) housed in a conical or cylindrical fixture. This type of lamp will give you wonderful amounts of light, see photo 93, for reading and working as well, lighting only specific areas. Thus others in the boat are not disturbed. And you are adding depth, life, and mystery to your surroundings, through strong light shade justaposition. (See Rembrandt)

To connect these lights I began with the foolish surmise that I'll run one wire the length of the cabin, splice other wires into it at designated spots, and lead the branch wires to where the lights will be located. Very stupid. This method results in hours of extra work by creating the need for extra splices, which will probably be buried in some inaccessible pit. The logical solution is to run both wires to each lamp, terminate them in the fittings in the lamp, and begin the wiring for the next lamp on the same point (with, of course, the lamp switch in between). In this way you have uninterrupted wire from lamp to lamp, and connections only in the lamps where access is immediate.

ELECTRICAL INSTALLATION

One note. I have found, to my dismay, that only a pathetically meager selection of 12 volt boat lamps are available. All others are made for recreational vehicles; thus they are ordinarily steel which will last no time in salt air surroundings. A simple way to circumvent this problem is to buy critical parts of brass (swivel heads, switch buttons, etc.) and paint or shellac the other parts. If you are young and foolish like us you can have them brass plated, but that usually costs more than the lamps themselves.

Because we wanted the lamps in pieces (easier than taking them apart) for plating, we went directly to the manufacturer and were able to pick up many spare parts, like bayonet sprockets, switches, and springs and bolts, all of which would be most difficult to replace abroad. Placed in a well sealed plastic bag; they may be your best friends some day.

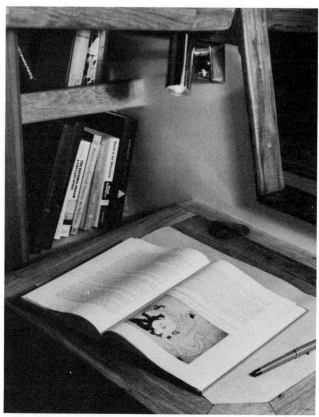

Photo No. 93 — My study wall light.

ELECTRICAL INSTALLATION

Chapter Twenty
PLUMBING

Boat plumbing requires few specialized tools and no specific esoteric skills. The tools needed, you will probably have available. The only items you are likely to be missing are a pair of hole saws for the different sized seacocks you use and a large channel lock which you must have to tighten the large inside nuts on the seacock through hull fittings. A countersink to create holes into which the ¼-inch flat heads for the seacocks will be recessed is also a must.

Seacocks

All underwater through hull fittings should be fitted with seacocks of the levered manual shut-off variety. No gate valve should be substituted.

Wilcox-Crittendon and Groco make very good seacocks to choose from. If you're offered others, check to make sure that the T-bar shut-off holds, and that the T-bar shut-off locks and opens with a positive feel but with some facility.

Seacocks must, of course, be bronze, for plastic ones do harden after which levers and attachments can be snapped off with little force. Be sure the bolts, nuts, and washers you buy for them are also bronze and not red-brass, or you'll be inviting electrolysis.

The installation is self-explanatory, but a few points should be mentioned. Refer to figure 46.

1. Placement

Be absolutely sure that the location of each seacock will be such that ready access will not be hindered by cabinetry, wires, or hoses. Try shutting off and opening them in their final locale using both

BOLT NUT + WASHER

MAHOG. BLOCK

HULL

SEAL WITH POLY SULPHIDE

Figure No. 46 — Seacock installation.

T-bar and the lever arm. Make sure you can do it in any circumstance. Make sure that if the necessity to dismantle arises you'll be able to get to all parts with tools without having to hack away through cabinets or dismantle half the boat.

a) Engine intake. It may be a very good idea to have two intakes so if one gets clogged or covered by a floating plastic bag you'll have an alternative intake. Whether one or two are used, they should be guarded by exterior screens, see photo 94, which will limit the entry of most floating debris.

b) Head. Make sure that your head intake is placed forward of your head outlet. Then if your boat is in motion (usually forward), the refuse will not be immediately returned by the intake pump. An obvious point, you may say, but I've seen the most basic of mistakes

Photo No. 94 — Thru-hull screen.

made on a friend's boat by a supposedly professional marine plumber.

Place the head outlet below the head intake, as most water logged refuse sinks or is forced downward because of the turn of the bilge. Pumping your refuse back into the boat is not only esthetically unpleasant, but it is most hazardous, as clumped toilet tissue can plug your intake solidly shut. I think it is also wise to install a forementioned screen over this intake to minimize the possibility of such an occurrence.

2. Fittings and sealing

Dry fit all your seacocks. You may find, either because of hull irregularity or the drastic bilge curvature, that your seacock will not lie flush against the glass at all points. The remedy is simple. Grind the hull with a small disc sander until a perfect fit occurs; otherwise, you'll be inviting leaks.

Use a plywood donut inbetween the hull and the seacocks. The donut will take up some of the compression when you're trying to put the last half or quarter turn to get your seacocks aligned, see photo 95.

Be sure to use only polysulfide base sealers. Dolfinite drains out in hot weather and silicone sealer doesn't seem to stand up to

PLUMBING   **299**

salt water too well. Acrylic sealant is out of the question, because it is not waterproof. As redundant as this advice may be by now, I urge you to wipe all surfaces to be sealed with acetone to assure the best possible adhesion.

When tightening nuts, tighten only to the point where you can feel it begin to take hold. I did undergo the misfortune of stretching a soft bronze bolt over ¼-inch by relentlessly turning and tightening the nut.

If you install a seacock on the engine exhaust, you can keep nasty following seas out of your engine, according to most experienced skippers. You don't need such an elaborate precaution on a yacht with blunt transom, as a simple flap made of leather or rubber and installed on the outside will work well. It should be top hinged so it will open only if the exhaust pressure forces it to.

The above is not a practical solution on double enders, however, where a following sea would hit the flap on an angle, forcing it open and rendering it useless. A more feasible idea would be installation of a seacock right at the through hull. The seacock should, of course, be all bronze (some bronze ones have neoprene or plastic turning drums) to stand up to heat. And above all, it must be placed in a very accessible location where nothing will be stowed about it,

Photo No. 95 — Seacock.

PLUMBING

possibly knocking the lever into shut position. It is an excellent idea to lock the seacock in the "open" position; lock it shut only if drastic following seas occur. Opening and shutting the seacock constantly may result in the grave condition of foregetting that the thing is shut, starting up the engine, and drowning it.

You may reason that this seacock is a costly luxury, but you can actually use the spare seacock you save by not installing a drain for your head sink. I'm not sure that a head sink is a vital necessity; but if you do have one, arrange to drain it into the head. You then take double use of the head through hull, instead of providing the seldom used sink with its own costly through hull. Besides, the fewer holes in your hull, the better. Neither can one forget how appreciative any marine head would be if it were occasionally cleansed and flushed with nice soapy water.

Fuel

1. Tanks

Materials to be used for tanks were described in an earlier chapter, so they will be left out here. Refer to figure 47 for installation. Most discussion required was touched upon in the chapter on what to buy. Here are a few parts that were omitted.

2. Tank vents

These vents are required for all fuel and water tanks. Fuel tanks

Figure No. 47 — Tank installation in the bilge.

should vent overboard so diesel fumes or over filling will not foul the interior of the boat. Standard bronze vents exist for this purpose, available at most marine hardware stores. They should be installed as high up as possible to keep them as dry as possible. To prevent water entry, fill the vents with copper wool. And to help it even more, angle the vent hole about 45° aft off vertical so your bow wake, or water throw when heeled, will have a tendency to flow by instead of in. If you turn the hole higher than this angle you're inviting rain water.

As a further measure, it's good practice to put a loop into your venting hose. The hose itself can be clear plastic tubing, which is easy to work with. Be sure your loop isn't of such small radius that you overstrain or "break" the hose. Common hose clamps (all stainless) serve fine, and most plastic or rubber hosing will seal perfectly well onto plastic or bronze hose-barbs without requiring any additional putty or sealant.

The deck fills for diesel (should be bronze) should, if possible, be located directly over the tank's intake fitting. If so you will be able to use an ordinary piece of wood as a measuring stick to establish fuel level. Granted, other consideration should be given to fills (like not putting them where one may sit because they get awfully hot in the sun) to satisfy specific needs, but "stick-check" potential should be a foremost consideration. The fills, of course, should be the screw down variety, see photo 96, of which keys are always lost, so have a few extras on hand. Bed the fills generously in bedding compound and cover the screw holes with a bead of it before installing the screws. The best fill-to-tank connector is an accordian hose, see photo 96. These bases are soft and pliable. They will guarantee an excellent seal even if the deck-fill and tank fitting are slightly out of ideal alignment. They come in different lengths, so get the best suited for you. See figure 48 for fuel tank connections.

A danger that is more likely to occur with gasoline engines is a spark of static electricity jumping from the fuel station's pump nozzle to the bank. If you are using a rubber accordian hose without a ground, this possibility is almost a certainty and it will mean a healthy explosion. To prevent such an occurrence run a piece of copper wire from the deck-fill to the tank. It is simple to solder one end onto the intake fitting and even simpler to attach the other to the screw that holds the small chain to the deck-fill. (The chain keeps the deck-fill from disappearing when unscrewed.)

Just as a reminder, put some sort of cushioning beneath the

Photo No. 96 — Deck fill.

tank, then strap or block or tie the tank down to something firm as heavily as you can. The cushioning should be very dense foam or better still rubber bedding. Not only will this material cushion the tank but it will also keep it from sliding about. I find this technique most critical on stainless steel tanks where the spot welds are usually covered by solder pads. These pads seem to be high spots on the tanks. They therefore are the initial supporters of the tanks, thus the first to be subjected to rubbing and wear. Rubber tape, at least under each seam, is strongly recommended. Do not place the tape in a closed pattern; be sure to leave openings in the pattern so that water will not be trapped below the tank but can flow out easily.

If you are using straps, either steel or nylon, as hold downs for the tanks be sure to observe the following simple procedure: Wherever a strap touches the relatively sharp corner of a tank use a short piece of sliced rubber tubing laid over the corner of the tank. Not only will this tubing keep the straps from sliding about and becoming looser, it will also act as a chafe preventer for the straps.

The type of hold down strap to be used is critical. I have heard of only two that have worked relentlessly without failure. One is stainless steel, the other heavy woven nylon (like the ones used for seat belts). The stainless steel ones can be adjusted by using a split strap system with a piece of allthread (a stainless rod threaded from end to end) as a connector, see figure 49.

The nylon strap usually comes with buckles of some kind. I strongly advise against using the quick release type for this type

PLUMBING   **303**

FUEL FILL

FUEL TANK WEDGES

TO ENGINE

Figure No. 48 — Fuel tank connections.

may release the tank at the least desirable moment. The old-fashioned friction buckle system seems to work well. To pull them tight requires a great force so put them in such a way that you can "pull" toward you using the aid of your weight. "Pushing" on a strap is no easy task.

PLUMBING

Your fuel line should be of the best quality aviation hose. This hose is of thick walled rubber with mesh reinforcing that will stand great pressure. All bronze to bronze, or brass to brass fittings should be generously basted before threading together for the final time with liquid aviation gasket or equivalent. Don't tighten your brass fittings too hard; that is, don't brace your feet on the hull and yank with two hands. Brass is soft and can be easily stripped.

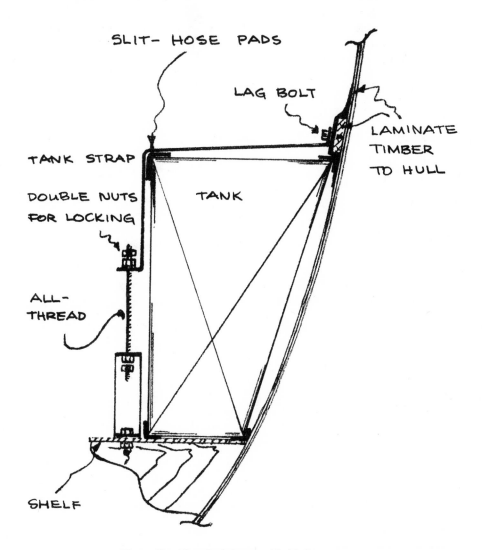

Figure No. 49 — Stainless steel hold-down strap.

Water Tanks

Water tanks require less attention. See figure 50 for their construction. Their vents need not go overboard since water fumes aren't usually foul, so a length of hose run up inside a cabinet, well out of the way, and as high as possible will suffice. All fresh water plumbing in the boat can be taken care of by easy to buy, easy to bend, easy to use, and easy to mend ½'' clear plastic FDA approved hose. For hot water under pressure, one should use reinforced spinnaker hose. It is not as expensive, nor as hard to use, nor as dangerous to solder as copper; and it is less prone to damage from banging, vibration, or kicking.

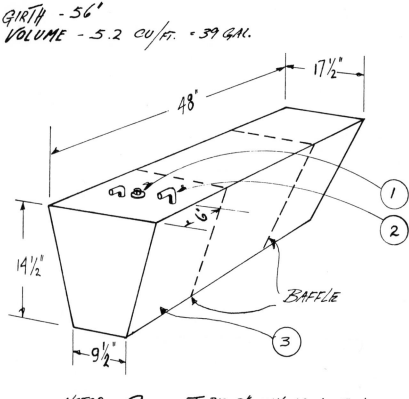

GIRTH - 56'
VOLUME - 5.2 CU/FT. = 39 GAL.

NOTE: - COPPER TUBE 2" MAX. ABOVE TANK

Figure No. 50 — Water tank construction.

Water tank intakes should not be run from the deck. A simple accessible fitting right on the tank is preferable. Deck-fills are prone to be the same size as a hose end, thereby totally cutting off escaping air. If the water comes in, in great quantities, and under a lot of pressure it's extremely likely that the seams of one's tanks will open wide and let the water run out. A friend had just finished his whole cabin sole, all teak covered when he first thought of filling and trying his tanks. He stuck in a hose, went inside his house to answer a phone call, and was very surprised when he came back to find his cabin sole undulating with water coming up through the cracks. If you think it's more difficult to drag a water hose into your cabin than to tear out, resolder, and reinstall tanks; then go ahead and put in as large a deck-fill as your heart desires.

With water tanks, selective plumbing is a must; that is, you should be able to use one or the other or both tanks at the same time, see figure 51 for connections. For this purpose, accessible gate valves, see photo 97, are sufficient, but make sure you grease them occasionally to stave off corrosion.

Hoses
1. Exhaust
Wire reinforced rubber hose is excellent for the purpose. Be sure you get the exact size for both exhaust fitting and through hull fitting. Stretching or down-clamping a hose of this wall thickness can result only in eventual seepage problems, see photo 98.

2. Scupper drains, sink drain, engine & head intakes
Here again, the pressure resistant reinforced rubber hose is ideal. Again be certain that the diameter is exactly matching your fittings, see photo 99.

3. Fresh water plumbing
As mentioned before, the ½'' clear plastic FDA approved hose is ideal, although others could be substituted here. Try to avoid rubber, for in a warm climate it adds a disgusting flavor to the water.

The rest of the installation is simple, requiring only hose clamps and the occasional adapter, see figure 52. Make sure all hoses fit onto tapered hose barbs; trying to fit a hose over a threaded fitting is very foolish.

As with wiring, use tye-wraps to fasten hoses to interior or cabin entry to keep them out of harm's way and to make the job more sightly. But never bend a hose too drastically; as soon as you see ribs on the inside of the curve you know you have gone too far,

Figure No. 51 — Twin tanks with select plumbing.

HOSE CLAMPS

GATE VALVES

BRASS TEE

TANK

PLUMBING

Photo No. 97 — Gate valve.

Photo No. 98 — Supporting exhaust hose.

Photo No. 99 — Thru-hulls with and without hose barb.

PLUMBING   **309**

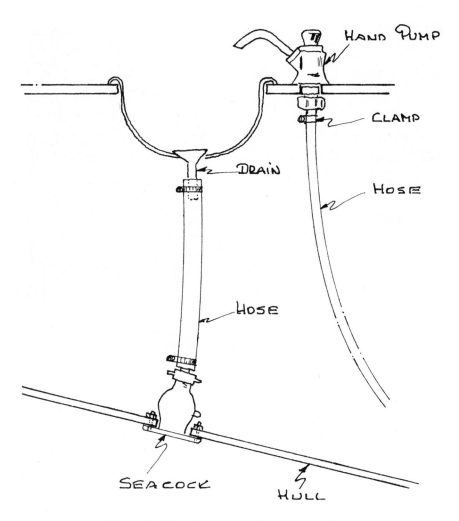

Figure No. 52 — Fresh water plumbing installation.

so ease off and your hose will have a longer life.

When attaching hoses to through hulls, one should not be frugal. Go ahead and double clamp all hoses, see photo 100, just in case one clamp fails or breaks.

With hose clamps as with brass fittings, use brain and save the brawn. Tighten them only expediently. Once you see tiny particles of rubber or plastic drizzling through the cracks in the clamp, take the hose off, throw it away and begin over. You've destroyed the hose, dummy. Think and tighten only to seal, not to demolish.

PLUMBING

Photo No. 100 — Double clamped hose.

Chapter Twenty-One
PORTLIGHTS

Portlights should be installed as soon as possible, that is, as soon as the cabin side liner is in place. Their location varies with each boat as does their size, but a mention of the type to use may be worthwhile.

If at all possible, use bronze. The heavier the casting, the better, for it is less likely to warp if over-tightened by the unthinker. The glass should be at least a quarter-inch thick even if the light is as small as 6'' diameter. Double dogs, see photo 101, are almost a necessity once 4'' diameter is exceeded to guarantee an even seal. To help the dogs, the adjustable hinge rod offered by a few of the companies should be seriously considered, see photo 102. On this variety, two small set screws grace either end of the rod. These screws vary the tension that the hinge applies to the rubber sealer when rubber fatigue or ring warpage occurs.

To install portlights, I found it most rapid to trace the spigot onto the exterior of the fiberglass cabin side. After drilling but one hole to allow entry of the saw blade, I slightly over-cut the scribed line with a saber saw.

Use only very sharp blades. Heavy-duty hack saw blades are the best but even they dull rapidly, overheat, and break. I don't think I'm exaggerating when I say I annihilated at least one blade per 1½ portlights. By over-cutting slightly, you will save yourself the hideous task of trying to file or in some other miserable fashion trim bits and chunks from (hopefully) ¼-inch thick fiberglass.

When cutting these holes be sure to wear a mask and goggles (blessed are the near-sighted who wear glasses).

Photo No. 101 — Double-dogged portlight.

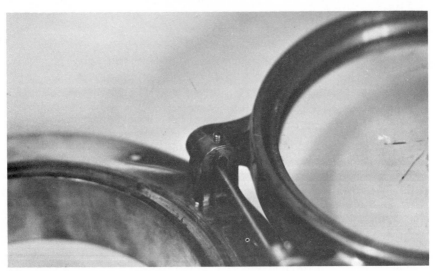

Photo No. 102 — Adjustable hinged rod.

It is most unhealthy to inhale exiguous floating glass particles and even more painful to have one of the critters lodge in your eye. I mention the following here in case it escapes my memory elsewhere.

I think it quite intelligent to have a bottle of eyedrops aboard from commencement of construction. Since glass particles are angular and they cling tenaciously, it is most difficult to exhume them by other methods than flushing with eyedrops.

After the hole is cut to size, you have to dry fit your porthole and drill the bolt holes. But first a hint. Install your portlights so that the hinge is on top. True you won't be able to open it as one does a bathroom window. But it will be in a position where both dogs can be tightened most effectively. It is quite a simple matter then to open them wide by placing a hook in the cabin top above the light. Install an eye in a position so the hook can be set into it tightly to prevent it from flapping noisily about when not in use.

Back to fitting. Do not go on the naive assumption that the bolt holes in the portlight will match the bolt holes on your outside back up ring. They may, but I have not yet encountered such a happy circumstance. I have, however, found a very simple remedy. Drill the topmost hole first by aligning the two holes by eye. If you don't hit the first time, bore about until you do. Put a bolt through the hole and tighten only to the point where the portlight and outer ring remain parallel.

You then drill through from the outside inward. The wood liner on the inside is easier to ream out than the glass if you miss the hole. And there is no danger of leaks here from an oversized opening. Put all your bolts through to make sure they penetrate. It is easier to catch them now than after the whole thing is oozing polysulfide from every pore.

After the portlights have been dry fit, acetone well. Apply generous amounts of unbroken polysulfide beads on the inside of the exterior rings. I used two beads, one on the inside of the bolt holes and one on the outside, see photo 103. A bead of goo around

Photo No. 103 — Caulked portlight rings.

PORTLIGHTS   315

the edge of the hole can't hurt. Now re-assemble the puzzle (hope you marked the top hole on the outside ring so you won't have alignment problems). Have a lot of rags handy and a large can of acetone to clean the mess.

When tightening, make sure that excess caulking squirts out all around the outside ring. Only then can you be certain that every water route is closed off. Don't try to wipe all of the goo off with rags. Use scrap pieces of wood (they don't scratch the gelcoat) to scrape off the bulk.

Chapter Twenty-Two
BEGINNING INTERIOR TRIM

This area requires a lot of preparation and its installation is time demanding. But you can limit the amount of time required by doing as perfect a job as possible with the assembly of the rough interior. Except for searails, berth rails, and grab posts, trim is used primarily to cover mistakes. Keep them to a minimum; your finishing work will be less and your boat won't look like a ginger-bread house with a little scrap here and another scrap there and a small chunk everywhere.

Searails

Height here is a primary consideration. The primary function of a searail is to keep things from flying off tables and counters when the boat is undergoing heavy motion. I think that a two-inch height around the galley is not excessive; if it is less than that, things are prone to tip over a small rail.

The only other matter of importance is to keep the corners open. Open corners will make cleaning of the top child's play; otherwise, you will forever leave crumbs and other half-dead things squatting in sharp, hard-to-clean corners.

The shape can be whatever you like. We tapered the tops of ours to ease the bulky effect. Dimensions of the typical rail we used are in figure 53. One can see from the drawing that milling out of ¾-inch teak stock is simple. "A" and "B" require one table saw adjustment each; run through vertically once and run through horizontally once.

Please note the "pusher" used in figure 54. A pusher should

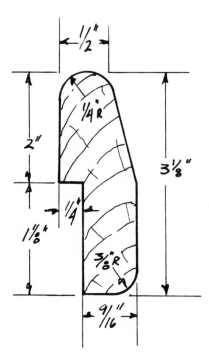

Figure No. 53 — Searail.

be permanently placed near the saw and used always when milling any piece of wood. It can be easily made of scrap plywood to the rough dimensions in figure 54. Make a few at a time because the pushing lip will be cut off after a few tight cuts where the blade penetrates its lower edge.

The sloped face of the searail can be cut on a table saw at whatever angle you desire. It is best to figure out how much rail you'll need for the whole boat ahead of time. That way you'll have to set the saw only four times to mill all the rails for the boat. Once the rough stock is milled there remains only a simple job of running the rail through the router, using a 3/8'' bull-nose to round off edges 1, 2 and 3. Don't bother fine sanding until the rails are attached in place. You'll put a few nicks and dents in before you're through. Use a lot of glue when attaching searails, screw every six or eight inches, and make sure that the glue seals the top seam everywhere.

Searail Corners

Photo 104 and figure 55 should be self-explanatory. I can offer little assistance, as searail corners will require hand-filing or the

Figure No. 54 — Table saw pusher.

Photo No. 104 — Open searail corner for sweeping out dirt.

COUNTER TOP W/ CORNER
TRIMMED

SEA RAIL CORNER

SEA RAIL

Figure No. 55 — Searail corners.

BEGINNING INTERIOR TRIM

occasional touch of the disk sander. One note. When attaching searail corners make sure that you have left at least 3/16'' extra thickness on the outside radius. You will be able to shape it with a belt sander once it is in place. It is less work to get a finer fit even if it means pulling out the screws and redrilling deeper because the first countersink holes were undersized.

Berth Rails

If the berth is to double as a settee, four inch cushions are advisable. To hold them in place, yet not cut off the circulation in your thighs, the same rails you used on the counters can be utilized. On berths used primarily for sleeping (pilot and forepeak), make the center portions as high as the cushions (mostly four inch). I think it quite shippy and extremely reassuring in a rough sea to have at least the last 18 inches made about four inches higher. In light seas these rails will provide sufficient bracing without necessitating use of leeboards. Their milling and attachment should otherwise be the same as searails.

Deck Beams

Most fiberglass boats have a cabin structure strong enough to eliminate the need for deck beams in all areas except the support bulkheads. Beams do look romantic though; and since you'll probably have to make a few, you may as well make a few more. They are messy, but simple to make.

First measure the crown necessary for each beam. To measure, run a string from one side of the cabin top to the other at the location of each beam and measure at the three points indicated in figure 56. On the edge of a bench, set up the required height blocks at points x, y and z, using 2'' x 8'' stock. It is desirable if you have about three beams with almost the same crown, because then you can use seven inch wide planks and rip them in three after laminating. Don't worry if the crowns aren't precisely identical. Something will give and bend enough to make up the slight divergence.

At any rate, cut from ¾-inch stock (gives you 2¼'' thick beams) three — 7'' wide pieces of whatever wood you want to use. Try to avoid teak because it requires expensive resorcinal glue to laminate acceptably and even then the results can't be guaranteed. Be generous and cut each piece about 8 inches too long. It is much easier to trim the ends then to add on a piece. Spread glue on both sides that are to meet in the lamination, then place them over the jig. With big C-clamps, clamp tight at the two ends as well as at x, y,

To Construct a Camber Curve:

Determine the higth of the camber-curve and full breadth.
Find the centerline and scribe a quarter circel, divide the circle @ the base — and peri' - meter line in equal parts.
The vertical dimension is the higth at points!
Connect all points with a spline and scribe the curve

Figure No. 56 — Measuring crown of deck for beams.

BEGINNING INTERIOR TRIM

and z. use blocks on top so that the clamp shoes don't mark your wood.

The crown is now defined. For even lamination, put as many clamps as you need to pull the three pieces together, see photo 105. When dried (leave at least 24 hours) you can rip the 7-inch wide stock into three 2¼'' wide beams.

Photo No. 105 — Clamping laminations.

Fitting is quick. Since most cabin sides slope in at the top, just bring the beam up beneath the deck, mark in the angle on both ends, and cut. Don't try to fit it the first time. Overcut generously; then repeat the process and trim less and less off each end as you get toward the top. If you leave the beam snug at the ends, it can be a structural help. The best method of attachment is through-bolting as shown in figure 57. If the beams are to strengthen bulkheads, it is

Figure No. 57 — Through bolt deck beams.

BEGINNING INTERIOR TRIM

advisable to use No. 14 self-tapping screws coming in through the bulkhead after through-bolting the first beam, see figure 58.

The shape and size of the rest of the trim will, of course, be determined by the size of the mistake they are assigned to cover. Use your imagination, but do it the simplest way possible, see photos 106 through 110 of different trimmings like knees and end trim. Whatever trim you install you'll have to plug the countersink holes made for the fasteners. Plugging is no mystery; it is simplified

NOTE:
1. USE 1/4"-20 X 3 1/2 CARRIAGE BOLTS
2. USE WHITE ACRYLIC SEALER SEALER AROUND THE HEAD
3. USE 3/4" MAH. PLUGS
4. CUT SQUARE IN FIBERGLASS DECK
   TO SEAT BOLT PROPERLY

FASTEN BLKD. TO AFT
DECK BEAM W/ N:12x2"
F.H. W.S. ON 4" ℄

"A-A" DETAIL

FWD. ⟶

Figure No. 58 — Using self-tapping screws.

BEGINNING INTERIOR TRIM   325

Photo No. 106 — Example of trim piece.

Photo No. 107 — Example of trim piece.

BEGINNING INTERIOR TRIM

Photo No. 108 — Example of trim piece.

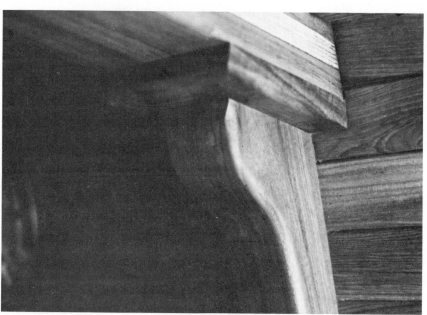

Photo No. 109 — Example of trim piece.

BEGINNING INTERIOR TRIM

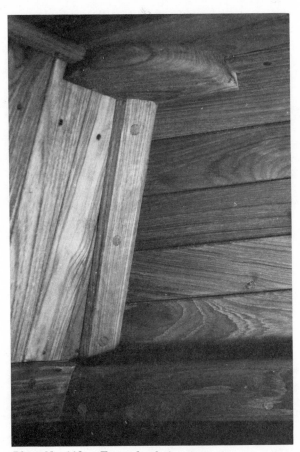

Photo No. 110 — Example of trim piece.

even more if sharp countersinks are used (see tool section) with a vertical unyawing pressure on the drill, for then you will not ream out the hole and make a perfect fit impossible.

If you have a drill press or at least an attachment into which a common drill motor fits, you can cut your own plugs from the mountains of scrap you'll have available. A plug cutter costs only $3.00 or $4.00 and it may come in handy in the corner of the world where they won't have heard of precut plugs. It is nice if your countersinks and your plugs are the same size. The fit of the plug upon insertion should be tight, but not so tight that the plugs split the wood when tapped in with a hammer. Plugging, as bonding, is best left until all the pluggables are completed. Then with a few hundred plugs, a few cups of glue, a small hammer, and a very sharp chisel you can be busy for a day or two.

The best glue pot for plugs we found was a paper cup cut down to about an inch and a half height with the bottom filled with ¼-inch of glue. You can then grip the plug in two fingers, align its grain with the grain of the wood it's going into, and dip it in the cup (if you have more than ¼-inch of glue in the bottom of the cup you will get glue all over your fingers and arms). Then insert the plug into the hole. When you have put in about ten plugs, go back and give each of them a firm tap with a hammer. Repeated bashings will either bury the plug too deep or cause it to crack and disintegrate, both very undesirable results.

It's preferable to have at least 1/8'' of the plug sticking out after hammering. You can now take your chisel and with the beveled edge against the surface of the wood and going with the grain, trim a little of it off the top, see figure 59 and photo 111. You will then be

Figure No. 59 — Trimming off the plug.

Photo No. 111 — Trimming off plug.

able to see whether the grain is true to the chisel or whether the tool must be turned 180 degrees and chiseled the other way so that the plug will not chip out deeper than the surface of the wood. Once grain has been established, you'll learn to clean off the head almost entirely with the chisel, necessitating very little following sanding.

It is most vital that all this chiseling be done before the glue has set. If you break a plug below the surface you can still easily dig it out as in figure 60, without chipping the surrounding wood and replace it. I heard from old shipwrights that they like to use shellac or varnish instead of glue to set plugs into. This idea may be excellent, making removal of the plugs possible at a later date without the danger of chipping out the surrounding wood.

I think it is advisable that all trim be oiled after plugging; then if drops of paint or unwanted goo of other sorts fall upon it, it will be easier to wipe off without the risk of rapid penetration.

Figure No. 60 — Digging out a broken plug.

BEGINNING INTERIOR TRIM

Doweling

You may find that you have to make a wide plank from two narrow ones for things like rudder cheekplates, icebox lids, etc. This effort can be accomplished by edge glueing and bar-clamping two pieces; but to have a long life, dowels should be used as a mechanical assistance. Without a jig, it's very difficult to perfectly align the holes you must drill in both pieces for the dowels. Therefore, it's advisable to attach the rough cut pieces to each other before you cut them to the final shape or size.

To guarantee a fairly close fit, clamp the two pieces side by side. Then with a thick ended square, draw lines across both of them at each location where the dowels are to be (every 8'' should be fine), see figure 61. Now comes the tough part. With a compass,

₵. FOR DRILLING

Figure No. 61 — Doweling.

scribe in the center line for the holes as close to the center of each plank as you can. If you don't, the pieces won't match and you'll spend hours trying to even off the surfaces.

Once the centers of the holes have been marked, use a center punch to set a starting point for the drill bit, then drill in. Be generous with the depth. There is nothing worse than with all holes perfectly matched and centered, dowels inserted, and pieces fit together you come to find that the holes are too shallow. Drill deep, then apply a good coat of glue to the edges, the holes, and the dowels. Insert the dowels in the holes, then fit and clamp on the other piece. If you were very accurate with your measuring and your drilling, everything should fit like a glove; if not, hit it with a sledge hammer.

Chapter Twenty-Three
DOORS & DRAWERS

Almost every boat that I've ever seen had a different solution, different materials, different patterns for the doors and drawers. I hope that this situation continues, for I love going aboard strange new yachts and seeing new solutions to old problems. Therefore, I will tell you only what we have done and why.

Doors

For openings in the backs of settee berths where we will be leaning or falling against doors, we used solid teak pieces, see photo 112. The only detail put on them was a "deep bull-nose" which was achieved by setting the edge of the bull-nose a bit higher than the routing table. It then cuts deeper into the wood than normally. This solid door is costly in materials but extremely cheap in labor because it takes so little time to make one. For all other doors we used 2½" teak frames (with the same detail) with cane insert. Figure 62 shows door frame detail for inserts. Using cane is more expensive because it is terribly time consuming and the woven caning, covered with dust in some junky furniture repair place, cost a usurious $3.20 per square foot. It would have been cheaper to use solid teak, but we wanted the ventilation. This reason is probably a lie; I just thought that cane looked good, so we used it. Ventilation was a nice excuse, though.

Inserting thin plywood panels into teak frames is also common practice. I've seen very thin strips of woven teak that worked nicely. At any rate, we caned and here is how:

We routed a 3/8" x 1/4" rabbett into the inside of the frames

Photo No. 112 — Solid settee door.

with a 3/8'' rabbett bit (see tools). We used dado blades to cut away the ends of each piece of door frame, see figure 63. Then we used resorcinal glue, a square, and clamps to clamp all of the corners. We were advised by the usurer to soak the cane in hot water for fitting. We did so, then rough cut the pieces (about one inch over required size) and laid them over the hole.

Using ¼-inch quarter round and brass tacks, we stretched the

Figure No. 62 — Door frame cross-section.

Figure No. 63 — Dadoing.

cane as much as possible and nailed down the edges, see photo 113. For extra safety, we used glue in all areas, i.e., between wood and cane, and quarter round. While still wet and soft, we trimmed with scissors whatever excess we could off the overhanging cane, leaving only a very short stubble. We waited until the stubble had dried and hardened, then we used a belt sander to remove it. When the cane dried it became tight between the frames; nevertheless, I sprayed both sides with transparent, no-gloss sealer to be certain of keeping potential moisture out.

Photo No. 113 — Laying in cane.

DOORS & DRAWERS

For handles, we used the world's most obvious method — the finger hole. They look quite pleasant if cut to 7/8'' diameter and bull-nosed. Apart from providing some ventilation in solid doors, it gives access to what I consider the best looks for a sailing boat, the positive locking elbow catches, see photos 114A and 114B.

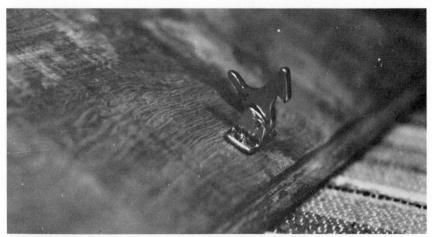

Photo No. 114 — Positive locks.

DOORS & DRAWERS

Drawers

Our drawers are of very standard construction. The simplest way to learn how to do them is to have a close look at your home cabinetry (the older, probably the better the work). We did; however, replace the nails or staples ordinarily used with stainless steel screws. The faces are solid teak with the aforementioned detail and handles. The simplest sliding system we found (although not necessarily the best) is the precut wood runners, see figure 64, and

Figure No. 64 — Drawer slides.

plastic slides available at most pedestrian hardware stores, see photo 115. They require only a square and a level for accurate installation. Drawers are kept from sliding out in rough seas by 1/2" x 3/8" notches cut in the front ends of the sides, see photo 116.

Sliding Doors

Keeping doors shut at sea is quite a problem. Most snap-locks, bayonet grips, and magnets are inadequate. There is nothing more annoying in an already madly rolling boat than stupid doors slamming shut every 14 seconds. So if you don't like positive locks, the second best solution is sliding doors. They also have the undisputable advantage that they require no space when opened. I

DOORS & DRAWERS   337

Photo No. 115 — Plastic drawer slide.

don't particularly like them for what reason I don't know, but I would encourage their use in galleys and other places where countertops may have to be cleared of pots, etc. before a conventional door can be opened. Their construction is simple, requiring

Photo No. 116 — Drawer lock notch.

DOORS & DRAWERS

pre-milled slides and little else as shown in figure 65. The only other words I have on doors is a strong encouragement to put one on your engine room access. I didn't. I have drop boards and I'm sorry I do because they are a giant pain if they have to be pulled out at sea and set down somewhere only to fly up in the first sea and smash you in the achille's tendon. A door with a hasp and an eye to keep it still, once opened, is an absolute dream in comparison.

Figure No. 65 — Construction of a sliding door.

Chapter Twenty-Four
CABIN SOLE OVERLAY

Little needs to be mentioned here, for all methods of construction discussed in counter top overlay apply here. I would not use stock thinner than ½-inch because it would be difficult to plug and more likely to warp or wear or crack. I believe teak to be the best wood to use, even though we used ash. We wanted the contrast in a teak satiated boat. Of course bedding compound should be used instead of glue.

For access to the bilge be sure to undercut your hatches by at least 3/16'' or the thing will swell shut never to reopen. To keep these hatches (or large lids on the counter tops) from warping, use strong backs of good dry hardwood, see photo 117. To lift hatches, the flush fitting pull rings are probably the most ideal solution.

I won't even mention how to lay carpeting into a boat, because any serious cruising boat will have its carpets constantly soaked. I think it's a great idea for mobile homes. You can, however, have non-absorbant carpet and a warm, non-slippery surface. A former mobile home owner used this material in his first boat to protect the teak cabin sole. Its well-known name is Astro-Turf and it was the most disgusting tasteless thing I have ever set eyes on. If you want me to hate you and your boat, use it.

I think we have come to the end of interior finishing. With the exception of the engine, there are many small points. But I think they have crept up periodically in other sections either on planning or scrounging or tools or what to buy. Many fine points were left out in order to keep the book a readable length. With what's absent, use your imagination and best of luck.

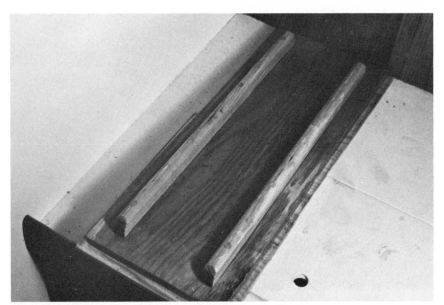

Photo No. 117 — Bilge hatch strong-backs.

CABIN SOLE OVERLAY

Chapter Twenty-Five
ENGINE INSTALLATION

One tends to shake and tremble at the thought of installing one's own engine. I'm not sure whether fear is activated by the number of esoteric-looking parts or by the sheer bulk of the thing. But it appears universally accepted that engines and their handling are best left to the experts, fatuous as they may be.

The work involved is truly no great mystery. The few hours of studying the engine, the manufacturer's brochure, and the parts such as stuffing boxes, cutlass bearings, shaft logs, engine pan, etc. will give you a more familiar, confident outlook on the whole situation.

As I mentioned before, I will be discussing only diesel engines, although admittedly most of the procedures described herein are applicable to diesel, gas, steam, or whatever your phobia.

Engine Pan

If at all possible, an engine pan should be utilized. Engine pans are usually made of fiberglass, with a combination of either wood or metal.

Construction of the engine pan is important. So if you want to make your own, be sure to use only hand laid up mat and roving or mat and cloth. A lot of vibration will have to be tolerated by the pan and with alternative methods of construction such as chopper gun or all-mat, pans have a tendency to crack and check more easily. For the horizontal surfaces of the pan (bottom and engine mount shoulders) use a plywood core. I have heard of one manufacturer who installs steel plates in the two shoulders; thus, instead of having the engine mounts held down by nuts and bolts, you can simply *tap and die* the steel plates, then thread the bolts into them. Otherwise, you will have to devise a method whereby the bolt heads under the pan will remain stationary while you twist and tighten the nuts above.

Shaft Hole

The drilling of the shaft hole will have to be your primary task. Its location can be detected by measurement on the exterior of the hull. I will be concerned primarily with boats that have deadwood and propeller apertures in the rudder, see photo 118.

Free-standing spade rudders are not the most ideal for cruising; however, the task of locating their shaft holes is not too demanding. The engine can be placed on its mounts, then a

Photo No. 118 — Aperture in rudder.

ENGINE INSTALLATION

shortened broomstick can be inserted into the coupling to detect the most comfortable place for the shaft to pass through. You will be governed by the angle at which you may set the engine, but follow the manufacturer's recommendations; otherwise, the more level the shaft, the better the performance of the propeller is likely to be.

For boats with the aforementioned aperture in the rudder, you must locate and drill the shaft hole first, then align the engine to it. You have to hit the shaft hole in the center of the aperture, both athwartships and vertically. Otherwise, at best, you will get a disturbed flow of water and plentiful cavitation from the propeller passing too close to either the top or bottom of the aperture. At worst, if the shaft hole is placed drastically low or high, the propeller will have a tendency to slice the rudder in half like a salami cutter.

So locate the center, mark it, and use a hole saw that will very snugly accommodate the shaft log, be it bronze or fiberglass tubing. If your engine is to be level and your shaft likewise, drill the hole as horizontal as possible. In a respectable fiberglass boat, you'll be drilling through an inch of fiberglass. Thus any deviation may cause misalignment which can cause the cutlass bearing to be prematurely worn. Once the hole is cut, you'll be ready to install the engine pan.

Engine Pan Installation

It is most advisable to have the engine at hand in order to take accurate and lucid measurements from it while installing an engine pan. You will need to make up a jig locating engine mount and coupling levels. Although most engines come with extremely accurate graphic renderings of all elevations, there is nothing quite like having the real item at hand to get a more accurate "feel."

Once you have located the mounts on the pan, mark their places. Or better still, screw down temporary pads which you can use as a base for the jig to set up a temporary shaft to assist you in pan alignment, see figure 66. Care should be taken with mount locations, because some boat builders design a pan for a certain engine but choose to use adapters or at least modifications of the mounts so that they become unrecognizable to the uninitiated. These modifications are done in order to accommodate hull narrowness or bilge curvature. If you are thoroughly confused, get in touch with the manufacturer and have him clarify.

Once you have screwed blocks in place of the mounts, you'll have to make a jig for the mock shaft. First, find the distance between the aft edge of the pan and the center point of the coupling. Fabricate a wood crutch to accommodate a broomstick or whatever you will substitute for the shaft. Make sure that its center will be at the exact center of the coupling when it's eventually fitted.

Next, from the specifications of the boat builder, determine the angle in degrees at which the shaft will sit in relation to the engine pan. Now fabricate a crutch in the foreward part of the pan to enable the broom handle to maintain this alignment. Once the jig is perfectly aligned and secured in the pan, lower the pan into the space where it is to go. It's advisable to predetermine the center line

Figure No. 66 — Engine pan jig.

of the boat just before you begin so that the pan can be aligned on center. If the boat is level, the measurement along the engine room bulkhead will give you a good location in combination with the center of the shaft hole. Position the pan with jig as close to the center line as possible. Then insert the "broomstick" through the shaft hole, set it, and secure it onto the jig. You can now maneuver the pan-jig until the desired shaft angle is achieved. Use a protractor and level for this exercise.

Fore and aft location of the engine is important, although not critical. Ascertain that your fly wheel will not mascerate your engine room bulkhead or other items, yet keep the engine as far forward as possible in order to carry the bulk of the weight toward the middle of the boat. To this end, it may be quite advisable to refrain from ordering your engine shaft until the final fore and aft location of the engine has been determined. Then measure for the length of shaft required and specify at the machine shop.

Be sure that you bring the broom-shaft through the very center of the shaft hole. You may require blocks and wedges to hold the pan in position, for very few fit perfectly snugly against the hull. Once it's perfectly located, put some temporary bonds onto either side of it to hold it in place. While you're bonding, be certain you don't hit or jiggle the pan or you can push it out of alignment.

Once the bonds have set, mix up a goodly batch of mill fibers and resin, then fill in all the voids between the pan and the hull. Mix the concoction very thick so it won't run out. Try not to miss any spots. Remember, this fill-in will be the foundation of your engine pan.

Some manufacturers neglect to tape off the edges of the pans to allow for bonding. Under no circumstance should you bond over the gelcoat. You must grind it all off down to the bare fiberglass, then acetone it, and then bond.

If you have a plywood core in your engine pan, you will have to take your engine mounts to a welding shop and have them weld the mounting hold down bolts onto a stainless steel plate, see photo 119. This plate will act as a large washer. More important, it will hold the bolts so that you can adjust the nuts without fear of the bolt falling into the bilge. It will also allow you to adjust the nuts without holding the bolt heads below the engine pan with a wrench.

If your engine pan maker has bonded pieces of steel into the pan instead of plywood, you will need only *to tap and die*, then insert the bolts from the top. Otherwise, locate the mount positions and tighten them loosely in place.

Your next step is to haul your engine up to your boat and lower it into the pan. The least troublesome method is to rent a small crane or a high forklift. They usually cost $25 an hour. If you're prepared for their arrival the whole operation should not take more than 10 to 15 minutes. You will have to pay travel time for the crane, so it's better to have one come from close by even if his hourly rate is a bit higher.

Once your engine is sitting on the mounts, put on the mount-

Photo No. 119 — Engine mount hold-downs.

nuts, but don't tighten them. Insert your proper propeller shaft and attach it to the coupling. Tighten the coupling bolts so that the shaft is as close to its permanent location as possible. Now, with all your weight off of the engine, check to see how well the shaft is centered in the shaft hole. It has to be exactly in the center before you can install the shaft log. If it is not, get ready for a couple of hours of shimming and trimming.

A note of advice concerning engine shafts may be appropriate here. When ordering the length of your engine shaft, take into consideration the fact that you do not want too much nor too little shaft sticking out of the hull. It's ideal to be able to remove your propeller without removing your rudder. Therefore the shaft cannot be too long or this task will be impossible to perform. On the other hand, you must not make the outhang of your shaft too short. It's advisable to have a zinc sacrificial anode on the shaft for which you will have to allow. In addition, if your deadwood is of any width, you should get your propeller as far aft of it as possible or the turbulent flow of water will cause serious cavitations, annoying with its sound and lack of performance.

Back to shimming and trimming. You will need a come-along, see photo 120, for this operation. The cheapest way to secure one is

ENGINE INSTALLATION

Photo No. 120 — Come-along.

to rent it, but I suggest buying one (about $25) for you can never tell in what dark corner of the world you may have to remove your engine without any other hands than your own to help. So, shift and shim your engine both horizontally and vertically until the shaft passes through the hole dead center.

One has a great temptation to use open-sided washers as in figure 67 to eliminate the need of pulling the engine from the mounts each time another spacer is to be added. I'm not sure if the use of these washers is the right approach. Granted it is easier to slip them in by raising the engine only slightly, but it is also easier for them to slip out after a few years of vibration. At any rate, align your engine, then tighten every nut until they scream.

ENGINE INSTALLATION **349**

Figure No. 67 — Open sided washers.

Shaft Log

Two different shaft logs are in common use. One is the bronze log with a flange, see photo 121, and the other a flangeless fiberglass tube, see photo 122. Both methods work well. The first uses mechanical aids (two bronze bolts); the other is bonded into place. Both are equally simple to install and both have functioned admirably in the past.

a) Bronze with flange. Thoroughly clean the shaft hole and surrounding hull area for about a six inch radius on the inside. Remove all paint, grease, scrap, and dust. Cover the outside of the bronze log thoroughly with mold-release wax. With the cutlass bearing inside, set the log in place over the shaft with the flange on the inside of the hull. Mix a thick but very even batch of mish-mash. Cautiously fill it in all the area around the shaft log on the inside of the hull. You are trying to make a supportive housing for the shaft log, so be thorough and build a strong well rounded dam. If the hull is close on either side, fill in the space completely, little by little, and be sure to leave no voids. If you can squeeze a little between the log and the shaft hole walls, so much the better. But don't force or nudge the shaft or the log or you might put the whole thing out of alignment.

To avoid having to taper the forward shoulders of the mish-mash dam to a fragile point, a plywood donut cut to the shape of the shaft log flange can be used as a forward supporting wall of the dam. Smooth out the dam and leave it to go off. Use only a mild amount of catalyst in this mixture; for, as you know, the slower the curing the better the adhesion.

Photo No. 121 — Bronze and rubber shaft log.

Photo No. 122 — Fiberglass tube stuffing box.

Once you're done, get out of the engine room and stay out. On your way, don't even breathe on the shaft or engine or you'll put it out of alignment. Allow it to set at least overnight, then gently tap out the shaft log and pull it right out of the hole. If you have applied the mold-release wax judiciously, you'll have no problem.

Now check the sides of the mish-mash tunnel to ascertain that you have left no flaws or voids. If you find some, you have to chisel out the whole dam and start again because if you leave a dam in with a large void, the log may be allowed to wallow and vibrate, causing the ocean to come in little by big.

If you find no voids, slip the log back in and drill two holes for the flange bolts. Drill as horizontally as you possibly can, as you will then get maximum support from your bolts. If you drill straight, you should come out at top and bottom of the cutlass bearing. A pair of hex nuts locked against each other with a flat washer will then forever keep your dams from moving, but don't tighten them yet.

Pull out the shaft log and wash off the mold-release wax until you can see your face in the bronze. Now wash the tunnel out with acetone also. Coat the log and the tunnel walls with polysulphide, then slide the log back in. You will have goo all over you again, but it's a small price to pay. Put some polysulphide in the flange hole, slip in the bolts; tighten the nuts; and you're almost secure. Wash off the excess polysulphide on the inside. Then on the outside lay large beads all over the heads of the bolts and right around the entire shaft log to cover the joint between it and the hull, see photo 123. Work the beads into swirls with a stick to be sure no voids exist inside the polysulphide scarf.

Photo No. 123 — Polysulphide around shaft log.

b) Fiberglass shaft log. The installation of this type of log is measurably simpler since, as mentioned before, it requires no bolting. The engine must be aligned in the same manner. Once aligned the log should be pulled and cleaned. Here it is unnecessary to apply any caulking. Simply shove the log back into its place. Then proceed to build on the inboard end a plywood crutch of at least ¾-inch thickness, made to conform to the hull. The usual length of the inward piece of the shaft log in the case of fiberglass tubing is about one foot. Placement of the plywood crutch can be about 2'' from the end. This crutch should then be bonded to the hull. Over the top half of the fiberglass tube, a similar crutch can be made to keep the tube from moving upward. This crutch should also be bonded to the hull.

Once the bonds have gone off and the tube is securely in place, fill the empty cavity between plywood dam and aft end of the hull with a semi-runny solution of mish-mash. Again, be sure to avoid leaving any sort of voids as well as to avoid knocking the shaft or the shaft log. And again, let the mish-mash harden overnight before going back to do any other work inside the engine room.

Stuffing Box

If you have not yet put your stuffing box over the shaft, pull the shaft out now and do so. Do not bang on the crown nut that holds the propellers nor the propeller itself, to try to get the shaft out of the coupling. Rather, try to find a shaft puller, as shown in photo 124, and tap it gently. If you hammer the shaft or the prop, you may bend the shaft or alter the prop's pitch. Neither result is too desirable.

Once your stuffing box is on the shaft, put four separate rings of 3/16'' diameter flax packing against the inside end of the cutlass bearing, see photo 125. Stagger the joints of the four rings so that water won't have a nice clean path. When cutting the flax, slightly overlap a complete loop, then cut both pieces with a razor, see photo 126. This way, your loops will be exactly the correct length, with no gaps in between. Now, gently push the stuffing box over the flax and tighten with your hands only.

When you can tighten no more, put a half turn on it with a wrench. Then tighten it no more. If you do, you will crush the flax resulting in no possibility of future tightening when the packing wears and develops a leak at a later time. The entire idea behind this technique is that you can, at a later time, tighten down the packing instead of having to re-do it every time a tiny leak develops. More important, if you think you have over-tightened, don't back the nut off now. If you do, you can be sure of a leak at the moment of

Photo No. 124 — Puller for propeller.

Photo No. 125 — Cutlass bearing.

Photo No. 126 — Cutting flax.

ENGINE INSTALLATION

launching for you have crushed the packing then backed off, creating a nice viaduct.

Believe it or not, your engine is now installed, aligned, and sealed. All that is left is hooking in your exhaust, clamping on your fuel lines, and securing your battery cables.

Exhaust Installation

Two basic types of marine exhaust silencers are commonly used, the "Aqualift," see photo 127, and the "stand pipe" or "riser," see photo 128. The installation of the riser is documented with engine installation instructions by most manufacturers such as Westerbeke and Perkins. The only item they do not point out is that the manifold undergoes tremendous vibration. They usually provide a single additional support arm that goes back onto the engine. But if you can fabricate a second one, you may be able to prevent premature failure of fittings.

Under no circumstances should you try to brace the riser by attaching it to a support arm whose other end is attached to a shelf or fixed bulkhead or anything but the engine. If you do, you will cause even earlier breakage of couplings or fittings. It can be compared to a piece of paper being flapped in the air by one hand. It flutters and shakes and it is undamaged; however, if a motionless hand holds the other end, the paper will tear as soon as the first hand starts to move violently.

The Aqualift variety requires no such precautions because as the photographs illustrate it is solidly mounted on the engine. And because of its bulk and hefty attachments, it will not experience exaggerated flexing.

But another sort of precaution is necessary with the Aqualift. Unless well guarded against, following seas can come in through the exhaust and flood the engine. To this end an installation such as is illustrated in figure 68 should be used. Notice that the hose is run as high as the deck will allow.

Use of the gate valve exhaust thru-hull fitting is highly recommended. This valve should be closed only in broken following seas where danger of flooding is accentuated. A safeguard system should be devised to prevent the possibility of the gate valve being left closed as the engine is started up. Storing the ignition key beside the valve at all times might be a solution.

One note: avoid any drastic bends in the exhaust hose. Most hoses are wire-reinforced and tape-fortified rubber, thus very strong. But a violent bend can cause the wire to cut right through the casing and ruin the hose. It is best to use the U's as in the

Photo No. 127 — Aqualift exhaust.

Photo No. 128 — Riser exhaust.

Figure No. 68 — A qualift safety precaution.

illustration to avoid this. All fittings should be exactly the correct size. If the hose is of too great an ID it can and will slip off and leak. If it's too small you can ruin the hose by forcing it over an over-sized fitting.

Hooking in Fuel Lines

This procedure was discussed to some degree in plumbing; therefore I will only touch upon it. Fuel hoses should be the high pressure aircraft variety just to be sure, and all hose clamps should be stainless. Be certain that you look for the engraved words "all stainless," because some stainless bands have galvanized screws which will rust once the galvanized has been scraped off.

If possible, tanks should have their inlets and outlets on the top to avoid the possibility of leakage through a bottom fitting, which could empty the tank's entire contents before discovered and checked. If the outlet is on the bottom of the tank, a shut-off valve must be installed before any hoses are run.

Fuel filters, see photo 129. At least a double fuel filter for every tank should be used, apart from the filter on the engine. CAV filters with a settling bowl for water, as shown in figure 69, have stood the test of time well, although I have heard of a newer type with a coalescer. This device separates water from the fuel by taking tiny

Photo No. 129 — Fuel filters — you can't have too many.

FROM TANK ⟶ TO ENGINE FUEL PUMP

FROM 2nd TANK
(WHEN FITTED)

NOTE:
FOR FUEL RETURN SEE
ENGINE MANUAL

CAV

Figure No. 69 — Fuel filter.

358   **ENGINE INSTALLATION**

droplets out in suspension, then causing them to bead and settle to the bottom of the bowl. The double filter per tank system illustrated in Don Street's *Ocean Sailing Yacht* is a fine concept, for it allows continuous running even though one filter may get clogged.

Once your fuel lines are hooked up, fill your tank with a couple of gallons of fuel (just in case they leak diesel). Bleed the system starting from the top most filter and working your way down to the injectors. The operation is simple. Loosen the bleeding screw until fuel starts flowing instead of air, then tighten it and go on to the next one. But be sure you tighten one before you descend to the other, or you are wasting your time because the top one will be letting in air.

Controls

Engine controls are of two types: the monoshift single lever which acts as a throttle and gear shifter at the same time and the dual shift which has a separate lever for each purpose. The monoshift has a tendency to fall out of adjustment somewhat more readily, but you will never have to worry about anyone going from forward to reverse at very high rpm's.

When you are installing your control cables, use as much caution as you do with your hoses. Don't force them or bend them too sharply or they will snag and bind; such a situation may stop you from shifting when you most need to . . . like when coming into a concrete dock. Also, be sure that they are out of the way of feet desperately looking for a foothold on the engine room sole in rough seas. This practice also holds true for other items such as fuel lines and battery cables. Keep them out of the way of traffic or you will have nothing but unexpected problems.

Now hook up a garden hose to your engine intake seacock. You may need an adapter for a good fit. Check your engine oil level, hook up your batteries, be sure the engine intake seacock and your exhaust gate valve are open; then turn the battery selector switch to "All," turn the breaker switch marked "Engine" to "on," put the gear shift lever into neutral, give her a bit of throttle, turn on the water in the hose; then turn the ignition key, and listen to it start on the first attempt. . . That's why I say, get a diesel.

Check for fuel, water, and exhaust leaks. Correct them now. Check to see if water is coming out of your exhaust thru-hull; if not, shut off the engine and check your connections and water pump.

I must say that having the engine hooked up and running properly makes one think that completion cannot be too far distant.

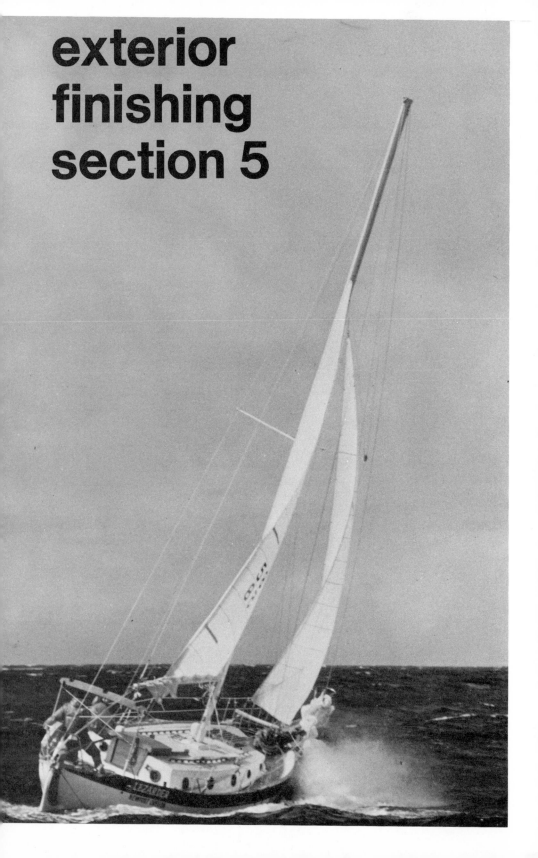

exterior
finishing
section 5

The majority of exterior operations requires more conformity to the manufacturer's plans than the interior. On the whole, they demand exact measurements or predefined assembly methods as with chainplates, tangs, stanchions, etc. Hatches you may be able to vary somewhat, but most molded decks come with molded openings and slide beds so you will be rather limited in your creative divergences.

Chapter Twenty-Six
HARDWARE

Chainplates and Tangs

Since you will most likely be using the standard rigging or at least the plans for it, you should pay strict attention to chainplate and tang instllation. I have seen far too many production boats of all types where the chainplates were misaligned or the angles on them were wrongly bent. When installing chainplates, the rigging plans will usually give measurements from the bow to the center line of the center chainplate. From this point, they'll give distances to the lower and upper ends of the two lower shroud plates. These measurements are critical for they determine whether your chainplates will line up correctly with the shrouds or not. If they don't line up, undue strain will be put on one or two bolts, see figure 70. If you're not satisfied with the plan, consult the architect and ask him to verify.

If your hull is thinner than ½-inch at the sheer line, it would be an excellent idea to beef up the laminates by at least two layers of cloth and mat in the areas where the chainplates will be placed. You can then use either 1/8'' thick x 3'' diameter stainless steel back-up plates for each bolt. Or here's a very bright idea which I once saw executed. A man made up a replica of his chainplates and installed them without the top bent portions on the inside of the hull. Be sure that the bolt holes will match perfectly and this solution should be very strong.

Once the angles and measurements have been computed for the chainplates, drill the holes cautiously. Be absolutely certain that the drill bit size matches the bolt size exactly. If the bit is smaller,

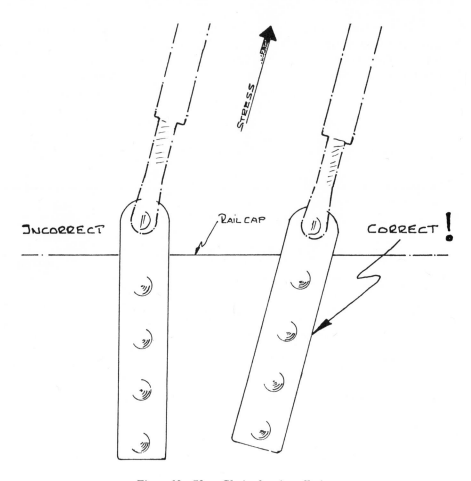

Figure No. 70 — Chainplate installation.

fine, it can be filed out. But if the holes are too large, you've wasted all of your alignments because the bolts will work around in the loose holes, become looser, and leak. Then clean and caulk and use nylon collared lock nuts on the inside.

When placing a liner over the hull, make sure that you leave access holes to each nut on your chainplates. You will have to tighten or recaulk someday. The same practice must be followed with tangs. The one-piece back-up plate mentioned on the previous page has one failing. If a liner is placed over the chainplate bolts and a leak does develop, it would be almost impossible to remove the one-piece back-up plate without tearing the ceiling apart.

If your boat is of traditional rig like ours, you'll have to suffer a bowsprit and perhaps a boomkin. In both cases, you'll need tangs for whisker stays, which continue the work of the forestay and backstay, see figure 71. To be of optimum value, installation of these tangs should be left until both the bowsprit and boomkin are permanently in place. Since each tang has two bolt holes in it, its alignment and installation at this point will be simple. If you already have your rigging, hook it up to the eye-band or boomkin tangs, turnbuckles and all, then dangle the tangs from their ends. Set your turnbuckles at a point where a little less than half the threaded rods are inside the barrel (the wire may stretch one day and you will need to tighten the turnbuckle; wire very seldom shrinks).

Figure No. 71 — Whiskerstay tangs.

Now find the approximate location; then mark, drill, and bolt the bottom hole of the tang. Put a hand turn on the turnbuckle to tighten the stay. The whole system now will be perfectly aligned. Drill the second hole.

If you don't have your rigging, use a piece of string tied to the eyeband. Be sure that it's approximately the right length to fit the rigging plans. It doesn't have to be exact, because your rigger can cut the whisker stays to whatever length you like. If you plan to change the length of these stays by relocating the tangs, think sufficiently ahead. You don't want to end up trying to drill through a four foot wide bulkhead end on. Use polysulphide to caulk.

Stanchions

It is rather difficult to be specific on this topic because there are so many different varieties of stanchions. Generally, optimum triangulation of fasteners should be attempted. Of course, the fasteners should be through-bolted only with judicious size back-up plates. The only valuable advise here is to caulk everything with polysulphide sealer and tighten the bolts well or the stanchions will work and areas around the fastenings will leak. One valuable note perhaps: if you have high bulwarks as we do, with no structural bracing in between, where the stanchions are to be mounted, blocks of wood well treated with Cuprinol or zinc chromate should be wedged between the hull and the deck as shown in figure 72. You can then put your bolts through these blocks and end up with an attachment that won't have as much play nor as great a potential for leaks.

Figure No. 72 — Stanchion blocks.

Other Hardware

Other deck ware such as blocks, travelers, tracks, pad-eyes, leads, fairleads, anchor rollers, etc. should be through-bolted, back-up plated, and mercilessly caulked inside and out. All the nuts used in these installations should be the locking type; or at least lock-washers should accompany a common hex-nut. Also, pay particular attention everywhere to drill bit size, to assure that you don't over-bore.

Chapter Twenty-Seven
HATCHES

You only need to consider two main types of hatches: the sliding and the coaming (lift up) varieties. I prefer calling the lift ups coaming hatches because coamings are the most vital aspect of them if they are to be made leak-proof. I firmly believe that only the double coaming variety is worth building.

Whether this hatch will be hinged or lift up, the coamings make it absolutely watertight, see figure 73 and photo 130. This feature requires the lower bed-log to be of 1¾" stock. Then ¾" high lips on it should be high enough to stop all the water and low enough to remain not too fragile. The inner coaming should be at least one inch higher than the bed-log. Then if any water makes it past the first one, the inner will surely stop it. Half-inch drain holes in the four corners of the bed-log will easily let brave water drops drain away. If you are not varnishing the hatch and coaming, make the hatch a loose fit over the bed-logs; otherwise, the first moisture will seal it shut, never to reopen. Another very acceptable method of double coaming is shown in the diagram.

Sliding hatch coamings are no more complex to fabricate. The slides themselves will prevent water from entering. They can be fabricated as shown in figures 74 and 75. We used all teak on the exterior; but less expensive woods, such as mahogany, will suffice if kept well varnished. Whichever you use, bed it well in either Dolphinite or polysulphide. And whichever you use, make sure you have learned to drill and screw into fiberglass before you attempt building a hatch. I am emphatic on this point, because I had problems of all varieties before the method was taught to me by a

Figure No. 73 — Sliding hatch coaming, Method I.

Photo No. 130 — Double coaming.

shipwright who has been working with fiberglass for years.

As I mentioned before, the hole cannot be either too large or too small. In the first case, the screw will spin freely and in the second, the head will snap off when the threads can turn no more even though the screw may be only halfway in.

Figure No. 74 — Single coaming

Figure No. 75 — Sliding hatch coaming, Method II

Therefore, use only the tapered drill bits shown in the tool section. Set the bit at the right depth as shown in figure 76. Plug the holes immediately, so that no rain water or dew can seep down into the plywood deck core and rot it. To make the forward end of the hatch waterproof presents a larger problem. This area is critical, likely to take on head seas; so take care. We used a dual purpose baffle system on ours as shown in figure 77. Here the baffle not only keeps water out, but also interacts with the coaming to stop the hatch from sliding backwards and out of the groove. We screwed our baffle onto the hatch from the inside. Then we used bedding compound instead of glue so if we ever have to remove the hatch from its track, we can unscrew the baffle and slide the hatch off.

HATCHES 371

Figure No. 76 — Tapered bit and countersink setting.

Figure No. 77 — Dual purpose baffle system.

HATCHES

I must admit, we did something else as an extra precaution. We built a solid teak hatch cover over our hatch, see photo 131. It does double duty by acting as a base for dinghy chocks as well as helping to keep water out of the cabin. The hatch cover is fastened permanently to the deck. One vital point if you are installing a hatch cover: before final installation of your hatch put a generous coating of some sort of preservative onto the underside of the hatch cover. It will keep all moisture away from the wood, thereby avoiding problem-causing swelling. Preservative of any color is fine here for it will never be seen.

Photo No. 131 — Our hatch cover.

Although hatch coamings are the critical part, the construction of the hatches themselves is also vital if they are to remain strong, unwarped, and leak-proof. I would hesitate to build hatch frames smaller than 1¾'' stock. Not only will ¾'' or 1'' stock warp without a doubt, but rabbetting or dove-tailing the corners results in not much more than slivers at the joints. Such areas are much too prone to warp or crack or both when exposed to the weather.

The corner joints can be dove-tailed if you have a jig, or lapped, see photo 132. Lapping can be assisted by screws and resorcinal glue for a very satisfactory joint. Dovetails are admittedly more traditional, but they tend to crack and split more easily than lapped joints because of their fragile size.

Photo No. 132 — Lapping the joints.

Hatch tops, if made of wood, can be laid into rabbetted shelves cut into the inside of the frames as shown in figure 78. Whether painted or teaked or mahoganied, the procedure is comparable.

Since most hatches are at least 22 inches wide, a one inch thick shell is necessary to provide long lasting resilience to jumping and falling bodies. This requirement is no problem, as one inch could be built up of any combination of plywood or plywood plus teak or other solid wood thicknesses. If teaked, ½'' plywood with ½'' overlay of solid wood works well. As mentioned before, anything less than ½'' is difficult to plug with any dependability.

Since all our hatches have a crown, we had to curve our

HATCHES

Figure No. 78 — Installing wooden hatch top in frame.

plywood. To curve ½'' ply presents tension problems during work as well as after construction. Not only will it be difficult to bend the plywood into place, but even after it's bedded and screwed to the frames it will have a tendency to flatten out and, as in the case of our hatch cover, cause the originally free-sliding hatch to be incessantly trapped.

To avoid this problem, use two layers of ¼'' ply laminated together. Fit and attach the first layer to the frames; then place the second ¼'' on top of it. Gluing and screwing ½'' x 1½'' teak slats atop this base will provide a nice effect. Screws should be no farther than 8 inches apart and well countersunk or the plugs will be very shallow and will pop out after only a few months of contraction and expansion.

Here, as with the countertop liner, you may want to use wider than 2 inch slats. If so, you'll have to put two screws side by side in each spot or the unfastened edges will rapidly curl up, see photos 133 and 134. Surfacing can be done either with tight butt joints or caulked open seams. The first is recommended for varnishing, the second for oiling, where the wood will undergo much work through moisture absorption and drying. On companionway hatches, the central rib should be installed to add sufficient rigidity. A two by two is adequate.

If additional light below is desired, dead-lights can be cut into wood hatches, as shown in photo 135, or the plywood-teak central surface can be replaced by plexiglass. Large unprotected surfaces of

HATCHES   **375**

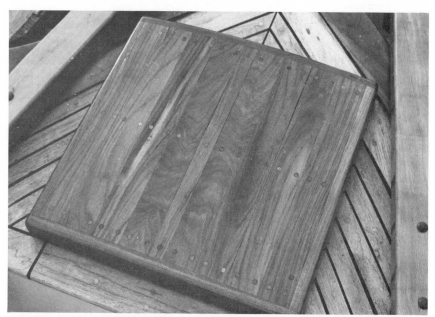

Photo No. 133 — "Solid" hatch.

Photo No. 134 — Caulked hatch.

HATCHES

this material scratch easily and warp in the heat. One inch thick laminate or solid plexiglass is needed on companionway hatches and ½-inch on smaller ones.

To alleviate the worry of scratching transparent plexiglass, it can be purchased opaque to start with, or regular plexiglass may be made opaque by sanding the surface lightly with 400 grit sandpaper. The second method may be cheaper, as you will be able to purchase second hand or salvaged plexiglass which has undesirable scratches in it. If exterior visibility is desired, it's advisable to use teak slats, see photo 136, to prevent major scratches and to provide a non-skid surface when wet.

Photo No. 135 — Deadlight in teak hatch.

If possible, hinge the forward hatch both fore and aft. Equip the hinges with quick release pins. The combination hatch will assist the ship's ventilation whether anchored from the stern or the bow.

Lazarette hatches, which cannot be made fast from below, need a method of dogging tight from the outside. A well-fitted hasp and eye on either side will enable you to lock it as well as close it tight. A chain attached to the hatch and the coaming will keep it from floating away if left unattended.

The question repeatedly arises whether to use drop boards or doors on a companionway hatch. I believe that when all has been considered, it is simply a matter of taste unless you have to mount your compass on the aft face of the trunk cabin like we did. In that

Photo No. 136 — Teak slats on plexiglas.

case, doors, if ever left open would completely hide the compass card. Drop boards are usually fairly large, so it's best to use at least 13/16'' stock to avoid drastic warpage which can render the critters immobile. Adjoining boards must be rabbetted, as in figure 79, to keep out driving rain and nasty following seas.

Figure No. 79 — Drop boards for companionway.

HATCHES

Chapter Twenty-Eight
GRABRAILS

These handy handholds should be abundant topsides. The minimum requirement is a pair atop the cabin running fore and aft. If available, they are best bought pre-milled, for unless you have a jig their fabrication can consume tremendous amounts of time. If you must make them, be sure to cut them from clear stock (no knots) and make them good and heavy. You might do well to use 1¾'' stock. Be sure to leave plenty of wood between the handholds for screws. Make sure you leave the handholds deep enough that one can move a hand quickly if need be.

Installation is quite simple from here on, especially if your cabin top is at least ¼'' thick fiberglass with a plywood core. In such a base, No. 14 self-tapping stainless steel flatheads will hold very well even if a 400-pound behemoth comes for a visit, see figure 80. If your cabin top is of plywood with only a thin covering of glass, screwing would be folly, because the chances of it holding under any conditions would be marginal. You have to through-bolt.

This procedure is more complex because it will require a person below with nuts, washers, a socket wrench, as well as some previous provisions for a reinforcing base under the headliner. The best solution here may be to install the grab rails before any interior insulation or liner has been begun. You may have to build around nuts, but it will still provide the strongest method of fastening. On the other hand, replacement of this hand rail, if it were broken, would be impossible without ripping off the headliner so that the nuts can be pulled.

Whichever system you use, fit and drill your grab rails dry

NOTE: USE BEDDING BETWEEN HANDRAIL & HOUSE TOP

Figure No. 80 — Grabrail installation.

BORDER OF HOUSE SKID

ELEVATION

1½"

5"

5"

1½"

¾"

FASTENING
14 X 2½ FH.S.M.S

GRABRAILS

(without bedding compound). If you are doing it yourself, it's ideal to put in the screws temporarily. Then the thing won't flip-flop about in the wind while you're drilling the other holes. When all holes have been drilled, remove screws and grab rail. You will see between the wood and the glass a tightly packed little mound of glass powder that the drill bit pushed out. This powder has to be cleaned off from both wood and glass. If you pre-caulk everything, then drill the holes and insert screws without any dry fitting first, these hard little mounds will remain under the rail. As well as preventing a tight fit and good seal, they'll cause a teeter-totter effect which will cause the grab rail to work loose and leak prematurely. So clean it well, caulk it well, and screw it down tight. But remember, you're using flat heads with a wedge shoulder and if you force the screws you'll split the teak. I know; I did it twice in one afternoon.

If you do split one, don't panic, spread the opening, fill it with resorcinal glue, clamp it and leave it for at least 24 hours. It will be better than new. I still wouldn't splinter them on purpose though.

Chapter Twenty-Nine
BOOM GALLOWS

See photos 137 thru 140 for several types of boom gallows. I cannot recommend too much the installation of a boom gallows. Not only will it enable you to set the boom off to one side so you won't

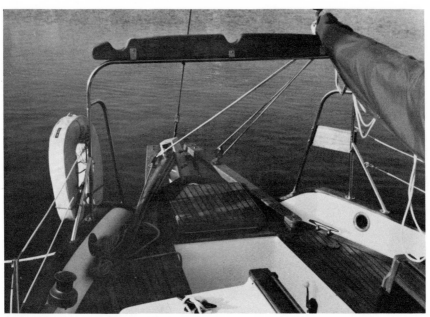

Photo No. 137 — Example of boom gallows.

Photo No. 138 — Example of boom gallows.

Photo No. 139 — Example of boom gallows.

BOOM GALLOWS

Photo No. 140 — Example of boom gallows.

open your skull every time you climb the companionway steps, but it also provides a marvelous place for an awning. Most of all, however, it makes a beautiful stern pulpit to which you can cling in desperate night storms when you're lucky enough to draw watch. It's the most comforting companion you can have.

A variety of boom gallows are shown. All require some expert welding for either stainless or brass and very little else. The gallows itself should be cut from 1¾'' stock (preferably teak for it won't rot or check as easily as others). The best tool to use is a large 4-inch hole saw to cut out the area where the boom sets. If you don't have one, a saber saw will do. Whatever your design, make sure the gallows gets through-bolted and be certain that you triangulate the base, see photo 141, to help it withstand the force of your body against it.

Make the gallows solid and permanent. Removable ones are complicated, require a place to be stored, and begin to work loose in the first seven seconds of use. Avoid them.

BOOM GALLOWS 385

Photo No. 141 — Triangulated base of boom gallows.

Chapter Thirty
SCUPPERS AND HAWSE PIPES

If your boat has bulwarks (as it should), you'll need some apparatus by which water will drain from the decks. If your bulwarks are of solid wood, the solution is simple; cut a few 1½'' holes or build double caprails, see figure 81, to start with.

Figure No. 81 — Double cap rails.

If your decks are the double-walled fiberglass bulwark type like ours, the ideal solution for scuppers is a fitted set of sleeved brass scupper pipes as shown in photos 142 and 143. Larger ones can be used for hawse pipes to lead mooring lines; fairleads on top of the caprails can be substituted for this purpose). Perko and a number of other companies make hawse pipes of cast bronze. The problem with cast pipes is that they do not fit together as the spun sleeves can, thus they have to be filled or fiberglassed. And the great forces

Photo No. 142 — Sleeved brass hawse pipes and scuppers.

Photo No. 143 — Sleeved brass hawse pipes and scuppers.

SCUPPERS AND HAWSE PIPES

on a mooring line would work then loose in little time and cause them to leak.

The spun brass ones, see figure 82, fit together snugly and can be firmly caulked where they do. They are each screwed into the fiberglass. It is ideal to use stainless steel sheet metal screws even though they contrast visually with the brass, for they are threaded all the way to the base of the head, thus providing a superior grip. If the space between your bulwarks is accessible, caulk the inside seams also. It can't hurt.

Figure No. 82 — Spun brass hawse pipes.

Chapter Thirty-One
DETAILING

At the joyous moment when the completion of your boat flutters just above your fingertips, you will be faced with the grand-pop of all icebergs. Somehow, somewhere, someone christened this horribly fidgety, monstrously time-consuming, and usuriously unrewarding task, "detailing." This cultured term refers to resanding, repainting, regelcoating, recleaning, and generally rebuilding the entire boat. Nowhere but here do things seem quite so futile because each job seems to mess up the one you just finished.

At any rate, there are a few short cuts and precautions which can be pursued to achieve a completely satisfactory job in minimum time. The greatest time saver, of course, is sufficient preparation and careful rough assembly. If you did the job well, the task now facing you will be minimal.

Painting

It seems, through practice, that short grain woods like mahogany make for a better surface than wider grained ones like fir. Though you may be considering covering your plywood cabinetry with paint, it may well be worth the extra two dollars per 4 x 8 foot sheet to use mahogany plywood instead of fir. You may argue that with dedicated sanding the fir can be brought to just as fine a finish. Quite the contrary. The more you sand, the deeper will be the softer grains and the more highlighted the more pitchy, harder ones.

One solution that does improve fir is painting the wood while still unsanded with a coat of undercoat, then sanding, then painting, then sanding, etc. By this process the softer grained areas will be protected by semi-hard covering. I had to use this method on one-piece of fir plywood that I recklessly substituted for mahogany. Not only did sanding take an unimaginably long time, but it possessed the added featurette of covering the minutest surface with a thorough coating of white dust that lifted and thickened the air every time I blinked. So try to use mahogany; if you can't, suffer.

Your painting chores will be much easier if you mask unpainted adjoining areas with tape. This practice is admittedly time-devouring, but not nearly as bad as scraping blobs of paint from wood. Since the paint will penetrate into most woods (the drier the deeper) overslop could lead to major problems. To get out all the unwanted paint, you will need to carve irrepairable gulleys with sandpaper. In solid wood, such repairs are less noticeable than on plywood. On plywood, very slight over-zealousness can result in your penetrating the thin (with teak plywood only one mil thick) top layer of veneer. I have not yet heard of a satisfactory method of veneer repair.

So tape off the perimeter of your areas and you will save hours of frustration. To help even further, seal off the area adjacent to the masking tape with a clear wood sealer and acid brush. This procedure should prevent any paint from seeping under the tape. If it does not, at least the paint will not penetrate the sealed wood and it will be easy to remove.

On the painted surface, use a quick drying undercoat. Z-Spar 105 is very satisfactory, although I'm not convinced that other oiled-based undercoats perform any less commendably. Even if you use mahogany ply, it is a good idea to sand well between coats. The first undercoat will be almost completely removed if you want a good job. Brush strokes are left by the finest brushes; if left unsanded, they will become more accentuated with each following coat. I'm not advocating a formica-like finish, but a soft smooth finish will bring hours of pleasure in silent dawning light.

Although Z-Spar 105 is a wonderful undercoat, I cannot recommend Z-Spar products for subsequent layers. Their finishing paint is very thick (I'm told that a good finish paint should be no thicker than fresh milk) resulting in a multitude of runs and brush marks. Apart from this problem, it has the irritating habit of never drying, thus clogging up a four-cent quarter-piece of sandpaper on the first stroke.

Interlux makes excellent finishing paints in many beautiful quick-drying shades. It also is difficult to sand, not because it fills the sandpaper, but for quite the opposite reason. It's a very hard protective finish.

A good rule is to use two undercoats (as mentioned, the first is all but sanded off completely) and two finishing coats. Some people advocate four or five finishing coats, but then some people mow their front lawn five times a week. After the last coat of paint has dried, don't leap to tear off the masking tape. If you do, you'll tear half the paint with it. Some paint will have overflown on to the tape and you will find a tendency for this overflow to pull the other paint with it instead of breaking conscientiously where the tape ends. To avoid pulling off paint take a sharp razor knife and literally cut the paint around the tape's edge. You can then pull the tape off cleanly and admire your masterpiece.

Masking tape will come in handy during procedures other than painting. If you are sanding a surface which is at right angles to another, you will be endlessly either hand sanding grooves into the other surface, or gouging it repeatedly while you use a vibrator or belt sander. To avoid the unnecessary repairs that will have to follow, tape the edge of the surface you won't be sanding, the wider the tape the better. This tape will allow some protection against sandpaper.

As exceptionally beneficial as masking tape is, it does have one villainous quality. If left on over a long period in a place where direct sunlight hits it, the glue will penetrate the surface it's on and cling tenaciously while the paper backing will crumble in your hands. We once left a strip of tape all around the fiberglass bulwarks when we caulked our teak decks. Absurd as it may seem, Candace and I spent eighteen tearful hours scraping off sixty-four feet of one-inch wide tape. It was about as much fun as practice bleeding.

Sanding

If you are sanding wood, no matter how solid and thick it is, use sandpaper of no rougher grit than 60. You can still shape wood rapidly with 60 grit, if necessary. Any rougher grit will leave a deep gouge in your wood (especially if you are going cross-grain) which will be very difficult to remove. Cross-grain sanding should be avoided if at all possible. On exterior surfaces, I can see no need to go finer than 150 at the most. If you are oiling exterior teak, to go finer than 100 is almost a waste, because the grain of the wood will raise drastically within two or three days no matter whom you know. If you are varnishing, you may consider going to 220 on your last run on the wood, but then varnish immediately because the grain will rise as soon as the dew falls. 220 is acceptable to use between coats, although some say to use 400 before your last coat.

If you can afford to (and you almost can't afford not to) buy sandpaper by the sleeve. A sleeve usually contains 50 or 100 sheets.

It is cheaper and you will end up using it all, especially common grits like 60, 80, 100, and 150.

On interiors, you may consider using 220 on all your woods. If you are varnishing, you will need to; and if you are oiling, you may as well for then you can oil the wood and immediately run over it with 220 to achieve a nearly hand-rubbed finish.

Oiling

The only important point here is to wash down the wood with acetone before oiling. Keep turning the rag you use to get all of the sawdust out of the grain. If you don't, it will have a tendency to darken once the oil is applied, rendering the wood lifeless and dark.

The first coat of oil you apply should be of a resin type, like Watco interior Danish teak oil. It does have a pungent odor, but it seals and protects wood better than wood sealers. Later coats can be of resinless variety, like lemon oil.

Be sure to wipe all excess oil (that which has not absorbed) no more than twenty minutes after application. If you don't, it will become tacky and attract every speck of dust and fluff as well as make the surface unsightly with patches of unequal sheen.

For the exterior, use oil recommended for that purpose only. Watco makes one that has a tendency to turn grey and unappealingly black within a very few weeks. Others, like Tip-Top Teak Oil, blacked to a lesser extent. Light sanding is highly recommended before a new coat of exterior oil is applied. A very fine product called "Te-Ka" cleans the wood better than sandpaper because it penetrates deeper. A very good idea after sanding a coat of varnish or a coat of oil, instead of using acetone which may be spilled and cause patches, would be to use a product by the name of "Tac-Cloth." It is a messy, toadish feeling cloth that is treated with a substance which absorbs fantastic quantities of dust from even the grainiest woods.

Varnishing

As mentioned, you may want to prepare the surface with 220 grit sandpaper. Then, a thinned-down sealing layer (about 20-25% paint thinner) should be applied followed by light sanding, then a full strength varnish coat. It is a fallacy that each coat has to be sanded to the point where no hairline is left untouched. Unless you want a glasslike finish, light sanding will do nicely. Apply the varnish in thin coats. Five thin coats are better than three thick ones which may run and curdle when touched, even four days after application. After sanding, wipe with a Tac-Cloth or similar product.

Be sure your varnish is applied at least three hours before the dew falls, if you are doing exterior wood. In climates where the day may have been cooler than 60 degrees, try to have your varnishing finished by mid-morning or the dew will ruin your precious work. For the eccentrics it might be a great matter of pride to use refrigerated varnish. Varnish, thus cooled, will have a tendency to dry "from the inside out" and consequently have a better hold. I was told this by an eccentric and I never did quite figure out what he meant, but it might be worth a try.

Do not be frugal. Buy a good quality brush and clean it meticulously after using. There's nothing worse than picking molting hairs or kernels of hardened varnish from your otherwise perfect surface.

Filling

Small marks which are deep or irrepairable can be drilled and plugged. A teak or mahogany plug out of place does not look as bad as a worm hole or a blob of white paint or a deep gouge. If the spot is large, patching could be considered. Patching is nothing more than the old art of inlaying wood. If you have a bad area, chisel it out very carefully and fill it with a piece of wood. If the grains match perfectly, that's wonderful. If they don't match at all, it looks good, and if you use entirely different kinds of wood, it looks even more intentional. Whichever you use, cut your filler piece to size first, then use it as a pattern on the damaged wood to scribe in the perimeter, then chisel out the damaged piece. Use a very sharp cutting tool or you will cause more damage through chipping than what you set out to repair to begin with. Keep a wetting stone handy.

If you suffer long splits in wood like we did with our hatches, the repair is simple. Many people use just glue or glue mixed with sawdust. I find either solution most unsatisfactory. You will end up with very dark colored seams or cracks which probably look worse than the crack itself. The best way to fill cracks in wood is to use wood. Cut long wedges, cover the sides with glue and drive them into the cracks with a mallet. Then chisel and sand off the remaining bulk.

If you pick your wood color to match, the inserted wedges will be unnoticeable.

Gelcoat Touch-Up

Many places on your boat the gelcoat will be chipped during construction. The best solution is to leave all repairs until the end. To prevent the problem of chipping and minimize necessary final cleaning, a coat of latex base protector can be applied before any work has begun, see photo 144. It will peel off easily even if left for a few months.

Photo No. 144 — Latex protector being peeled off.

If however, chips in the gelcoat do occur, follow this procedure:
1. Clean the area with acetone.
2. Fill the crack with body putty.
3. Sand with 400 grit sandpaper.
4. Spray on gelcoat.
5. Spray on sealer.
6. Peel off the tape before the gelcoat hardens.
7. Wash off sealer with water.
8. After it has gone off, sand the whole area with 600 grit. If you don't do your final sanding immediately following the catalyzation of the gelcoat, you may run into another problem, especially if you had taped off the area around which you sprayed. Very likely you will have a sharp edge of fresh gelcoat protruding which, if not feathered in immediately, may result in chipping. So sand with 600 grit and feather in.

DETAILING

Other Problems

If you do have stubborn problems with over-cooked masking tape or polyethylene which the sun baked onto your mast, deck, or caprail; only one economical remedy seems possible. People have attempted to use acetone, thinners, heat guns, and fingernails to no avail. The only thing that seems to work is steam cleaning. You can rent portable units or find companies who will come out to your aid. If your mistake is portable (like a boom) take it to the nearest do-it-yourself car wash and do-it-yourself.

Chapter Thirty-Two
TEAK DECKS

I have intentionally left this section as the final item in construction for I believe it to be a non-functional item, application or exclusion of which can be decided only after lengthy deliberation between you and your ego. I have always thought it would require a babbling moron to take a perfect solid non-skid waterproof and rot-proof fiberglass deck, spend $600 on teak and fasteners, then drill a thousand holes to hold the wood down, then spend $300 on caulking and bedding compounds to seal and waterproof the thousand holes he has just drilled.

Needless to say, we put teak decks on our boat at an expense of $1,000 and almost 200 hours of screamingly frustrating labor. But they are beautiful and they are non-skid and we do love them and I wouldn't trade them for a brand new Porsche . . . well, maybe a silver one. Here's how it's done.

Type of Deck and Wood Selection

Try to pick the straightest, least knotty pieces you can find. The longer, the better. If need be, shop around for long clean pieces. One of the worst jobs in doing the decks is butting ends together, so try to avoid too many joints. Knots look beautiful down below if oiled or varnished, but topsides they'll just weather and pop out, or if you are bending your planks they'll surely snap in two at the knot.

If you do have to have joints in your deck, be sure to place them in the area of least curvature, even if your planking is milled to as narrow as an inch and three-quarter each. It will be almost impossible to bend the last foot of a piece of teak, so try to get your joints to stagger, as shown in photo 145, and try to put them amidship where the curvature of the deck is at its least.

Try to predetermine the width of the planking you intend to use. If you are running your decking straight fore and aft without

Photo No. 145 — Straight fore and aft teak decking.

bending as in photo 146, the width of your planks is unlimited. Running them in this fashion is a traditional procedure and it is very simple to do, but only if your cabin sides themselves are uncurved or only slightly curved. If their curve is drastic, an attempt at straight

Photo No. 146 — King plank.

TEAK DECKS

decking can only result in a myriad of short, unsightly, slivery pieces. If you intend to have a curved deck with either a king plank, see photo 147, or herringbone foredeck, see photo 148, using planking wider than two inches will lead to grave problems during

Photo No. 147 — Herringboned foredeck.

Photo No. 148 — Staggering plank joints.

TEAK DECKS 401

bending unless the boat is very long on deck and of a very slight beam. If it is of this design, perhaps you could push the width of the decking to 2-3/8'' or to 2½''. I mention this tradeoff here because it's good to know your intended plank width before you buy your teak stock so that you will select only those widths which will lend themselves economically to your purpose.

The thickness of the stock should not fall below ¾-inch. Anything thinner will be very difficult to plug as well as more inclined to warp and crack with constant weathering. If the plug thickness ends up being less than ¼-inch, the plug is guaranteed to crack and pop out before the year is over.

Milling

Whether you use straight decks or curved ones, you should mill a caulk groove into the edge of each plank. You will need this groove into which to pour polysulphide sealant after your deck is laid. The caulking not only seals the deck and keeps water from entering into the plywood core through the screw holes, but it also remains flexible to allow the decks to shrink and swell without causing the wood to buckle or crack. The caulking groove need not exceed ¼'' x ¼''. I have seen some teak decks without groove like the ones shown in photo 149, but I have never known how they survive. The

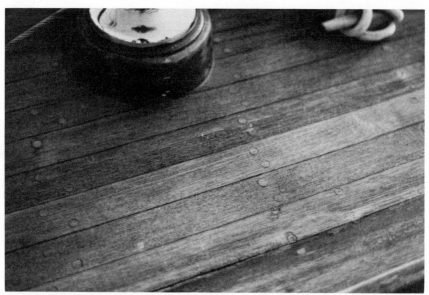

Photo No. 149 — Teak deck without caulking.

TEAK DECKS

grooves can be milled into the planks with either a dado or two cuts of a table saw.

Covering Boards

Making covering boards will probably be the single most time-consuming task in your decking. They should be cut with a band saw (if one is not available a saber saw will do) out of wide planking. I managed to cut ours on a table saw; if you set your blade at a height barely sufficient to cut through your wood and no more, you will be able to do it too if you concentrate.

To determine the shape of the covering boards, you will have to scribe them to fit the cabin and/or your bulwarks, see photo 150. To be sure that you don't waste expensive teak, cut templates for each board out of 1/8" thick veneer. The length and width of each board will be dictated by economy. The wider and longer you make your covering boards, the more scrap you will have. Boards 3½" wide look wide enough to seem intentionally different from the 2 inch planking and yet are narrow enough to be fairly economical. The length of each board will depend on how drastically curved your cabin sides or your bulwarks are. If they are curved as much as ours, the boards cannot economically exceed 5 feet.

Photo No. 150 — Scribing covering board.

TEAK DECKS   403

A side note: if you want teak decks, I think it practical to mill and lay them before you trim out the interior. The amount of large scraps from milling the decks is phenomenal, and all this scrap can be utilized inside for corner trim, shelf searails, etc.

If you have an extremely small radius at your cabin-side-to-deck or deck-to-bulwark turns, fitting the boards flush against the cabin or bulwark will be simple. If, however, you have a substantial radius, you must choose one of two alternatives. You can a) begin your decking at a distance from the vertical side where the curve will have no consequence as shown in photo 151; or b) hand plane the

Photo No. 151 — Teak decks started away from coamings.

bottom edge of the covering board to a curve large enough to accommodate the radius in the fiberglass. The butt end joints for the covering boards can be made using any number of traditional scarfs such as the ones shown in photos 152, 153, and 154. The structural integrity is virtually identical; thus, your choice will have to be based on taste alone.

Do not mill caulk grooves into the covering boards. For the long sides you can use the groove in the first plank; as for the scarfs, it is preferred that you bed and screw the boards down in their final position first, then belatedly chisel in the grooves. This way, if your

404   TEAK DECKS

Photo No. 152 — Traditional scarfs.

Photo No. 153 — Traditional scarfs.

Photo No. 154 — Traditional scarfs.

butting or alignment is not perfect (and they never will be even though the screw holes have been dry fitted), you will be able to cheat a little and chisel in a nice parallel sided caulk groove.

The King Plank

I am not sure that a single logical argument exists in favor of a king plank except that it is pretty. To do one is time consuming and painstaking. If you can get the pattern for it from someone you will be far ahead; but if not, you will spend many hours drawing in the lines and routing them out.

The fastest procedure involves laying the planks with roughly hacked off ends. The angle at the ends is irrelevant and the fit unimportant for the ends will be later overlapped by the king plank. Once the planks are all down, make a pattern out of thin veneer or cardboard for the king plank. The width of the plank and the angles you use will be of your own choosing. Cut out the plank from a solid piece of teak, lay it over the deck, and draw its shape onto the over-long planks. Now take the router and set it exactly the depth of your teak decking. If anything, leave it 1/16th of an inch shallower, because then you can easily penetrate the last bit of wood with an old chisel and remove the excess. This way you won't have your expensive router bit dulled by the fiberglass.

Now you can drop in your king plank and see how it fits. Don't worry about it being in perfect alignment. As long as your mistake is no greater than a sixteenth of an inch you will be able to correct it when you rout in the caulking groove between the king plank and the other planks.

Herringboning

This method is less demanding. It is quicker than a king plank, because it involves only the first stage in laying the deck. You must use more caution, however, in scribing your angles on the end of each plank to make certain you don't wander too far off the center line. But again, remember that a one-sixteenth or even a three-thirty-second mistake is allowable. You will then only have to rout in a center line caulking-groove to notch out the mistakes and complete the job.

An absolutely vital note, whichever method you employ, is to have the straight bit for your router sharpened just before you start working on your teak decks. If you can get a carbide-tip bit, so much the better; whatever else you may have heard, teak is a brittle wood and prone to chipping, if anything but the sharpest of tools is used.

Deck Laying

The first step in laying a deck should be shaping and fitting the covering boards. Dry fitting should include the placement of each board into its final position and putting at least a few screws into their final places.

When it seems you have done everything you can to make the covering boards fit perfectly, take out those screws you have just put in and lift up the covering boards. You will find little mounds of white fiberglass powder surrounding the mouth of every hole. Some of the powder will have stuck around the screw hole on the wood too. This powder must be wiped off completely or the board won't set evenly and even teeter over the little mound, which can cause it to perhaps crack. This procedure of dry fitting and cleaning off the dust mounds should be observed with every teak-to-glass joining to guarantee better joints. Once the dust has cleared you can permanently install the boards.

The first step in installation is to lay two unbroken beads of black polysulphide about one inch from either end of the plank onto the fiberglass. Many people have used Dolphinite as the bedding compound, but Dolphinite has the tendency to expand and ooze oil in very hot climates even a few months after laying. I've heard of some decks buckling because of the expansion. And even if buckling doesn't occur, the seam-caulking may be pushed away from the wood, allowing water to penetrate.

At any rate, lay down two beads of polysulphide, and just for safety pop a drop into each screw hole. If you think that's being over anxious, just try not doing it and see how you sleep at night. I didn't do it originally, only to end up four days later taking every fastener out of the deck, screw by screw, and popping in a belated drop of sealer, then putting the screws back in. That's being over-anxious.

Once the covering boards are in their final place, the fun begins. Use your table saw to cut about ten pieces of ¾-inch thick by 4" by 4" plywood blocks. Now gather up all the oak, ash, and teak scraps you have and cut them into wedges ranging from four inch by ten inch to ½" by 5".

The harder the wood you use, the better because you will be smashing these blocks with a hammer and you will want the wedges to last as long as possible under this onslaught.

Next, establish the athwartship points where you will be putting screws into the planks. The screws should be no more than twelve inches apart; if the bends are radical, use closer centers. At these twelve or whatever inch points draw a straight pencil line athwartships on the fiberglass. Nothing looks prettier than perfectly lined up plugs, and the pencil lines will help you prettify.

Now get your first plank, cut it to length, then take the ¾" ply blocks you have just cut and screw them into the deck 4" or 5" from the covering boards and about 12" apart. Use one screw only and use it in the center of the block so that the block can swivel when you insert different shaped wedges. Drive in this one screw deep, or the force of the wedges will cause the screw to bend, and it is almost impossible to pull a crippled screw out of fiberglass.

Now lay double seams of caulking down the length of the deck where the first plank will go. Spread it evenly and thickly. Be sure to put a bead right next to the covering board to seal the edges. Don't scrimp. It's easier to wipe off the mess that squeezes out than to try to fill the voids under a screwed down deck. Also have a couple of rolls of paper towels ready along with a can of acetone to wipe the goo from your hands, tools, and your left ear lobe. Rags are passable, but too frequently you'll end up wiping old goo onto your hands, instead of wiping the new goo off; so, use paper towels and throw them away. It's only money.

Now, summon the bulkiest friend you have and secure his loyalty for the next 4 days. You will need every ounce he carries. The longer his reach, the better.

With a screw gun and drill motor, some one inch pan-head sheet metal screws (remember flat heads split wood) and a couple of hammers, you will be set. You will also need about thirty tubes of polysulphide. Have them handy, for it's very ulcerizing to run out when you're raring to keep going on your job.

Now, with the goo spread evenly and with the large friend hanging onto the other end of your plank, bend the plank and place it behind the blocks. Once it's down behind the blocks, don't ever take your weight off it. Be sure to hold down both ends and both centers, and tell chubby not to lose his balance or the plank will spring up like a steel coil and smash his face in.

Now comes the critical point. Insert wedges between each block and the plank; begin to tap each wedge gently and evenly, one tap each at a time. Give your helper a hammer too, but tell him to be gentle and never to take his weight off the plank. As the plank is stressed more and more, the more vital this constant pressure becomes, because the greater the tension the greater the tendency of the plank to spring up and smash in the aforementioned face.

Be certain, also, that all wedges advance evenly. If one proceeds or lags behind the others by too much, the plank will crack and literally explode. Teak shatters in the most frightening fashion, taking its toll of skin and blood as it does. Try to keep the leading edge of the plank somewhat off the fiberglass. If the plank is squeezed down completely tight, you will be scraping off all of the preciously spread polysulphide; so, keep hammering gently until the plank is butted tight against the covering board.

Once in place, screw it down and screw it down tight immediately. Drill your countersink holes about halfway through the ¾" plank. If you drill any less you will not have a deep hole for your plug; as mentioned before, if the plug is less than ¼-inch it is guaranteed to crack and pop out very shortly.

If by some chance you hear a nasty cracking sound before you wedge the plank into place, don't start bashing the nearest portlight in anguish. As a matter of fact don't even move. Take a bit of resorcinal glue (which you should have sitting around ready mixed) and pour generously into the obviously cracked wood. Now hammer the wedges home and, as if nothing has happened, screw the plank into place. You may have to disturb the straight line of the plugs and put a couple of screws out of sequence to make sure the crack won't open up. Wipe off the excess resorcinal glue and try to forget about it. You may now get off the plank.

Move your blocks back about 2", screw them down, and start the whole process over again. Some people advocate not cutting the planks to length until they are laid in their final place. This idea is probably very good, for then you won't have to worry about getting the planks in exactly the right location. While you are attempting to bend them it's almost an impossibility anyway.

On the other hand, it's simple to set in a board, set it and screw it, then just wack the end off with a good sharp chisel. Use only the sharpest chisel or you will split the teak. Don't try to hack the whole end off in one oafish blow. Penetrate no more than 1/8" per blow; then chisel out the groove and do the next vertical penetration. Don't use this chisel to go right to the fiberglass. Nothing can ruin a good chisel quicker than a few blows at a steel-hard deck. Have a duller chisel at hand to cut through the last 1/16".

Other Things

There are a few problem items with teak decks, like nibbing, see photo 155, which I prefer to making wedges where the sheer line no longer parallels the cabin sides. Nibs can be angled and lengthened to taste. Other problems like corners, deck fills, cockpit trim, etc. are shown in the photographs above.

TEAK DECKS **409**

Photo No. 155 — Nibbing.

Caulking

Once you have finished laying the deck, the fun is just beginning. Your next job is to plug the 1,000 screw holes. Make sure you align grains of the plugs and tap them in good and deep. It is preferable to use a clear epoxy glue on the plugs insted of resorcinal, for resorcinal is a very dark red color which leaves a very dark brown ring around the plug, no matter how great your care.

Now go back, and with a chisel wack off the tops of the plugs. Don't bother to get them flush at this time. Just get rid of the bulk, so that if someone kicks one, it won't break off and require replacement.

Now get the most powerful vacuum cleaner you can find and clean all the scrap and dust from the caulking grooves. Make sure you unlodge every piece of junk you find.

Now go shopping and take a lot of money. You will need about three gallons of "Grove" two-part polysulphide. About ½-pint of hardner comes with each gallon kit, and each gallon kit cost about $35. You will also need to buy about 40 empty caulking cartridges, a quart of Grove teak primer, a gallon of acetone, and a lot of paper towels.

I mention the trade name of the two-part polysulphide here because I have not heard of anyone else manufacturing this. The only other name I've heard it called has been "black death." After you've half finished filling the first empty cartridge you will be completely empathetic to the etymology.

The one item you may have difficulty finding is the empty cartridges. I did, and when I found them I was so happy that the atrocious price of 36¢ each (for an empty cartridge??!!) gave me heart failure for no more than 49 seconds. You will get used to highway robbery like this throughout your boat building career. It seems that in boat building, the boat builder is fair game, so by no means hesitate to lie, cheat, and rob all you can (see chapter on scrounging). At any rate, secure about 40 of these tubes early and have them ready.

Now, using a small acid brush, primer all the immaculate caulking grooves thoroughly. Don't worry about getting primer on top of the teak deck itself. It will be sanded.

Caulk right away. To be economical time-wise, you will have to mix a gallon of caulking at a time. Mix in the catalyst thoroughly. This procedure is a demanding task, because the polysulphide is as thick as tar. Fortunately the catalyst is a light brown color so its path is easily traceable.

Stir the catalyst in completely but slowly, or you will trap a jillion air bubbles which will stay in the thick caulking compound. They will be transferred and trapped in the caulking grooves only to pop when you are sanding the hardened caulking. Once you sand off the top of the bubble, you will be left with gaping holes which you will have to open, clean out, and fill with more "black death." To this end save a quarter of a gallon of polysulphide and a bit of hardener. You will need almost that much for repair work.

Don't be afraid to let the polysulphide fill the grooves to overflowing, see photos 156A and 156B. When it hardens it will shrink and settle. It is a lot easier to cut off the excess than to fill the voids. Once the poly has gone off, trim off the overflow rubber with a sharp chisel. Then get a belt sander and about four 50 grit sanding belts (anything finer will have its pores filled in no time) and grind the caulking right down to the wood, see photo 157. If you find any air holes in the seams, fill them now.

You will find if you curve your decks that the edges of some drastically curved planks will have a tendency to turn slightly upward, necessitating very extensive belt sanding to bring it to an even level. After you have leveled the deck with the 50, use 80 grit paper to get out the cross-grain gouges, and finish off with 100. Then oil or let bleach or whatever you like. Watco makes an exterior teak oil with a very high resin content that has a tendency to turn

TEAK DECKS   **411**

Photo No. 156A — Filling in grooves to overflowing.

Photo No. 156B — Filling in grooves to overflowing.

black a few months after application. I have heard of "Te-Ka" oil used on the exterior with very good results.

You can see from the foregoing that laying a teak deck is not something you can leave for a dull Sunday afternoon. It does take time (as mentioned, approximately 160 hours) and quite a bit of money to do a satisfactory, lasting job. If you can afford it, by all means don't hesitate for there are very few sights to a sailor quite as heartwarming and satisfying as the sight of a freshly scrubbed, bright teak deck. . . Anyway, it's probably the best non-skid you can find.

Photo No. 157 — Belt sanding the caulking.

Chapter Thirty-Three
RIGGING

Mast

I waded for four months through people's opinions, prejudices, and whims, trying desperately to decide between a wood and an aluminum mast. My final decision came; not from conviction, but by default. And although I am overjoyed about my aluminum mast, I may have rationalized myself into this emotion.

I always felt slightly ill at ease about the vulnerability of a wood mast; the susceptibility to rot, the weakening it suffers from fastener holes, the potential delamination of the pieces, and the tremendous amount of upkeep it intransigently demands. Apart from the preceding, wood masts are difficult to find at a reasonable price. I finally did find a man who would build my 43-foot mast, spreaders, and booms (main and staysail) of knotless sitka spruce. The price was $600 plus freight. I would have had to install the hardware. However, he was in the process of moving his shop and the new place wouldn't have sufficient heat for gluing for two and a half months. I decided to rush and get the readily available aluminum mast.

Aluminum, of course, has its own disadvantages. Although it won't rot it will oxidize to a point where after a year or two one may find the removal of stainless steel fasteners impossible. It is advisable to use some sort of lubricating compound like "Graphite" to ensure future removal. The mast section selection was a problem. I wanted whatever would be the heaviest and strongest, but I was assured that it would be rather folly to get something beyond "overbuilt." The mast size would create extra windage and weight aloft (see chart for IXX and IYY measurements).

The wall thickness should be considered if two similar extrusions are being evaluated. The thicker the wall, the greater the number of threads that can be tapped into it. The more the threads, the greater the fastener's holding power.

Most sail tracks are riveted, but spinnaker tracks are through-bolted as are cleats and halyard winches. Here is where the greater help would be found in a thicker-walled mast. The thicker the wall the smaller the cross-section can be and still achieve the same IXX and IYY measurements, therefore the same strength.

Mast Heads

Welded aluminum mast heads are the lightest and most practical if well-welded. Look for smooth even beading on the welds. This level of quality is the sign of an artist. Installation of an extra sheave is desirable in case a halyard breaks, a sheave cracks or fouls, or if you intend to utilize twin running sails, see figure 83. The sheaves can be of either aluminum or phenolic. Both last and perform equally well it seems.

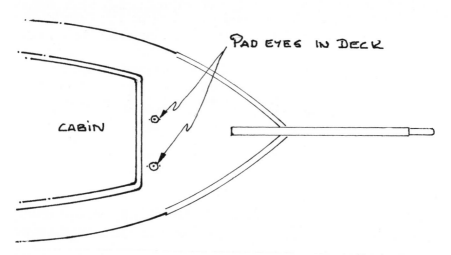

Figure No. 83 — Twin headsail rig.

In a mast of greater depth than five inches (and I hope you have this size on a cruising sailboat) a double set of sheaves should be installed (unless the mast is tapered) to keep the halyards from chafing on the mast, see figure 84. This mast head setup nicely distributes all forces over two pins. I do not much like tapered

Figure No. 84 — Double sheaves.

aluminum masts. A one-piece taper is much too expensive and the standard two-piece method (the bottom part unshaped, the top tapered, and the joints riveted) leaves me somewhat uneasy. If I wanted to feel uneasy I could have bought a wood mast.

Wiring must be run to the masthead for at least an anchor light and perhaps a strobe light. It is also advisable to install a radio coax for an eventual VHF or single side band antenna. If you are uncertain whether or not you will want this equipment, at least have a spare line installed to enable future wiring to be pulled through.

RIGGING 417

Regular 12 volt wires should be run through a PVC tube that's riveted to the inside of the mast. The tube will keep the wires from flapping madly, chafing themselves to death.

Mast Steps

Most aluminum masts are stepped on deck requiring a footing or mast step. The rims of the step should be quite high (¾" is not too drastic) to keep the mast in "step" if it has a tendency to jump about in its place, see figure 85. If the cabin top is well reinforced

Figure No. 85 — Mast step.

RIGGING

with the compression taken care of (see chapter 13, mast step support) this motion should never occur. Through the rim should be drilled at least two drain holes to allow any water that has found its way into the mast through the sheaves, rivet holes, etc. to drain off. Salty water will corrode anodized aluminum if the metal is closed off so that it cannot air.

A tabernacle mast step, see figure 86, is a very nice idea. Not only will it enable you to have greater freedom in roaming below low bridges through the canals of Europe and Asia. It will also enable the mast to drain completely and easily, and to air at all times. To prevent interior corrosion whether your mast is a tabernacle or not, it is a good idea to coat the lower three feet of the extrusion's interior with either primer paint or a thin layer of heavy grease. Either material will protect the mast and extend its life.

Figure No. 86 — Tabernacle Mast step.

The tabernacle mast has one great advantage over its unhinged counterpart. You can rake the mast at whatever degree you desire, while a standard mast has to sit evenly on the mast step. If you rake a standard mast too far forward or aft you will cause one end of it to lift from the step, putting all the compression strain caused by the stays on the other end. This strain can cause premature metal fatigue and potential buckling.

Sail Tracks and Slides

Another decision that should be made is whether to use internal or external slide track, see figure 87. The external type is made of stainless steel, looks less cumbersome, and will not corrode. The way the rivets are recessed in the center will allow for some rivets working loose and eventually protruding into the track groove. Since the sides are contoured in the opposite direction, a small protrusion will not interfere with their movement. On the internal track, however, the slides pass directly next to the track's face. In this

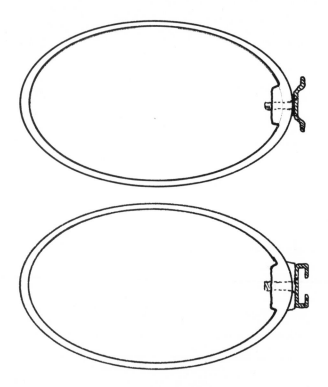

Figure No. 87 — Sail tracks.

case, a small rivet sticking out even a 32nd of an inch can snag a slide and necessitate a trip aloft to free it.

But, on the other hand, stainless steel track comes in short lengths requiring the use of a number of pieces to cover the mast length. Aluminum (most internal tracks are made of this material) comes in unbroken lengths, thus reducing the possibility of a foul at the joints. The aluminum track has, I think, another great advantage. Since it has its outside extremities resting on the mast, the central rivet has the support of these points whereas the stainless track tends to pivot around the rivet thereby greatly increasing the potential of it being worked loose with the constant and tremendous forces applied by the sails. I think this factor outweighs the advantages of the stainless steel track.

Slotted booms, I think, are more desirable than ones with tracks. There are fewer parts so that their potential for failure is reduced. Sails with rope along the foot that slide directly into the slot seem to have an esthetic advantage over the common slugs. Slugs tend to rattle menacingly in confused airs and disturb the occupants. On the other hand (as usual) the slugs allow for use of a rubber snubber or preventer by merely passing either of them through between the slugs.

Riveting

The spacing of the rivets in the sail tracks is essential. I think that three-inch centers are maximum, and the bottom and top four feet of the track should be double riveted (1½" centers). If you have reef points (and hopefully not roller reefing) it is advisable to double rivet the main track in the areas where the head of the sail will set when reefed and when double reefed. Eighteen inches above and below these points should be sufficient. The storm trysail track should be riveted every two inches with the top and bottom ends riveted at an inch and one half. The lower end of this track should come within a foot of the base of the mast so that the sail can be permanently bent on for quick use in any emergency, see figure 88.

Reaching Poles

If you intend to use any large head sails you will need to have a reaching pole to help your sail set. The length of this pole should be derived from a discussion with your rigger and naval architect. The fitting to be used on the inboard end, however, should be of only the bayonet type with no compromise, as shown in figure 89. The snap hook fitting is the more commonly used on small boats and it is indeed fine for weekend cruising or even racing where quick

DOUBLE RIVETS
8'

25'

INSTALL 7/8" SAIL TRACK
ON PORT SIDE OF MAST
FOR STORM TRYSAIL

21'

BASE OF GOOSENECK TRACK

DOUBLE RIVETS
5'

BASE OF MAST

12"

PORT ◄───────┼───────► STARBOARD

Figure No. 88 — Storm trysail track.

removal is necessary and longevity can be bypassed. The hook fitting with a ring stationary on the mast has no ability to swivel, or give, or twist, as the shape of the sail demands. The torque may be so much here that eventually the cast aluminum fitting can snap from excessive stress.

The inboard end should be as shown in figure 89. It is an open-ended arrangement that slips over a pin which in turn is attached to a car. This arrangement is infinitely better, for the pole can swivel without obstruction to whatever degree the sails demand.

422   **RIGGING**

The mast fitting itself is usually recommended only for boats over fifty feet, so I think it should be just adequate for a 32' cruising boat.

If you will be using a number of head sails with varying clews, you may be well advised to install a track of about eight feet in length on your mast. This track in conjunction with a slide fitting will allow numerous positions for the inboard end, guaranteeing a better fitting sail.

This method will of course lead to more paraphernalia, for you will need a topping lift and a down haul to adjust the slide's position on the track. An endless line is best used for this purpose to prevent

Figure No. 89 — Reaching pole end.

the possibility of it coming loose. The line will have to be secured with a pair of clam cleats or equivalents to prevent the pole from riding either up or down. The two cleats must work in opposite directions, and a generous space should be left between them to allow some slack to the line so that the extraction and insertion into the cleat can be accomplished with ease. Putting the cleats at least two feet apart should give you enough slack to enable easy maneuvering.

Goosenecks

In recent years the trend has been toward a mechanical down haul for the main boom, see photo 158. The trend came because it

Photo No. 158 — Mechanical down-haul.

was reasonable to assume that in time the main sail would stretch necessitating adjustment of the foot. This down haul created additional moving parts, and many failures in even the best built boats occurred because the down haul track worked loose on the mast. A recent resurrection of the fixed gooseneck is underway. This concept is more solid and it is one that can still allow for stretching of the sail by inserting a cunningham hole a few feet from the foot. Through the cunningham hole a line can be fed which can be made tight if stretching of the luff is necessary. I have the fixed version, as shown in photo 159; because of its simplicity and positive attachment, I do prefer it.

Photo No. 159 — Fixed gooseneck.

Riveting

Attaching sail tracks with rivets is not a great task. A pop-rivet gun is inexpensive, about $30, and no great magic is involved in its use. It works on the principle of drawing a large ball through a small tube, thereby enlarging the circumference of the tube which then becomes a structural shoulder or flange around the drilled hole.

The only thing to watch for is the drilling of the hole. It should be a good fit, but not a tight one around the rivet stem. The drilled hole will have to be perfectly straight. I heard from a veteran mast maker that he likes to put a dab of bedding compound around the rivet's base to seal the narrow space between the flange and the mast wall. This way moisture cannot settle in and oxidize the aluminum.

The question of whether or not a bedding compound should be used under the track keeps emerging. If you are willing to do a thorough job, I feel that it is an excellent idea. But a thorough job you must do or you will only create sporadic pockets in which moisture can settle. It will be an extremely messy operation working with bedding compound but well worth the effort if well done.

Tapping

Using stainless steel machine screws requires more time than riveting, but it becomes necessary for cleats, winches, and large fittings. Tapping the threads, see photo 160, is a basic operation requiring only a $15 tool. Drill a hole through the diameter of the machine screw's shank not taking into account the threads, then place a drop of oil or A-1 aluminum cutter fluid on the tapping tool. Hold it perfectly vertical and start to tap. Do not allow the tool to oscillate, for your result will be pitiable and worthless. Tap straight and true. For tapping each hole apply a drop of oil to the tapping tool to keep its grooves clear and make it work more effectively by enabling the cut aluminum to slide out easier.

If you have your halyard cleats near the base of the mast as you should, you may consider putting nuts on your machine screws for extra strength. If you use lock washers you should be safe; if you don't, the nuts can work loose and can fall off. You will then have the most infernal rolling and clanging in the base of the mast. Your only remedy lies in removing the mast and gathering the nuts. If you want to change cleat positions you will find removal of the machine screw impossible unless you send a very small and very slim person inside to hold the nut; so think twice before you indulge.

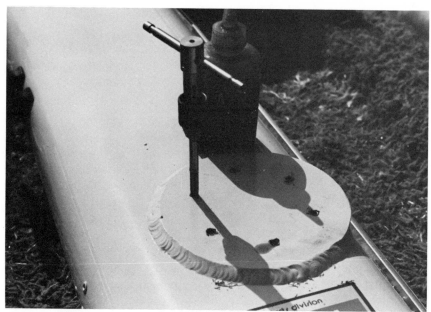

Photo No. 160 — Tapping mast.

Rigging

For a boat with a forty-foot mast I would not use less than ¼"
1 x 19 wire. This wire has a strength of 8,200 lbs., see table 4, more
than enough to guarantee that something other than it will fail
before it does. Heavier than 9/32" wire will add tremendous weight
aloft unnecessarily. This wire used with ½" turnbuckles (thread
and pin size) compares similarly in breaking strength with the
turnbuckles, see table 2. Over-rigging beyond this point shows a
lack of thought, for you must remember that rigging is a chain, and
if any link is weak (like a tiny tang somewhere aloft) the whole thing
will find its way overboard in little time. Swedging the marine ends
(eyes, forks, etc.) onto wires should be left to a good shop using a
multiple roller swedger to give an even thorough press. Cruisers
should consider Norseman fittings, for these can be attached to the
wire without specialty tools, a great advantage in the Amazon River.

Turnbuckles

One-half inch turnbuckles of the toggle toggle variety, as shown
in photo 161, are recommended. With toggles at two ends, an extra
joint is put in to relieve torque on the fittings. In ordering rigging,

RIGGING

427

1 x 19 NON-FLEXIBLE

PREformed

 ## FLEXIBLE 7 x 7

PREformed

 ## 7 x 19 Extra Flexible

PREformed

VINYL COATED WIRE

TYPE WIRE	BREAKING STRENGTH IN POUNDS									
SIZE WIRE	1/16	3/32	1/8	5/32	3/16	7/32	1/4	9/32	5/16	3/8
1 x 19	500	1200	2100	3300	4700	6300	8200	10,300	12,500	17,500
7 x 7	500	1200	2100	3300	4700	6300	8200	10,300	12,500	17,500
7 x 19	—	—	1760	2400	3700	5000	6400	7800	9000	12,000

VINYL COATED WIRE

TYPE	SIZE	
	WIRE	OUTSIDE
7 x 7	3/32	5/32
7 x 19	1/8	3/16
7 x 19	5/32	7/32
7 x 19	3/16	1/4
7 x 19	1/4	3/8

Table 4 — Wire Strength

Photo No. 161 — Turnbuckle toggle.

every attempt should be made to give a clear picture of the wire including all fittings. A simple sketch is recommended. Measure every shroud length between the centers of clevis pin holes and fittings or from center clevis pin to end of the threaded terminal.

If a turnbuckle is included, measure the length from center of clevis to center of clevis and turnbuckle with the turnbuckle two-thirds open, see figure 90. Ascertain if your choice of turnbuckle has the body threaded at least as deep as the circumference of the threaded rod. This qualification is most important in turnbuckles where the body and the rod are both stainless, because this combination tends to gall as most similar metals do. The more threads used, the less the pressure on each thread, so the less likely this eventuality will be.

Turnbuckles with naval bronze bodies and stainless steel rods will not be subject to this occurrence because one metal is softer than the other and thus it will always give sufficiently to guarantee movement. I do like the open-body turnbuckle, see photo 162, for one can readily see the amount of thread left inside the body.

I also prefer turnbuckles that use a locking nut as well as a cotter or ring pin to ones that rely on a cotter pin alone. A cap-like locking nut that slips part way over the body has a better chance of staying in place than the simple hex nut type. Do be careful of the pins you use to keep the body from spinning. A pin with any sharp protrusion on it could be a great menace to sails.

Boom Bails

Boom bails as shown in photo 163 should be used for main-sheet blocks, vangs, and preventer attachments. Use ones that have a positive, six machine screw attachment. This type is recommended for boats over 40-feet; again, almost sufficient for a 32-foot cruising boat.

Figure No. 90 — Measuring rigging.

Genoa Tracks and Deck Blocks

Genoa tracks and deck blocks should all be through-bolted with at least flat washers, better still back-up plates, on the underside. Use nylon-insert lock nuts to guarantee a good long-lasting hold. Wise planning would be reflected by allowing access to these nuts in case a leak develops or modifications need to be made. Cap or acorn nuts, see photo 164, can be used if the ends of machine screws are to be left exposed.

If you dislike tracks you can use pad-eyes as shown in figure 91,

430   **RIGGING**

Photo No. 162 — Open-body turnbuckle.   *Photo No. 163 — Boom bail.*

Photo No. 164 — Cap nuts and acorn nuts.

at two or three positions where your head sail sets best during beating, reaching, and running. A snatch block can easily be moved from one position to another depending on sailing conditions. This solution is not the ultimate, but it is a solution.

Figure No. 91 — Pad eyes.

Running Rigging

Nylon braid sized 7/16'' or ½'' is very good for sheets and halyards. Some people prefer ½-inch for this generous diameter makes for easier handling. All-rope halyards are recommended by many cruising people who feel totally opposed to wire halyards or even wire halyards with rope tails. The latter requires a splice to the rope tail. This splice may become a weak point in the halyard. Wire chafes noisily on aluminum masts and removes the paint. It also frays and develops fish-hooks which cut fingers deeply.

If you use heavy nylon line, look for a widely mortised block.

This solution will alleviate the need for unsightly oversized blocks. Blocks with plastic sheaves are sufficient for all rope running rigging. If you choose to use wire at some point, then sheaves of "radically wound phenolic or scored aluminum" should be used. Be sure that your sheave is large enough; too small a sheave can cause undue friction with rope halyards and can cause wire halyards to fray.

The following pointers are taken from a Schaefer catalog on hardware and I think paraphrasing would do them injustice.

Block Strength

We determine the ultimate strength of any block by a series of tests that stress it to the point of failure. Fifty percent of the figure we then advertise as its safe working load, allowing the remaining fifty percent as a safety factor. This is "insurance" against breakage. When selecting hardware be sure the advertised strength of the block is at its safe working load and not its ultimate strength.

Fairleads

Every block must be free to align itself with the rope that leads into and away from it. The rope should not chafe or the block bind in the performance of its function. In cases where the alignment does not vary appreciably (such as main and mizzen sheets and forestaysail sheets), there is a common tendency to use swivel shackle blocks which usually only tangle the sheet. A *front/side shackle block* should be used. On a spinnaker halyard, pole lift or main sheet lead block on deck, where the lead changes constantly, *swivel blocks* should be used. *Upset shackle blocks* are the answer for tangs that will only accept a shackle pin, boom down hauls, or where a shackle bail won't fit through the point of attachment, or where slight universal action is required.

Sheave Diameter, Score and Material

Many boat owners prefer to use heavier lines because they are easier to handle and to haul. If this is your preference, look for a wide mortised block that will accept the heavier line. This eliminates the necessity for a yachtsman to outfit his craft with blocks that are too big for the job.

Understand the job that you want done and choose a block designed to do it. As any block will break if misaligned or overloaded, respect their limitations. If you have any misgivings about the right piece of equipment for the job, see your nearest dealer.

BASIC MATERIALS AND PROCESSES

Aluminum

Although aluminum is well known for its lightness and resistance to corrosion, certain of its alloys are stronger than structural steel. Aluminum is also exceptionally workable. It can be easily stamped; cast or welded and accepts a wide variety of finishes. The alloy most widely used is 6061-T6, which has a tensile strength of 45,000 psi and a yield strength of 40,000 psi.

Anodizing

This process coats the surface of aluminum with a corrosion resistant protective film by subjecting the metal to electrolytic action. A hard-coat anodizing process adds about 1 to 1.5 thousanths of an inch of tough aluminum oxide to the aluminum. Hard coat anodized finishes have withstood corrosion for more than 1,000 hours in salt spray tests.

Bronze

Bronze and bronze alloys are used in turnbuckles, and in bushing for larger blocks. It is a copper alloy which contains maganese, zinc, nickel, tin and aluminum. Bronze bushings (a detachable metal lining used as a friction reducing bearing on shafts and axles) are impregnated with oil, which provides a strong and well lubricated bearing surface.

Electropolishing

Manufacturing processes such as machining, welding, grinding and sanding add impurities to the surface of stainless steel which can encourage corrosion. Electropolishing is an electrochemical process subjecting the stainless steel to a light electric charge while emersed in a sulphuric acid solution. This removes a thin layer from the stainless steel surface, giving it a hard brilliant finish as it removes most of the impurities.

Epoxy Coating

For applications where extreme abrasion is a consideration, such as on cleats, a black epoxy coating can be used. Epoxy coating is chip resistant, highly abrasion resistant and corrosion tests have been very successful.

Forging

The forging process forms metal to a desired shape through the use of pressure or impact, while maintaining a strong grain structure.

High Impact Plastic

Generally used are either Delrin or Lexan plastic. Both are extremely tough plastics with properties of high tensile, impact and shear strength. Lexan, in particular, possesses toughness and rigidity exceeding any plastic known.

Investment Casting

The first step in this process involves making a wax part from a master, or permanent die. The wax part is then used in making one, or a series of temporary molds, which have a high degree of accuracy. The actual parts are then cast from the temporary molds without any wear on the permanent die.

Passivation

Conducted with a nitric acid solution, this surface cleaning operation helps eliminate contamination which may cause corrosion or discoloration and permits the steel to generate its own protective oxide.

Phenolic

Phenolics are laminates thermoset under high pressure which have an extremely high resistance to frictional heat. Most synthetic line will burn before the phenolic begins to distort.

Stainless Steel

A steel alloy containing iron, carbon, silicon, manganese, nickel and at least 12% chromium (which makes the iron passive in air at normal temperatures). Generally used is type 304 stainless steel, whose combined properties of corrosion resistance, strength and elasticity make it ideal for marine use.

Contrary to the implication of its name, stainless steel is not totally rustproof. All stainless steel will rust to a certain degree, due to natural chemical reaction to air and salt water (particularly in areas of abrasion, friction and welding where a chemical imbalance in the metal might occur). The problem though, is mainly a cosmetic one and is solved with metal polish and frequent fresh water rinsing.

KNOWING YOUR HARDWARE

The hull of a sailboat has often been described as the platform upon which the process of sailing is performed. Gear and hardware are the tools used in this performance. Selecting these tools with care and intelligence not only keeps the process smooth, simple, and efficient, but adds greater enjoyment and safety to the sport of sailing.

To keep pace with the variety of jobs that must be performed on sailboats of all sizes, shapes and makes, producers of yacht hardware are developing and producing an ever increasing variety of equipment from which choices can be made. Helpful in the choice of proper hardware is a basic knowledge of its anatomy, terminology, and function.

The basic piece of marine hardware is the block. The following information should help you determine whether the block of your choice is strong enough, assumes a fair lead, has the right sheave and is made of the proper material.

Snap Shackle
Can be easily moved from place to place. Instant disengagement.

Upset Shackle
Used where the tang will only accept a shackle pin. Slight universal movement.

Swivel Shackle
Used where the rope angle varies. Allows block to pivot.

Front/Side Shackle
Used where the rope angle is reasonably constant.

Spring Mounting
SS spring keeps block upright while allowing block to swivel and tilt.

Becket
Used to dead end a line on the block in multi-part systems.

Slide
Used where block is mounted on track for rapid fore and aft or athwartship adjustment.

Exit Block
Leads internal halyards or other lines out of mast, boom or spinnaker pole. Specify a plastic sheave for use with rope. For use with rope and wire combinations, specify a scored aluminum sheave.

Fairlead Block
For use with genoa sheets and halyards. Block is shown in use with genoa sheet and is mounted on a slide (block should be used in conjunction with a turning block in genoa sheet applications). When used for leading external halyards aft from the base of the mast, no slide is used.

Turning Block

Used for turning spinnaker sheets and jib sheets. When turning jib sheets the turning block should be used in conjunction with a fairlead block. Usually mounted near aft end of boat, along the rail.

Cheek Block

Used for turning sheets and halyards. Mounts on spar itself (mast or boom) or on deck, deckhouse or coaming. Specify a plastic sheave for use with rope. For use with rope and wire combinations, specify a scored aluminum sheave.

Fiddle Block

For use in multi-part systems such as mainsheets and boom vangs. Has two or more sheaves. Can be ordered with or without snap shackle or with an adapter for use on traveller systems.

Placement of the basic types of hardware are shown.
1. Stemhead Fitting
2. Stanchion
3. Fairlead Blocks
4. Exit Block
5. Halyard Block
6. Traveller Block
7. Track
8. Spinnaker Pole Slide
9. Genoa Slide
10. Jib Furling
11. Boom Bail
12. Cheek Block
13. Cleats
14. Turnbuckles
15. Snap Shackles (for movable tackle, spinnaker, halyards, etc.)
16. Topping Lift Block
17. Turning Block

Winches

A discussion of winches could be an endless topic, consequently I'll barely touch upon them. Barlow and Barient print beautiful catalogs with intricate explanations and recommendations. Secure one of each and memorize them if you like.

Meanwhile glance over the enclosed winch guide, see table 5, for comparisons of the "name" winches.

I have found through longish research that a 30-45 foot cruising boat can usually utilize single-speed Barlow #16 or equivalent for all

SPEED SELECTION	BARIENT	BARLOW	GIBB	LEWMAR	MERRIMAN
Singlespeed	—	—	—	#5	#8
	#9	#15	#571	—	—
	#10H	—	—	—	—
	#10	#16	#573	#8	#10
	#16	#20	—	—	#16
Geared Singlespeed	#20	—	#847	—	—
Two Speed	—	—	—	#10	—
	—	#18	#848	#16	—
	#21	#22	—	#25	#20
	—	#24	—	—	—
	#22	—	#809	#40	#22
	—	#26	—	—	#25
	#26	—	#1049	#43	—
	#28	#28	—	—	#28
	#30	#30	#810	—	—
	#32	#32	#1043	—	#32
	#35	#34	#808	—	—
	#35 special	#36	—	—	—
Three Speed	#28	—	—	#45	—
	#30	—	—	—	—
	#32	—	—	#55	—
	#34	—	—	—	—
	#35	—	—	—	—
	#35 special	—	—	#65	—
Halyard Winches	#1	#8	—	#3	—
	#2-A	#6	—	#3	—
	#2	—	—	—	—
	#3-A	#5	—	#2	—
	#3	#4	—	#1	—

Table 5 — Winch Size Comparison

halyards including the main if it does not exceed 450 sq. ft. If you like for a 400 sq. ft. main the use of Barlow #20 or equivalent is almost warranted.

Winches for "jiffy reefing" need not be larger than Barlow #15.

Sheet winches on a boat over 30 feet should be at least Barlow #24, etc. If head sails of any size, like a genoa or drifer-reacher, are to be used. Any smaller winch will only suffer under the great strain of head sails over 400 sq. ft. Overall stainless steel winches are the strongest and not expensive. Bronze winches are only slightly less strong and do look more traditional. Shop around, the mark-up is sizeable.

Stepping the Mast

Before the mast is stepped, a few items should be checked. After you have outfitted everything to your liking on deck, attach all your turnbuckles to chainplates and tangs. Be sure to put them all "right side up." Most things tighten clockwise and untighten anti-clockwise. This order is fairly common and it is a universal expectation. Problems in times of crises can be avoided if your turnbuckles are installed conformingly. Have all of your clevis pins in place and ring-a-dings dangling. Now attend to your mast. With a battery and a light, check all mast lights and all wires. Repair and adjustment is made much more easily standing on unmoving pavement than dangling from a bo'sun's chair.

Check all your fittings and tangs, and tighten your bolts. Make sure that nothing has wedged its way into and around your sail tracks. Use a stiff paint brush with the bristles cut down to ¾-inch lengths to clean out everything. Spin your masthead sheaves and listen for a grinding sound which could indicate sand or other impediments present.

Now feed through your halyards, attach your shrouds, and tie the whole thing to the mast with line. Do be sure that everything is secured and will not wobble, chafe, or destroy while the truck is taking the boat down for launching. A loose stainless steel shroud can easily crack mast lights, chafe paint, or even, in extreme cases (like a trip from Arizona to San Diego) chafe away a part of the aluminum mast.

When the boat is launched and the crane is dangling the mast over the deck, take all your neatly packed wires and feed them through a protruding and well sealed PVC tube, see photo 165, into the cabin down below. Don't miss any wires.

Once the mast is on the step, take your fore and aft lower shrouds and anchor them fast to their appropriate turnbuckles to moderate adjustment only, just to be sure that all four are providing support. The crane is now free to leave; the lowers will hold sufficiently while you attend to the rest of your stays. After everything is attached, tune your rig. Loosen all the shrouds, but do

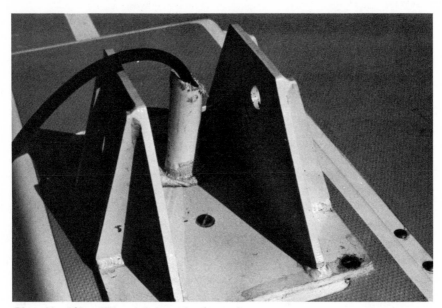

Photo No. 165 — Wires fed through tabernacle mast step.

not make them slack. Now set your forward and aft lower turn-buckles a few turns at a time. Shake each shroud heavily from time to time to see if they have equal amounts of "give."

If you have a bowsprit and/or boomkin, tighten your whisker stays first. These stays should be taut but not over-tightened to the point where they destroy the column of either boomkin or bowsprit. They must remain unbent. You can now adjust your forestay and backstay. The foremost point of reference for any adjustment is the mast step itself. Be sure that the mast sits squarely upon it. Gauge it all the way around to be sure that it is not squatting on its toe or heel or one side.

Tighten turnbuckles a little at a time, walking back and forth from one side to the other laying your face against the mast wall, looking up along it to make certain you're not "warping" the mast. It, as with the boomkin and bowsprit, must remain in column, unbent, and evenly supported. Do the same thing for your forestay and backstay and keep checking your mast. Once your shrouds are tight, calm yourself and don't tighten your turnbuckles anymore. With a large crescent wrench as an accomplice, you can easily overtighten the rigging and crack your deck with the tremendous compression of the shrouds.

Now walk about and check each turnbuckle extremely closely. You must have at least ⅓ of your threaded rod inside the barrel, but you must also have about ½ of the threaded rod on the outside. You will need, eventually, some space to tighten them. If any turnbuckle is closed tightly, call your rigger; your shroud is too long and it must be re-cut and re-swedged. If only the last few threads of your rod are inside the barrel, the shroud is much too short. Have it redone.

Make fast your halyards so that they won't fly away and tangle somewhere high in your rigging. Now step off the boat and back away. . . God what a beautiful sight. . . Mothers must feel ecstatic when they see their newborn. . . Don't back too far . . . beware of the short wharf.

RIGGING
IDEAS

The grandad of spinnaker-pole rigs.

Chafe guard on mooring line.

Rich man's chafe guard for genoas. Stainless steel tubing.

Belaying pins.

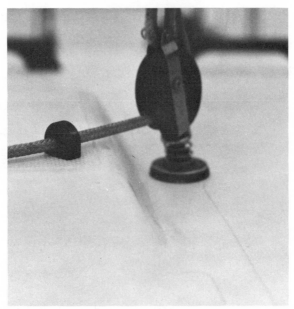

Turning block and bulls-eye fairlead.

Combination of deadeyes, lanyards, and turnbuckles.

appendix

MATERIALS & EQUIPMENT

FIBERGLASS

1. RESINS — POLYESTER

a. Laminating — basic resin for laminating hulls, decks, small parts and for bonding. Catalyze with MEK peroxide at ambient temp. of 77°F. 1.0% MEK will gel in 26 min. (1.0% = 38 c.c. per 1 gal.). A #10 can almost full is approximately ¾ gal. and needs about 30 c.c. of catalyst.

b. Surfacing — used for finish which can be sanded easily. Laminating resin cannot be sanded to give smooth surface. Surfacing agent added to laminating resin achieves same result.

2. GELCOAT

a. Mold — gelcoat sprayed 12-15 mils thick on hull, deck, parts. Thinned with 1:1 styrene/acetone for spraying consistency used for touchup of center line and imperfections. When used on exterior surfaces, must be sprayed with PVA.

b. Ramanel — air curing gelcoat used for boot stripe and sheer stripe.

3. MOLD RELEASES

a. Mold release wax — applied to mold surfaces to prevent adhesion of gelcoat to mold. Can be applied to any surface where easy removal of excess resin is required.

b. PVA — a liquid sprayed on mold surfaces to facilitate easy removal of molded part from mold. Must be sprayed over exterior gelcoat applications to obtain proper care.

4. CATALYSTS

MEK peroxide is the only commonly used catalyst. Must be thoroughly mixed with resin or gelcoat 5 c.c. to 70 or 80 c.c. per gallon of resin, depending on temperature and gel time required. Can be used with accelerators, such as DMA, if necessary *only* if mixed independently into resin. If catalyst and accelerator mixed together, a nice explosion will likely result.

5. SOLVENTS

a. Styrene — used to reduce viscosity of resin and gelcoat. Gelcoat may be thinned with a 1:1 styrene acetone mix at no more than 10% by weight.

b. Acetone — commonly used to clean brushes and other utensils and hands of resin. CAUTION: Acetone is highly flammable.

6. ASBESTOS MISH-MASH

a. A mixture of powdered asbestos and resin. Powdered asbestos is mixed with resin to the required consistency, either very thick, syrupy, or anywhere in between, depending on use. Thick mixtures are easier to use on vertical or near vertical surfaces. It is used to bond F/G to F/G or wood to F/G.

b. If very thick buildup is anticipated, chopped strand should be added to reduce cracking.

7. CABOSIL

A white powder mixed with resin to substantially thicken it to putty-like consistency. It can be mixed with a little gelcoat to fill hull or deck imperfections. As its main use is repair, surfacing agents should be added.

8. MICROBALLOONS

A lightweight red powder mixed with resin and used to fill voids in wood or fiberglass prior to laminating or bonding. Very easy to sand.

9. GLUES

a. Weldwood contact cement — or similar product — for cementing formica to table and counter tops. Strict adherence to container instructions is necessary.

b. Weldwood plastic resin glue — mixed according to container instructions. Used on all interior wood to wood joints. Should not be used on teak exterior joints. Wiping completed joints well with damp rag before glue sets minimizes clean up.

c. Weldwood Resorcinal plastic resin glue — must be mixed according to container instructions. Used on teak to teak exterior joints, and on submerged or continually wet wood joints. Care must be taken to avoid staining adjoining wood.

10. BEDDING & CAULKING COMPOUNDS

a. Dolfinite — all purpose bedding compound used on all fittings and wood parts fitted to deck or hull, such as teak decking to fiberglass, under cap rails and rub rails, under pintles and gudgeons, under deck hardware, etc. #2005 is the most common compound, 3905-TX is a fungicide compound for use where maximum resistance to rot and mildew is desired.

b. Boat Life — life caulk — available in three colors, black, white and mahogany. Black is used to caulk decks, seal bolts on gudgeons, bed shaft log and thru hull fittings. White Boat Life can be used where white color is desired. Both colors available in liquid form which is excellent for fixing leaks as it flows easily. When used on oily woods such as teak, Boat Life primer *must be* used to maximize adhesion. Boat Life needs about one week to cure.

c. Grove Specialties — Flo-Caulk — a two-part caulking compound used on decking. It cures in much shorter time (hours) than Boat Life. It also requires a primer on oily woods.

d. G.E. Silicone Seal — a white sealant with excellent bonding properties. Its quick curing time makes it useful for sealing cabinet to formica joints in galley where water seepage is a problem.

WOOD

a. Teak — deck — 200 B.F.
   Cabinsole (solid) — 60 B.F.
   Searails — (Interior trim) — 150 B.F.
   Caprails — 60 B.F.
   Rubrails — 20 B.F.
   Doors (solid + frames)
   Drawers } — 180 B.F.
   Trim
   Hatch Coamings } — 100 B.F.
   Hatches
   Plugs — Mahogany — 2000
   Plugs — Teak — 1400

b. Plywood
   ¾" — 12 sheets
   ½" — 25 sheets

c. Adhesives
   Resorcinal glue — 4 quarts
   Plastic resin glue — 25 lbs.
   White glue — 1 bottle
   Acrylic compound — 30 tubes

d. Caulking Compounds
   Polysulphide — seacocks — 25
                  other
   Dolphinite — caprails
                portlights
                other
   Silicone seal — above water — 10
   DECK — Polysulphide — 40 tubes
          2-part polysulphide — 3 gallons
          40 empty cartridges

e. Paint
Undercoat — Z-Spar 105 — 2 coats — 3 gallons
Inside cupboards only
Gloss — 2 gallons

f. Oil
Interior — 2 gallons
Exterior — 1 gallon

g. Varnish — 2 gallons

h. Acetone — 15 gallons

i. Paint thinner — 3 gallons

j. Resin — 25 gallons
Mat tape 6'' — 50 yards
Cloth tape 8'' — 50 yards

k. Catalyst — 1 quart

l. Resin brushes — 15

m. Plastic gloves — 20

n. Sandpaper
60 grit — 4 sleeves
100 grit — 2 sleeves
220 grit — 2 sleeves
400 grit — ½ sleeve

o. Paint remover — 1 can
Paint thinner — 3 gallons

FASTENERS

#10 x 1'' ss P.H.S.M. Screws — 2000
#10 x ¾'' ss, Pan Head, Sheet Metal Screw — 1000
#16 x 1¼'' ss P.H.S.M. Screw — 500
#10 x 1½'' ss P.H.S.M. Screw — 250
#10 x 2'' ss P.H.S.M. Screw — 50
#6 x ¾'' Brass Flat Head MS — 300
#8 x ¾'' Oval Head Wood Screws — 200
#8 x 1'' Oval Head Wood Screws — 100
#10 x 1'' ss F.H.S.M. Screws — 150
#10 x ¾'' ss F.H.S.M. Screws — 150
#8 x ¾'' ss F.H.S.M. Screws — 100
#8 x ½'' ss F.H.S.M. Screws — 100
#14 x 2'' ss P.H.S.M. Screws — 150
#14 x 1½'' ss P.H.S.M. Screws — 100

¼" x 1½" ss F.H. Machine Screws — 150
3/8" x 1" ss F.H. Machine Screws — 100
¼" ss Flat Washers, Lock Washers Hex nuts
3/8" ss Flat Washers, Lock Washers Hex nuts

ELECTRICAL

Battery Level Indicator
Battery Charger
Battery Switch — Perko 85A
Buss Bars
Cable Straps — Perko
Cable Outlet — Perko — 42Y Watertight
Circuit Breakers — 10A, 15A, 20A, 25A
Circuit Breaker Panel
Conduit 1" ID
Connector — Butt — 80
              Spade — 80
Duplex Receptacles & Cover
Fuse — one Time Buss Fuse 60 amp.
Lugs
Radio Coax
Shore Power Cord & Adapter
Terminal Junction Block — 4, 6, 8, 10 Post.
Toggle Switches
Wire Ties — "Tywrap" with and without Crew Eyes
WIRE
    4Ga Battery Cable
    10GA Black
    10GA Red
    14GA Black, Yellow, White, Blue, Green, Violet

PLUMBING

Bilge Pump — 1 Whole #10, 1 Whole #25, 1 Electric
Bilge Pump — Strainer — Wilcox
Bilge Pump — Switch
Bilge Pump — Thruhull
Head — Mansfield, Groco, Wilcox
Pump — Fresh & Salt
Sinks & Fittings
Tape — Mylar & Copper
Seacocks — 1½" x ¾"
Seacocks Tail pieces puc. (1 per seacock)
Throughull Fitting (Bronze, Plastic for cockpit)

Throughull Vents (Fuel)
Throuhull Deck Fittings
Hose Clamps #7, 8, 12, 16, 24, 28, 32, 36, 48
HOSE
    ½'' White Spinnaker Hose — Water — 100'
    3/8'' Clear Vinyl Tubing — Vents — 35'
    ¼'' ID Red Fuel Line Hose — Fuel — 25'
    1½'' ID Wire ins. Rubber Hose — Exhaust — 10'
    1¼'' Wire ins. Hose — Carlisle — Bilge Pump — 25'
1½'' Bronze Gate Valves — 1
¾'' Bronze Gate Valves — 3
Hose Barbs — Bronze & Nylon — 10 approx.
Elbows — Bronze & Nylon — 15 approx.
T's — Bronze & Nylon — 15 approx.
1½'' Bronze anti-Siphon Loop — 1
¾'' Bronze anti-Siphon Loop — 2
Hose Ties (tywrap)

TOOLS

Milling tools (power)
Table saw
Band saw
Planer
Router
Table sander

Milling tools (hand)
Chalk line
Scribe
Tape Measure
Square
Bevel Square
Pusher

Bonding tools and apparatus
Resin brushes
Milk jugs
Cardboard slabs
Squeegie
Rubber gloves

Construction (power)
¼'' drill motor
3/8'' variable speed drill motor

Saber saw
Belt sander
Disc sander
Vibrator sander

Construction (hand tools)

Level
Bevel square
Framing square
Scribe
Rasps (shoe, round bastard file)
Chisels (¼'' to 1'')
Hole saws (for drill motor)
Hand saw
Dovetail saw
Hack saw
Drill bits (tapered)
Countersinks (Fuller)
Hand drill
Hammer (claw
Hammer (machine)
Mallot
Center punch
Countersink (for rail heads)
Acid brushes
Glue cups
Caulking gun
Screw gun bit
Screwdrivers
Pliers
Crescent wrench
Vice grip
Wire strippers and crimp
Hand plane
Sur-Form
Pencils

Finishing

Vibrator sander
Sandpapers
Matte knife
RAGS

• MARINE EYE

WIRE SIZE	1/16	3/32	1/8	5/32	3/16	7/32	1/4	9/32	5/16	3/8	7/16	1/2
PIN SIZE	1/4	1/4	1/4	5/16	5/16	7/16	1/2	1/2	5/8	5/8	3/4	7/8

• THREADED TERMINAL

Wire Size	1/16	3/32	1/8	5/32	3/16	7/32	1/4	9/32	5/16
Thread Size	6-40	10-32	1/4-28	1/4-28	5/16-24	3/8-24	3/8-24	7/16-20	1/2-20
Thread Length	1	1-3/16	1-3/8	1-3/8	1-7/16	1-5/8	1-3/4	1-7/8	2″

(Specify RH or LH for right or left hand threads)

RIGGING DATA

- WIRE SPLICE EYE

- NICO PRESS EYE

Specify with or without thimble.
Specify loop size if without thimble.

- WIRE TO ROPE SPLICE

Wire to rope splices are available with
1 x 19 cable and Yacht Braid only.

Recommended sizes: 1/8″ wire to 3/8″ Yacht Braid
3/16″ wire to 7/16″ Yacht Braid
7/32″ wire to 7/16″ Yacht Braid
1/4″   wire to 1/2″   Yacht Braid
5/16″ wire to 5/8″   Yacht Braid

RIGGING DATA

• FORK

CABLE SIZE		1/16	3/32	1/8	5/32	3/16	7/32	1/4	9/32	5/16
PIN SIZE	DIA.	3/16	3/16	3/16	1/4	5/16	5/16	3/8	7/16	7/16
	GRIP	1/4	3/8	1/2	1/2	9/16	11/16	3/4	3/4	13/16

• EYE

CABLE SIZE	1/16	3/32	1/8	5/32	3/16	7/32	1/4	9/32	5/16
PIN SIZE	3/16	3/16	3/16	1/4	5/16	5/16	3/8	7/16	7/16

RIGGING DATA

APPENDIX

AVAILABLE DIESEL ENGINES FOR 25'-45' SAILBOATS

The following section contains specifications on some better known and time tested marine diesels. For options lists and further information, consult manufacturers or distributors.

BOTA 17 HP

These basic diesel engines are produced by KUBOTA, Ltd./ Japan, Asia's largest manufacturer of engines and farm tractors, with over 500 diesel tractor dealers in the U.S.

Specifications:

Model BOTA-750M
Type ....4 cycle, water cooled diesel engine
Number of cylinders 2
Cylinder bore x stroke ....3.00 in. x 3.23 in. (76mm x 82mm)
Total displacement ....45.3 cu. in. (743cc)
Combustion chamber type ....Spherical combustion chamber
Injection order 1-2
Compression ratio 21:1
Direction of revolution ....Counterclockwise, seen from fly
Measurements bobtailed ....20.30 in. x 18.07 in. x 23.47 in.
  (length x width x height)   (515.6mm x 458.75mm x 595.7mm)
Net weight bobtailed ....295 lbs. approximately
Fuel ....Diesel Fuel No. 2
Fuel injection pump ....Bosch "K" type mini-pump
Governor ....All speed mechanical control type
Starter 12v, 0.8kw
Generator ....12v, 120w (AC)
Lubrication oil ....DM grade
Lubrication oil capacity ....0.92 gal. (3.5 liter)
Cooling water capacity ....0.53 gal. (2 liter)
  Paragon SAO Vee-Drive, 1:1, 1.29:1, 1.67:1, and 2:1; weight 95 lbs. Paragon SAO 1:1, weight 55 lbs. or 2:1, weight 80 lbs. Paragon SSL 2:1 or 1.3:1, weight 25 lbs.

BOTA 17 HP

General Propulsion's marine execution of these diesel engines incorporates the following American manufactured equipment:
  "Motorola" alternators and tachometers.
  "Pincor" lightplant generators.
  "Stewart-Warner" instruments and fuel pumps.

"Morse" throttle and shift controls.

"Fram" diesel fuel filters and lube oil filters.

"Gates" belts, hoses, and pulleys.

"Warner" hydraulic marine transmissions, Vee-drives, oil coolers, and dampers.

"Walters" Vee-drives and off-set transmissions.

"Paragon" manual and hydraulic transmissions.

"Snow-Nabstedt" marine transmissions.

"San Juan" heat exchangers and thermostats.

"Jabsco" raw water pumps.

"Bushings" flexible and adjustable marine mounts.

"Vickers" hydraulic pumps.

"General Propulsion" marine water cooled exhaust manifolds, expansion tanks, bellhousings, flywheel adapters, marine engine supports, and mounting brackets.

Paragon SAO Vee-
Drive, 1:1, 1.29:1,
1.67:1, and 2:1
Weight 95 lbs.
Paragon SAO 1:1
Wt. 55 lbs. or 2:1
Weight 80 lbs.
Paragon SSL 2:1
or 1.3:1
Weight 25 lbs.

Gross b.h.p.
17 /2,800
16.3/2,600
15.4/2,400
14.4/2,200
13.4/2,000
12.2/1,800
10.9/1,600
9.4/1,400

BOTA 24 HP

These basic diesel engines are produced by KUBOTA, Ltd./ Japan, Asia's largest manufacturer of engines and farm tractors, with over 500 diesel tractor dealers in the U.S.

Specifications:
Model BOTA-1100M
Type .... 4 cycle, water cooled diesel engine
Number of cylinders 3
Cylinder bore x stroke .... 3.00 in. x 3.23 in. (76mm x 82mm)
Total displacement .... 68.04 cu. in. (1.115 cc)
Combustion chamber type .... Spherical combustion chamber
Compression ratio 21:1
Injection order 1-2-3
Direction of revolution .... Counterclockwise, seen from fly
Measurements bobtailed .... 24.00 in. x 18.07 in. x 23.47 in.
  (length x width x height)   (610mm x 458.75mm x 595.7mm)
Net weight bobtailed .... 360 lbs. approximately
Fuel .... Diesel Fuel No. 2
Fuel injection pump .... Bosch "K" type mini-pump
Governor .... All speed mechanical control type
Starter 12v, 1.0kw
Generator .... 12v, 120w (AC)
Lubrication oil .... DM grade
Lubrication oil capacity .... 1.4 gal. (5.3 liter)
Cooling water capacity .... 0.92 gal. (3.5 liter)
  Paragon SAO 1:1, weight 55 lbs. or 2:1, weight 80 lbs.

BOTA 24 HP

General Propulsion's marine execution of these diesel engines incorporates the following American manufactured equipment:
  "Motorola" alternators and tachometers.
  "Pincor" lightplant generators.
  "Stewart-Warner" instruments and fuel pumps.
  "Morse" throttle and shift controls.
  "Fram" diesel fuel filters and lube oil filters.
  "Gates" belts, hoses and pulleys.
  "Warner" hydraulic marine transmissions, Vee-drives, oil coolers, and dampers.
  "Walters" Vee-drives and off-set transmissions.
  "Paragon" manual and hydraulic transmissions.

"Snow-Nabstedt" marine transmissions.

"San Juan" heat exchangers and thermostats.

"Jabsco" raw water pumps.

"Bushings" flexible and adjustable marine mounts.

"Vickers" hydraulic pumps.

"General Propulsion" marine water cooled exhaust manifolds, expansion tanks, bellhousings, flywheel adapters, marine engine supports, and mounting brackets.

Paragon SAO 1:1
Weight 55 lbs.
or 2:1
Weight 80 lbs.

Gross b.h.p.
25.5/2,800
24.7/2,600
23.6/2,400
22.1/2,200
20.4/2,000
18.4/1,800
16.6/1,600
14.5/1,400

FARYMANN DIESELS

FARYMANN A 30 M

Standard Equipment:

Vertical one-cylinder four cycle marine diesel. Direct injection. Thermostat controlled seawater cooling. Reverse gearbox, reduction 2:1. Specially tuned 2-point flexible marine mounts. Flywheel and rim gear fully enclosed. Service points and accessories at front end of engine for ease of service and maintenance. Engine in running condition including self-priming waterpump and thermostat. Fuel filter. Rimgear on flywheel. Reverse reduction gearbox. Fuel transfer pump. 2-point flexible mounts with ready-to-install bearers. Tool kit. Starting handle. Maintenance manual and parts list.

Optional Equipment:

Electric starter motor 12V and marine alternator 420 watts. Panel with wiring harness. Exhaust elbow with water injection. Remote control for engine and gearbox. Complete water intake and exhaust kits including hull fittings, hoses, seawater strainer, and waterlift silencer respectively. Flexible shaft coupling, etc.

FARYMANN DIESEL A 30 M

Specifications and Data:

Continuous shaft output . . . . .12 hp
Cubic displacement . . . . .582 cm^3
Engine speed . . . . .2500 rpm
Engine type . . . . A 30/watercooled
Number of cylinders 1/vertical
Combustion system . . . . .4-cycle direct injection
Valves . . . . .Overhead
Output (continuous) . . . . .12 hp SAE (8,8 kw)
10 PS DIN (7,36 kw)
Engine speed (cont.) . . . . .2,500 rpm
Maximum torque . . . . .2,9 mkp (21 ft. lb.)
Bore . . . . .95mm (3,74 in.)
Stroke . . . . .82mm (3,2 in.)
Cubic capacity . . . . .582 cm^3 (35 cu. in.)
Dry weight including gearbox, elect.-start,
   flexible mounts . . . . .144 kp (317 lbs.)
Install. angle . . . . .15° (27%)

Sump capacity . . . . .2,25 liters
Fuel consumption . . . . .1,9 liters/h (full load)
Reverse gearbox . . . . .Reduction 2:1
Propeller rotation . . . . .Clockwise

	B	D	E	F	G	H	K	L	M	N	O	S	U	W
mm	480	140	392	215	58	470	22	711	108	45	75	180	155	77,5
inch.	18,89	5,51	15,43	8,46	2,28	18,5	0,86	28,00	4,25	1,79	2,95	7,00	6,10	3,00

FARYMANN R 30 M

Standard Equipment:

Two cylinder four cycle marine diesel in V-configuration. Direct injection. Thermostat controlled seawater cooling. Reverse gearbox, reduction 2:1. Specially tuned 2-point flexible marine mounts. Flywheel and rimgear fully enclosed. All service points at front end for easy maintenance. Engine in running condition including self-priming waterpump and thermostat. Oil-cooler. Fuel filter. Rimgear on flywheel. Watercooled exhaust manifold. Fuel transfer pump. 2-point flexible mounts with ready-to-install bearers. Tool kit. Starting handle. Maintenance manual and parts list.

Optional Equipment:

Electric starter motor 12V and marine alternator 420 watts. Panel with wiring harness. Exhaust elbow with water injection. Remote control for engine and gearbox. Complete water intake and exhaust kits including hull fittings, hoses, seawater strainer, and waterlift silencer respectively. Flexible shaft coupling, etc.

FARYMANN DIESEL R 30 M

Specifications and Data:

Continuous shaft output . . . . .24 hp
Cubic displacement . . . . .1170 cm^3
Engine speed . . . . : . . . . .2500 rpm
Engine type . . . . .R 30/watercooled
Number of cylinders 2/V-configuration
Combustion system . . . . .4-cycle direct injection
Valves . . . . .Overhead
Output (continuous) . . . . .24 hp (SAE)
20 PS (DIN 6270)
Engine speed (cont.) . . . . .2500 rpm
Maximum torque . . . . .5,7 mkp/2000 rpm, 42 ft. lb.
Bore . . . . .95mm (3,74 in)
Stroke . . . . .82mm (3,2 in.)
Cubic capacity . . . . .1170 cm^3 (71 cu. in.)
Weight dry, including gearbox, elect.-start,
flexible mounts . . . . .205 kp (451 lb.)
Sump capacity . . . . .2,3 liter
Maximum angle . . . . .15° (27%)
Fuel consumption . . . . .2,3 liter/h (full load)
Reverse gearbox . . . . .Reduction 2:1

Upon request: B1 = 555 mm (21,8")

	B	B1	D	E	F	G	H	U	K	L	M	N	O	P	S	W
mm	570	630	146	443	255	60	400	178	18	816	110	45	85	11	220	77,5
inch	22,4	24,8	5,7	17,44	10,04	2,35	15,74	7,01	0,70	32,13	4,33	1,79	3,35	0,43	8,66	3,05

FARYMANN K 30 M

Standard Equipment:
Engine ready for operation including reverse reduction gearbox. Cooling water pump and thermostat. Fuel filter and transfer pump. Rimgear on flywheel. Flexible mounts complete with engine bearers. Tool kit, sump drain pump, manual and parts list.

Optional Equipment:
Electric starter with 90 watt generator or 420 watt alternator. Two or single lever remote control. Panel with wiring harness. Flexible shaft coupling. Exhaust bend with water injection. Complete kits for water intake and exhaust system including hoses, hull fittings, seawater strainer and waterlift silencer respectively, etc.

FARYMANN K 30 M

Single cylinder four cycle marine diesel engine in vertical configuration. Direct injection. Thermostat controlled seawater cooling. Easy-shift reverse gearbox, reduction 2:1. Specially tuned 2-point flexible mounts. All service points at front end.

Specifications:

Engine type	K 30/watercooled
Number of cylinders	1/vertical
Combustion system	4-cycle direct injection
Valves	Overhead
Output (continuous)	6 hp (SAE)
	5 PS (DIN 6270)
Engine speed (cont.)	2500 rpm
Maximum torque	1,5 mkp/2000 rpm — 11 ft. lb.
Bore	68mm (2,7 in.)
Stroke	82mm (3,2 in.)
Cubic capacity	298 cm³ (18,2 cu. in.)
Weight dry, including gearbox, elect.-start, flexible mounts	96 kp (211 lb.)
Maximum angle	15° (27%)
Sump capacity	1,4 liter
Fuel consumption	0,9 liter/h (full load)
Reverse gearbox	Reduction 2:1

P.T.O. flange

	B	D	E	F	G	H	K	L	M	N	O	S	U	W
mm	460	15	305	201	60	442	9	622	103	33	50	170	175	78
inch.	18,11	0,59	12,01	7,91	2,36	17,40	0,35	24,49	4,06	1,30	1,97	6,69	6,89	3,07

PERKINS 4.108 M

Specifications:

Maximum brake horsepower . . . . .50 at 4000 rpm
Engine type . . . . .4 In-Line
Displacement . . . . .107.0 cu. in.
Bore/Stroke . . . . .3.125 x 3.5 in.
Operating cycle 4
Compression ratio 22:1
Firing order 1-3-4-2
Bobtail . . . . .490 lbs.
With reduction gear . . . . .624 lbs.
Installation angle . . . . .0° to 17°

Engine Features:

Cylinder block. High strength cast iron.

Cylinder liners. Cast iron, dry type, press fit easily replaceable.

Cylinder head. High strength cast iron alloy, dual valve springs standard.

Combustion chamber. Perkins "H" pre-combustion system insures clean burning and excellent fuel economy throughout wide operating range.

Crankshaft. Forged chrome-molybdenum steel, case hardened journals statically and dynamically balanced.

Main bearings. Three main bearings, pre-fit precision replaceable type, thin-walled, steel backed aluminum tin lined.

Pistons and rings. Silicon aluminum alloy piston for high strength, lightweight, good heat conductivity, three compression and two oil control rings.

Connecting rods. Molybdenum alloy steel with high strength "H" section shank. Rod bearing cap includes positive locating machined serrations. Piston pin bearing — replaceable steel backed lead/bronze lined precision bushing.

Valves. Intake valves are chromium steel, exhaust valves are silicon-chromium steel.

Camshaft. High strength cast iron, case hardened.

Intake manifold. Aluminum alloy casting dry bronze gauze air filter incorporating closed ventilation system.

Exhaust manifold. Fresh water cooled, corrosion resistant aluminum alloy.

Fuel system. Rotary distributor type fuel injection pump provides even fuel distribution to all cylinders for smooth performance from idle to full power. Automatic advance and retard mechanism insures fast starting and quick acceleration through speed range.

Injectors easily accessible on cylinder head for ease of maintenance.

Lubricating system. Engine lubrication full pressure feed, rotor pump driven. Control valve in pump body maintains maximum pressure.

Cooling system. Heat exchanger, thermostatically controlled, fresh and raw water pumps engine-mounted.

Electrical equipment. 12 volt, 42 amp alternator and 12 volt Delco starter standard equipment.

Tachometer drive. Standard, angle drive, SAE.

Engine mounts. Rubber: standard 18 inch centers.

PERFORMANCE CURVE:

Curve indicates horsepower ratings at 30.00 inches of mercury barometric pressure and 60° Fahrenheit air temperature.

Optional Equipment:

Front power take-off. 1½ inch diameter x 1-7/8 inch extension shaft bolted to steel serrated crankshaft pulley, allowing accessory drives to 20 lb. ft. torque.

Marine gears. Hydraulic — Warner 70 CR type, Paragon, manual.

Marine gear reductions. Up to 3:1 ratio.

R.H. rotation. Warner 1:91 ratio or as available from other manufacturers.

Electric tachometer. Alternator powered.

Alternator. 12 volt, 60 amp Delco.

MODEL 71
WARNER "V" DRIVE

PERKINS 4.236 M

Specifications:

Maximum brake horsepower .85 at 2500 rpm
Engine type . . . . .4 In-Line
Displacement . . . . .235.9 cu. in.
Bore/Stroke . . . . .3.875 x 5.0 in.
Operating cycle 4
Compression ratio 16.0:1
Firing order 1-3-4-2
Bobtail . . . . .840 lbs.
With reduction gear . . . . .1,026 lbs.
With Mod. 80 outdrive . . . . .1,068 lbs.
With Mod. 81 outdrive . . . . .1,213 lbs.
Installation angle . . . . .0° to 12°

Design Features:

Cylinder block. High strength cast iron; cylinder block extends below crankshaft center line for additional rigidity.

Cylinder liners. Cast iron, dry type, press fit, easily replaceable.

Cylinder head. High strength cast iron alloy, cadmium plated valve springs standard.

Combustion chamber. Direct injection into toroidal chamber in piston crown insures fast starting and maximum fuel economy.

Crankshaft. Forged chrome molybdenum steel, case-hardened, statically and dynamically balanced.

Main bearings. Five bearings, pre-fit replaceable precision type, thin-walled, steel backed, aluminum tin lined.

Pistons and rings. Silicon aluminum alloy piston for high strength, lightweight, good heat conductivity; three compression and two oil control rings.

Connecting rods. Molybdenum alloy with "H" section shank; fitted with precision type aluminum tin lined "big end" bearings and lead/bronze replaceable "small end" bushings; full floating piston pin.

Valves. Intake valves are high silichrome steel. Exhaust valves are stellite-faced for longer life.

Camshaft. High strength cast iron, case-hardened.

Intake manifold. Aluminum alloy casting; dry bronze gauze air filter mounted on manifold intake incorporating closed ventilation system.

Exhaust manifold. Heavy-duty, cast iron, water jacketed.

Fuel system. Rotary distributor type, fuel injection pump provides even fuel distribution to all cylinders for smooth performance from idle to full power. Automatic advance and retard mechanism insures fast starting and quiet running through speed range. Injectors accessible on cylinder head for ease of maintenance.

Lubricating system. Engine lubrication full pressure feed, rotor pump driven. Control valve in pump body maintains maximum pressure.

Cooling system. Heat exchanger, thermostatically controlled. Fresh and raw water pump engine-mounted.

PERFORMANCE CURVE:

Curve indicates horsepower ratings at 30.00 inches of mercury barometric pressure and 60° Fahrenheit air temperature.

Electrical equipment. 12 volt, 42 amp alternator standard equipment. 12 volt Delco starter standard equipment.

Tachometer drive adaptor. Standard, angle drive, SAE.

Engine mounts. Rubber; standard 22½-inch centers.

Optional Accessories:

Front power takeoff. 2 inch diameter x 3½-inch extension shaft bolted to steel serrated crankshaft pulley, allowing accessory drives up to 175 lbs. ft. torque.

Marine gears. Hydraulic — Warner 71 CR type, Pleasure Craft 72 CR Work Boat.

Marine gear reduction. Pleasure boats up to 3:1 ratio.

R.H. rotation. Warner 1.91:1 ratio, or as available from other manufacturers.

Electric tachometer. Alternator powered.

Alternator. 12 volt, 60 amp Delco.

Inboard/Outboard drive reductions. 1.3:1, 1.6:1 for 14½ and 17'' props.

MODEL 80 OUTDRIVE

PERKINS 4.154 M

Specifications:

Maximum brake horsepower . . . . .62 at 3000 rpm
Engine type . . . . .4 In-Line
Displacement . . . . .153.9 cu. in.
Bore/Stroke . . . . .3.5 x 4.0 in.
Operating cycle 4
Compression ratio 21.5
Firing order 1-3-4-2
Bobtail (dry) . . . . .668 lbs.
With reduction gear (dry) . . . . .830 lbs.
Installation angle . . . . .0° to 10°

Engine Features:

Cylinder block. High strength cast iron.

Cylinder liners. Cast iron, dry type, press fit, easily replaceable.

Cylinder head. High strength cast iron alloy, ''cross-flow'' design. Cadmium plated valve springs standard.

Combustion chamber. Perkins ''H'' pre-combustion system insures clean burning and excellent fuel economy throughout wide operating range.

Crankshaft. Forged chrome molybdenum steel, induction hardened, statically and dynamically balanced.

Main bearings. Five bearings, pre-fit replaceable precision type, thin-walled steel, aluminum tin lined.

Piston and rings. Silicon aluminum alloy piston for high strength, lightweight, good heat conductivity; three compression and two oil control rings.

Connecting rods. Molybdenum alloy with ''H'' section shank; fitted with precision type aluminum tin lined ''big end'' bearings and lead/bronze replaceable ''small end'' bushings; full floating piston pin.

Valves. Intake valves chromium steel. Exhaust valves, composite steels.

Camshaft. High strength cast iron, case-hardened.

Cooling system. Combined corrosion-resistant aluminum alloy header tank/exhaust manifold with serviceable copper alloy heat exchanger. Engine coolant thermostatically controlled. Fresh and raw water pumps engine mounted and belt driven. Fresh water cooled dual lubricating and gearbox oil cooler.

Fuel system. Rotary distributor type, fuel injection pump provides even fuel distribution to all cylinders for smooth perform-

ance from idle to full power. Automatic advance and retard mechanism insures fast starting and quiet running through speed range. Injectors accessible on cylinder head for ease of maintenance.

PERFORMANCE CURVE:

Curve indicates horsepower ratings at 30.00 inches of mercury barometric pressure and 60°F air temperature.

Lubricating system. Engine lubrication full pressure feed, rotor pump driven. Control valve in pump body maintains maximum pressure. Spin-on filter.

Electrical equipment. 12 volts, 42 amp Delco integral regulator alternator standard. Delco 12 volt starter. Engine mounted harness.

Front P.T.O. stub shaft. 1.50 diameter, 2.00 long standard allowing up to 30 lbs. ft. torque.

Engine mounts. Rubber; standard 22½-inch centers.

Optional Equipment:
Engine shutdown. Electric solenoid actuated.

APPENDIX

Alternator. 12 volt, 60 amp Delco integral regulator.

Electric tachometer. Alternator actuated.

Tachometer angle drive. Will accept .093 square drive 1:1 ratio.

Instrumentation. Plug in panel.

Marine gears. Warner type 71C hydraulic drop center R.H. and L.H. rotation with ratios up to 3:1.

**MODEL 71
WARNER "V" DRIVE**

PISCES DIESEL

A unique fresh water cooling system circulates only anti-freeze through the engine block and cylinder head. Cooling raw water enters only the oil cooler and heat exchanger, both constructed of corrosion resistant copper. To assure a good start, even in the foulest weather, preheating glow plugs are a standard feature.

All three PISCES, the two, three and four cylinder diesels were designed to use interchangeable parts, increasing serviceability and reducing cost.

Standard Features for All Models:

Thermostatically-controlled fresh water cooling system insures optimum operating temperatures, smoke-free operation, and prolongs engine life.

Pressure lubrication system with full-flow spin-on oil filter for ease of replacement and protection of your engine.

Piston-type full injection pump with low pressure feed pump and hand priming feature.

Transmission with 2:1 reduction-reverse ratio.

Adjustable rubber engine mountings.

Pre-wired instrument panel with tachometer, water temperature gauge, amp and oil pressure warning lights, and key switch.

35 amp alternator with integral regulator.

Engine wiring harness for ease of installation.

Zinc anodes in both fresh water and raw water systems to guard against electrolysis.

Engine glow plugs for quick cold starting.

Fuel filter with replaceable element.

Throttle and shift connection brackets.

Engine lifting rings.

Raw water pump with neoprene impeller.

Water by-pass connections for hot water heater or water maker.

PISCES 60

Specifications:

Model . . . . Pisces 60
Engine type . . . . 4-cycle, fresh water cooled, overhead valve, in-line
Engine performance
   With transmission, 35 amp alternator, sea-water pump
   Governed maximum output . . . . 60 hp/3000 rpm
Maximum torque . . . . . . 98.3 ft./lb./2000 rpm (13.6m-kg/2000 rpm)

Number of cylinders 4
Firing order 1-3-4-2
Bore and Stroke ....3.39 x 4.02 in. (86 x 102mm)
Piston displacement ....144.2 cu. in. (2369cc)
Compression ratio 20:1
Fuel injection pump ....Bosch type, in-line
Fuel ....Amber No. 2
Governor ....Mechanical, all speed controlled
Alternator ....35 amp, 12 volt
Starter motor ....3.0 hp (2.2kw), 12 volt
Lubrication oil capacity ....5.8 quarts, series 3
Coolant capacity ....8 quarts, 50% anti-freeze
Wet weight
  Bobtail ....563 lbs.
  With 2:1 transmission ....605 lbs.
Maximum inclination ....15°
Transmission ....2:1 reduction-reverse
Propeller rotation ....Right hand*
*Will change with transmission option.

PISCES 60

PISCES 40

Specifications:

Model . . . . Pisces 40
Engine type . . . . 4-cycle, fresh water cooled, overhead valve, in-line
    Engine performance
    With transmission, 35 amp alternator, sea-water pump
    Governed maximum output . . . . 40 hp/2800 rpm
Maximum torque . . . . . 75.9 ft./lbs./2000 rpm (10.5m-kg/2000 rpm)
Number of cylinders 3
Firing order 1-3-2
Bore and Stroke . . . . .3.39 x 4.02 in. (86 x 102mm)
Piston displacement . . . . .108.5 cu. in. (1777cc)
Compression ratio 20:1
Fuel injection pump . . . . .Bosch type, in-line
Fuel . . . . .Amber No. 2
Governor . . . . Mechanical, all speed controlled
Alternator . . . . : . . . . .35 amp, 12 volt
Starter motor . . . . .2.4 hp (1.8kw), 12 volt
Lubrication oil capacity . . . . .5 quarts, series 3

                        APPENDIX

Coolant capacity .... 7 quarts, 50% anti-freeze
Wet weight
  Bobtail .... 549 lbs.
  With 2:1 transmission .... 591 lbs.
Maximum inclination .... 15°
Transmission .... 2:1 reduction-reverse
Propeller rotation .... Right hand*
*Will change with transmission option.

PISCES 27

Specifications:

Model . . . . Pisces 27
Engine type . . . . 4-cycle, fresh water cooled, overhead valve, in-line
Engine performance
   With transmission, 35 amp alternator, sea-water pump
   Governed maximum output . . . . 27 hp/2800 rpm
Maximum torque . . . . 51.6 ft./lb./2000 rpm (7.0m-kg)
Number of cylinders 2
Firing order 1-2
Bore and Stroke . . . . 3.39 x 4.03 in. (86 x 102mm)
Piston displacement . . . . 72.3 cu. in. (1184cc)
Compression ratio 20:1
Fuel injection pump . . . . Bosch type, in-line
Fuel . . . . Amber No. 2
Governor . . . . Mechanical, all speed controlled
Alternator . . . . 35 amp, 12 volt

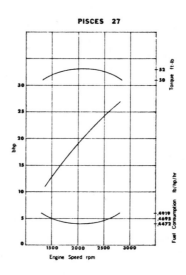

PISCES 27

Starter motor ....1.6 hp (1.2kw), 12 volt
Lubrication oil capacity ....3.5 quarts, series 3
Coolant capacity ....5 quarts, 50% anti-freeze
Wet weight
    Bobtail ....439 lbs.
    With 2:1 transmission ....477 lbs.
Maximum inclination ....15°
Transmission ....2:1 reduction-reverse
Propeller rotation ....Right hand*
*Will change with transmission option.

VOLVO MD2B

Volvo Penta MD2B is a 2-cylinder, 4-stroke marine diesel engine with direct injection. The exceptionally compact outer dimensions and the considerably powerful propeller thrust make the engine specially suitable for installation in small fishing boats, work boats, pleasure boats and as an auxiliary unit in sailing craft.

MD2B is a further development of the well-known MD2 engine. It has many components in common with MD1B and MD3B, which gives special advantages from the viewpoint of service and parts supply.

Direct injection ensures immediate starting on diesel fuel oil without any preheating, for example, with glow plugs.

The MD2B is very economical. To a great extent this is due to the effective design of the combusion chamber and also to the fact that the fuel injection pump is fitted with a centrifugal-type governor, which always supplies the engine with the correct fuel quantity for the varying loads and speeds.

MD2B is delivered with the easy operating ''Mono-Shift'' reverse gear which requires specially small forces.

The reverse gear is built on the cone clutch in the well-known aquamatic drives. Both speed and reverse gear are operated with the same control lever e.g. ''fingertip control.''

The engine is supplied with the following alternative equipment:

1. With manual start and reduction/reverse gear type RB ratio 1.87:1.

2. With starter-generator and reduction/reverse gear type RB ratio 1.87:1.

3. With starter motor, alternator and reduction/reverse gear type MS ratio 1.91:1.

4. With starter generator and reduction/reverse gear type RB ratio 3.42:1.

Specifications:

Operation .... 4-stroke diesel with direct injection
Continuous output, hp (DIN[1]) at rpm 25/2500
Maximum torque kpm (lb.ft.)/rpm .... 7.2 (52)/2000
Bore, mm (in.) 88.9 (3.5)
Stroke, mm (in.) 90 (3.54)
Capacity, cm[3] (cu. in.) 1120 (68.4)
Valves .... Overhead
Compression ratio 17.5:1

Maximum inclination while running ....15°
Net weight, including reduction/reverse gear,
    approx. kg (lb.) 220 (485)

DIMENSION DRAWINGS (engine with reduction/reverse gear
A = RB; B = MS)

ENGINE DIAGRAM

VOLVO MD6A

Volvo Penta MD6A is a new compact marine diesel engine which is ideal from an installation and servicing point of view. The compact outer dimensions make the engine specially suitable as an auxiliary unit in medium size sailing crafts and for installation in small pleasure and work boats of the displacement type.

The two-cylinder four-stroke engine is fully balanced dynamically and this ensures smooth and vibration-free running. The MD6 has direct injection, which makes for good cold starting and low fuel consumption — at full output it uses up only about 2 quarts of fuel per hour of operation.

The compact reverse gear type Mono Shift is designed on the well-known cone clutch in the Aquamatic drive and is particularly easy to maneuver. All operation of both the engine speed and reverse gear is done with a single control lever.

The engine is supplied with the following alternative equipment:

1. With starter-generator and reverse gear type MS, ratio 1:1.

2. With starter-generator and reduction-reverse gear type MS, ratio 1.91:1.

3. With starter-generator and reversing mechanism type Combi, ratio 1.42:1, complete with propeller equipment and 2-blade, adjustable propeller.

Other technical advantages which are characteristic for the Volvo Penta MD6:

Injection pump of rotor type with hydraulic governor for particularly accurate speed control.

Feed pump with hand primer for fuel and with effective fuel filter.

Automatic cold starting — makes starting easier in cold weather.

Decompression device and recess for starting crank at front facilitate manual starting.

Effective lubricating oil filter of the so-called "Spin-On" type — easy to change.

Thermostat-controlled, sea-water cooling system means that the engine runs at its most favorable operating temperature. Easily accessible sea-water pump with impeller made of neoprene rubber.

Effective intake silencer and particularly good balancing — gives us an engine with quiet and smooth operation.

Special, marine type electrical system, complete instrument panel, starter-generator 135 W maximum output and 1 hp starter motor output. A 12 V — 28 A (450 W) alternator can be fitted as extra equipment.

VOLVO MD6A

Specifications:

Operation . . . . .4-stroke diesel with direct injection
Continuous output, hp (DIN[1]) at rpm 10/2400
Maximum torque, kpm (lb.ft.)/rpm . . . . .3.1 (22.4)/1900
Number of cylinders 2
Bore, mm (in.) 70.0 (2.75)
Stroke, mm (in.) 82.0 (3.23)
Capacity, cm^3 (cu.in) 631 (38.5)
Valves . . . . .Overhead
Maximum inclination while running . . . . .15°
Net weight, including MS reverse gear,
    ratio 1,91:1, approx. kg (lb.) 170 (375)
[1] Output acc. to DIN 6270 Dauerleistung B

VOLVO MD21A

The MD21A is one of the most modern diesel engines on the market and provides an outstandingly advantageous combination of low weight, high output and good running economy.

Because of its high output — 75 hp SAE at 4500 rpm — in relation to its low weight, the MD21A is equally suitable for lightweight planing boats as it is for boats of the displacement type. Its low consumption of diesel fuel means that the MD21A is a particularly economical engine, especially for use in boats which are in constant use during the season or work boats. In relation to its output, the MD21A is one of the absolutely lightest and most compact marine diesel units on the market. Its compact design means that the MD21A is suitable even in confined space.

Other advantages provided by this engine include:

Five-bearing crankshaft, guaranteeing a long lifetime and vibration-free running.

Thermostat-controlled fresh-water cooling. Fully water-cooled exhaust manifold ports and water-cooled exhaust elbow.

Fuel injection pump of the distributor type fitted with a mechanical governor and a separate feed pump. Ricardo swirl-type combustion chambers and glow plugs.

Easily cleaned oil cooler. Full-flow lubricating oil filter of spin-on type.

12 V electrical equipment with 240 W generator (maximum 360 W) and a 1.8 hp starter motor.

All the electric cables are collected in one single harness between the engine and the instrument panel — this facilitates installation considerably.

The MD21A is supplied with the patented Volvo Penta reduction/reverse gear, ratio 1.91:1 or a hydraulically operated reverse/reduction gear of the Borg Warner Velvet Drive type with ratio 1.91:1 (right hand rotaion) and 2.1:1 or 2.91:1 (left hand rotation).

Instrument panel with electric revolution counter, electric temperature gauge, warning lamps for charging and oil pressure, mechanical stop control (separate delivered), combined glow plug switch and starting key as well as a control resistor.

Specifications:

Operation .... Four-stroke diesel engine with turbulence chambers
Type designation MD21A
Maximum output, pleasure boats (SEA)/rpm[x] 75 hp/4500
Maximum output, other installations (SMMT)/rpm[x] ... 51 hp/3000

Number of cylinders ....4 in-line
Capacity, cc (cu. in.) 2112 (129)
Bore/stroke, mm (in.) 90/83 (3.54/3.27)
Valves ....Overhead
Total weight including RB reduction/reverse gear,
   approx. kg (lb.) 275 (605)
Maximum engine inclination ....18°
x) Max. output only permitted for short periods of time.
   Cruising speed is 200 rpm lower than maximum engine speed.

DIMENSIONS DRAWING (engine with RB reduction/reverse gear)

ENGINE DIAGRAM

VOLVO MD3B

Volvo Penta MD3B is a new 3-cylinder, 4-stroke marine diesel engine with direct injection. Exceptionally compact and robust, it is designed for the toughest possible marine operating conditions.

The MD3B is a further development of the well-known and well-tested Volvo Pentas 1- and 2-cylinder marine diesel engines MD1 and MD2, and this in itself is a guarantee of top operational reliability and durability. Since all three units have many components in common, the MD3B has many special advantages from the viewpoint of servicing and spare parts.

High output — 36 hp at 2500 rpm — compact measurements and low fuel consumption are some of the properties which make the MD3B a really attractive engine choice, e.g., for middle-size, relatively heavy work boats and pleasure boats of displacement type and also as an auxiliary unit in large sailing crafts.

The engine is supplied with the following alternative equipment:

1. With electrical starter and reduction/reverse gear, ratio 1.87:1 (no hand starter).

2. With electrical starter and reduction/reverse gear ratio 1.91:1 and hand starter in front and rear end.

3. With electrical starter and reduction/reverse gear type RB, ratio 3.42:1 (no hand starter).

Here are some of the features included in the standard equipment:

Feed pump with hand primer for fuel and highly effective fuel filter.

Automatic cold-start — makes starting easier in cold weather.

Full-flow lubricating oil filter of so-called "Spin-On" type — easy to replace.

Thermostat-controlled sea-water cooling — ensures that the engine always runs at its most favorable operating temperature.

Effective intake silencer and particularly well-balanced crank-shaft — guarantee a quite, smoothly running engine.

Decompression device and raised hand starter — a reliable stand-by for manual starting.

Special marine type electrical system, complete instrument panel, alternator 12 V-38 A (450 W) with fully transistorized charging regulator.

Starter motor 1.8 hp.

Specifications:
Operation . . . . 4-stroke diesel with direct injection

Continuous output, hp (DIN[1]) at rpm 36/2500
Maximum torque kpm (lb.ft.)/rpm ....10.4 (75)/2000
Number of cylinders 3
Bore, mm (in.) 88.9 (3.50)
Stroke, mm (in.) 90 (3.54)
Capacity, cc (cu. in.) 1680 (102)
Valves ....Overhead
Ratio, reduction/reverse gear type RB 1.87:1
Ratio, reduction/reverse gear RB with auxiliary gear 3.42:1
Maximum inclination while running ....15°
Net weight, including reduction/reverse gear,
  approx. kg (lb.) 290 (640)

DIMENSION DRAWINGS (engine with reduction/reverse gear, ratio 1,91:1)

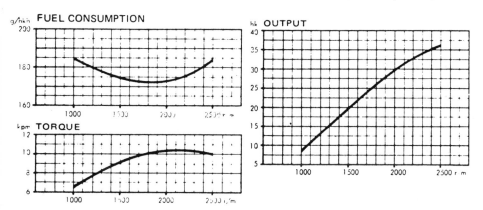

WESTERBEKE PILOT 20

Standard Equipment:

Built-in reverse and 2.5:1 reduction gear; electric starter/generator; lube oil filter, sump pump; centrifugal governor; water-cooled exhaust manifold, thermostat, zinc rod; air intake filter and silencer; fuel lift pump, secondary fuel oil filter; high-low engine mounts; 1½'' IPS exhaust flange; 1'' solid shaft coupling; control panel with key switch; mounting brackets for controls; stop and decompression control cables; standard set of tools; detailed operating manual.

Optional Equipment:

1.5:1 and 2:1 reverse and built-in reduction gear; deluxe instrument panel with electric tachometer, ammeter, oil pressure and water temperature gauges; flexible adjustable engine mounts; 1'' flexible shaft coupling; 3-groove front end pulley; 55-amp 12-volt alternator kit complete with mounting and transistorized regulator; water-cooled exhaust elbow; high efficiency silencer; spare parts kit.

WESTERBEKE PILOT 20

Specifications:

Type . . . . 2-cylinder vertical four-cycle diesel
Displacement . . . . .58.8 cu. in.
Bore . . . . .3.35 in.
Stroke . . . . .3.35 in.
Power . . . . 20 hp at 3000 rpm. See power curve
Compression ratio 21.5:1
Weight with starter/generator and reverse/reduction gear . 430 lbs.
Installation angle . . . . .15° max.
Lubrication . . . . Wet sump system (full-flow type) including
        pre-filter, main filter, pressure gauge and sump pump
Fuel system . . . . Camshaft-driven fuel lift pump
                        Automatic injection timing
Cooling system . . . . Raw water pump with thermostat
                        and protective zincs
Electrical . . . . 12v starter/generator. 13 amps output
Transmission . . . . Reverse and built-in 2.5:1 reduction gear

WESTERBEKE FOUR-91

Specifications:

Type . . . . .Four cylinder, four-cycle vertical in-line diesel
Displacement . . . . .91 cu. in.
Bore . . . . .2-7/8 in.
Stroke . . . . .3½ in.
Power . . . . .25 hp at 2500 rpm (see power curve)
Compression ratio 23:1
Weight, basic engine . . . . .470 lbs.
Combustion system . . . . . . .CAV distributor type injection pump and
CAV Pintaux nozzles working in conjunction with
Ricardo Comet V combustion chambers
Cylinder block and head . . . .High quality iron castings, mono block
Crankshaft .Forged steel, counterbalanced
Camshaft . . . . .Forged steel
Connecting rods . . . . .Forged steel
Pistons . . . . .Aluminum
Bearings . . . . .Tri metal, heavy-duty
Lubrication . . . . . . .Eccentric rotor pressure pump, camshaft-driven,
supplies 60 psi pressure to all parts
Exhaust manifold . . . .Fresh water cooled with exhaust outlet
at either end
Cooling system Closed circuit system with heat exchanger cools
engine and exhaust manifold with fresh water for long life
Angle of installation . . . . .12° max.

ENGINE WITH PARAGON SA0 DIRECT DRIVE REVERSE GEAR.

Electrical system . . 12-volt grounded system with 55-amp alternator
Reverse & reduction gears . . . . paragon manual type SAO —
          direct drive and 2:1 reduction. Type SAOV Vee-drive —
                    1:1, 1.67:1 and 2:1 reduction.
                Hydraulic transmissions — all ratios
Mounting . 16''-18'' mounts standard. 3-point suspension available.

Standard Equipment:

Fresh water cooling complete with pumps and heat exchanger mounted; 12-volt, 55-amp alternator; adjustable flexible mounts; propeller shaft coupling; fuel filter; full flow lube oil cooler and filter with spin-on element; fuel lift pump and hand primer; electric cold weather starting aid; flexible hose connections for fuel supply and return; sump pump and hose; mounting bracket for control cables; threaded exhaust flange, 1½'' IPS; key switch panel.

YANMAR YSE 8 and YSE 12

Design Features:

Cylinder block. Cast iron, incorporated water jacket, crankcase and oil pan in one block. Lower profile horizontal cylinder design permits under-floor installation and lower center of gravity.

Cylinder liner. Special cast iron, wet type for high abrasion resistance.

Cylinder head. Cast iron, intake and exhaust valves are made of heat resistant steel.

Combustion chamber. Swirl precombustion chamber for sure starting and better fuel economy.

Crankshaft. Carbon steel, forge-mounted construction. Pin and journal parts are induction hardened and grounded.

Main bearing. Kelmet metal.

Piston. Aluminum alloy, oval construction.

Connecting rod. Carbon steel.

Fuel system. Deckel type injection pump, pintle type injection valve and paper filter fuel strainer are used.

Lubricating system. Complete forced lubrication by trochoid pump and full-flow type auto-clean lubricant oil strainer for excellent durability.

Cooling system. Direct sea-water cooling by rubber rotary pump, (V-belt driven); no need extra water to carry on board.

Gear system. Constant mesh type reduction and reversing gear with wet single disc plate mechanical clutch connected to the flywheel directly. Output shaft (propeller driveshaft) designed below crankshaft permits optimum shaft angle for maximum efficiency.

Governor system. Centrifugal all-speed governor.

Starting system. Hand starting and electric starting are both available.

YANMAR YSE8 and YSE12

Specifications:

Model . . . . 4-cycle horizontal diesel
Number of cylinders 1
Bore x stroke . . . . 75 x 75
displacement 0.331
Continuous rating output, hp/rpm 5/2200, 6/2600, 7/3200
1-hr. rating output, hp/rpm . . . . —,—,8/3200

Model **YSE8**

1 = 2200rpm / 2 = 2600rpm / 3 = 3200rpm

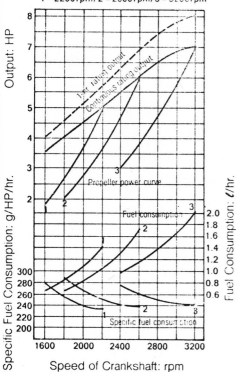

Output: HP

Specific Fuel Consumption: g/HP/hr.

Fuel Consumption: ℓ/hr.

Propeller power curve

Fuel consumption

Specific fuel consumption

Speed of Crankshaft: rpm

Model **YSE12**

1 = 2200rpm / 2 = 2600rpm / 3 = 3000rpm

Output: HP

Specific Fuel Consumption: g/HP/hr.

Fuel Consumption: ℓ/hr.

Propeller power curve

Fuel consumption

Specific fuel consumption

Speed of Crankshaft: rpm

APPENDIX

497

Reduction ratio (forward) 2/3
Propeller shaft rpm (cont. rating)...1127/751, 1332/888, 1639/1093
Crankshaft rotation ......Counterclockwise, viewed from flywheel
(stern side)
Propeller shaft rotation ......Counterclockwise, viewed from stern
Compression ratio 23.1
Combustion system ....Special swirl precombustion chamber
Lubrication system ....Enclosed full pressure lubrication
with trochoid pump
Cooling system ....Water cooling with rotary pump
Starting system ....Manual or electric with manual combination
Gear system ....Reduction & reversing gear with single disc plate,
mechanical clutch (wet type)
Dry weight, kg (lbs)
Hand starting 115 (253)
Electric starting 125 (275)

Cooling water inlet pipe
13/20 rubber pipe

Cooling water outlet
13/20 rubber pipe

Exhaust elbow
PT 1 1/2 Screwhole

425(447.5)

237
(289)

273.5 (275)

7.5(7.5)

4-14.5⌀ Holes M12 Bolt

180 (210)──·──180 (210)

360 (420)

25 (25)

25 (25)

YANMAR YSE12/YSE12G

Specifications:

Type .... 4-cycle horizontal diesel
Number of cylinders 1
Bore x stroke .... 85 x 90
Displacement 0.51
Continuous rating output, hp/rpm 8/2200, 9/2600, 10/3000
1-hr. rating output, hp/rpm .... —,—,12/3000
Reduction ratio (forward) 2/3
Propeller shaft rpm (cont. rating) 1113/718, 1316/849, 1518/980
Crankshaft rotation .... Counterclockwise, viewed from flywheel
(stern side)
Propeller shaft rotation ...... Counterclockwise, viewed from stern
Compression ratio 20.9
Combustion system .... Special swirl precombustion chamber
Lubrication system .... Enclosed full pressure lubrication
with trochoid pump
Cooling system .... Water cooling with rotary pump
Starting system .... Manual or electric with manual combination

Gear system ....Reduction & reversing gear with simple disc plate mechanical clutch (wet type)

Dry weight, kg (lbs.)
Hand starting 155 (341)
Electric starting 165 (363)

MODEL	Dia.	length	A	B	C	D	E	F	G	H	I	J	K	L	M·Q	N	O	P
YSE8	22	1800	32	52	65	57	54	88	35	46	35	46	90	60	2-14φHoles, 1/2" Coach screw	90	60	54
YSE8G YSE12	25	2000	32	52	75	76	73	100	38	50	38	50	100	65	2-14φHoles, 1/2" Coach screw	100	65	62
YSE12G	28	2400	40	60	80	75	73	110	41	56	41	56	110	75	2-18φHoles, 5/8" Coach screw	110	75	70

Note: Standard prop· · is of integrated 3-blade type, manganese bronze, with an area ratio of 0.36.

	Propeller shaft rpm	Propeller	
		Dia.(in)	Pitch(in)
YSE8	1127	14	9
	1332	13	8-1/2
	1639	12	7-1/2
YSE8G	751	18	12
	888	16-1/2	11
	1093	15	10
YSE12	1113	15	10
	1316	14	9
	1518	13	8-1/2
YSE12G	718	19	15
	849	18	13
	980	17	12

Detail of flexible mounting (optional)

2-11.5 φ Holes M10 Bolt

Detail of flexible coupling (optional)
8-M10 Bolts

CHECKLIST BEFORE STARTING ENGINE

1. DO NOT HOOK UP BATTERIES BEFORE SPARK TESTING ELECTRICAL SYSTEM!
   A. Hook up negative cable to negative (—) battery terminal.
   B. Turn main switch (red) to "ALL" and engine switch (switch panel) to "ON."
   C. Carefully tap positive terminal (+) with positive cable; if spark occurs there is *trouble!* In the circuitry, recheck wiring & spark test again — do not permanently attach cables until there are *no* sparks when testing.

2. BATTERY CABLES *MUST NOT* BE HOOKED UP WHEN WORKING ON THE WIRING!!

3. BLEED FUEL SYSTEM WITH HAND PUMP.
   A. Volvo — First at fine filter; second at injection pump.
   B. Perkins — First at filter on engine; second at injection pump.

4. CHECK LUBRICANTS (fill before installation of engine).
   A. Volvo usually filled — Check level of engine & gearbox — Top up with diesel lube oil (30) MS grade only. Both engine & gearbox use same oil.
   B. Perkins — Fill engine with diesel lube oil (30) MS grade only — gearbox with automatic transmission fluid.

5. CHECK KILL CONTROL: BE SURE IT WORKS *BEFORE* STARTING.
   A. Volvo must pull back against spring-loaded Stop and must not interfere with throttle opening. Be sure cable routing does *not* contact starter terminals — insulate if necessary.
   B. Perkins — Check out kill control solenoid — *does it work???!*

6. SET UP WATER INTAKE
   A. Close all drain cocks.
   B. Perkins: Fill fresh water tank and hook up hose to salt water inlet.
   C. Volvo: Hook up hose to salt water inlet.

7. START ENGINE.
   A. Disengage gearbox button.
   B. Move throttle to half-open.
   C. Volvo: Push cold start button (if button does not remain depressed, open throttle more).
   D. Start engine — Quickly *reduce* throttle opening to fast idle: 800-1,000 rpms. Check exhaust outlet for water flow. Check

oil pressure (gauge should read minimum 60 lbs. and alarm should be silent within a few seconds). Volvo warning light should go out; if not, kill engine, check alternator light on Volvo. On Perkins, meter should return to center within a few seconds.

8. STOP ENGINE.
   A. Recheck lubricant levels.
   B. Recheck fresh water tank on Perkins.
   C. Recheck shaft alignment.
   D. Winterize if necessary.

LIST OF SUPPLIERS

CATALOGS

Thomas Foulkes
Lansdowne Road
Leytonstone
London E. 11 3HB
England

Spyglass Catalogue
2415 Webster Street
Alameda, CA 94501

Lands' End Catalogue
2317 N. Elston
Chicago, IL 60614

Mariners Catalogue
National Fisherman and International
Marine Publishing Co.
Camden, ME

James Bliss Co.
Dedham, MA 02026

Manhattan Marine
116 Chambers Street
New York, NY 10007

SPARS

Le Fiel
Mast and Rigging, Aluminum
13700 Firestone Blvd.
Santa Fe Springs, CA 90670

Shepperd Woodworks
Wood Spars
21020 70th West
Edmonds, WA 98020

Super Spar
Masts, Aluminum
7231 Rosecrans Ave.
Paramount, CA 90723

Forespar
Spars and Fittings
3140 Pullman St.
Costa Mesa, CA 92627

Metal Mast Marine
Aluminum spars and related fittings
P.O. Box 471
Putnam, CT 06260

Sparcraft
Masts and assorted hardware
P.O. Box 925, 770 W. 17th St.
Costa Mesa, CA 92627

Forespar, Inc.
Rigging and spinnaker poles
3140 Pullman St.
Costa Mesa, CA 92626

WOOD

American Forest Products
All hardwoods and marine plywood
14103 Park Place
Cerritos, CA 90701

American Hardwood
1900 E. 15th St.
Los Angeles, CA 90021

Rogers Woodworking
Custom marine woodwork
874 W. 18th St.
Costa Mesa, CA 92627

Albano Marine Woodwork
Custom wood parts
% Wave Traders
1702 Bridgeway
Sausalito, CA 94965

H & L Woodwork
2965 E. Harcourt St.
Compton, CA 90221

RIGGING

Forespar
3140 Pullman St.
Costa Mesa, CA 92627

Hood Industries Rigging
951 Newhall St.
Costa Mesa, CA 92627

Ronstan (Alexander Roberts)
Running rigging
1851 Langley Ave.
Irvine, CA 92705

Universal Wire Products, Inc.
Rigging
222 Universal Drive
North Haven, CT 06473

DECK HARDWARE

American Precision Marine
Deck hardware
1260 Montauk Highway E.
Patachoque, NY 11772

Barient
Winches, etc.
936 Bransten Road
San Carlos, CA 94070

Barlow Winches
Alexander Roberts Co.
1851 Langley Ave.
Irvine, CA 92705

Clamcleat
Sneve-Nysether Co.
Box 1201
Everett, WA 98206

Gibb
Winches, turnbuckles, hardware, Hasler vang gear
82 Border St.
Cohasset, MD 02025

Harken
Blocks
1251 E. Wisconsin Ave.
Pewaukee, WI 53072

Hye
Deck gear
1075 Shell Blvd., #12
Foster City, CA 94404

Johnson Yacht Hardware
Lifeline hardware
Main Street
Middle Haddam, CT 06456

Lewmar Marine Yacht Hardware
Winches and rigging hardware
892 W. 18th St.
Costa Mesa, CA 92627

Merriman Holbrook
Complete line of deck hardware including winches
301 River St.
Grand River, OH 44045

Navtec Inc.
Rigging hardware
P.O. Box 277, Maynard Industrial Park
Maynard, MA 01754

Nicro-Fico
Complete line of hardware for running rigging
2065 N. Ave 140th
San Leandro, CA 94577

Ronstan (Alexander Roberts)
1851 Langley Ave.
Irvine, CA 92705

Schaeffer Marine
Complete line of deck and running rigging hardware
Industrial Park
New Bedford, MA 02745

Wilcox-Crittendon
Complete line of marine hardware
Middletown, CT 06457

GENERAL HARDWARE

Harding Machine Marine Parts
Individual custom hardware
1733 Monrovia Ave., Suite N
Costa Mesa, CA 92627

Harris Marine
Individual custom hardware
1281 Logan
Costa Mesa, CA 92626

Vic Berry
Best fuel and water tanks in the whole world
760 Newton Way
Costa Mesa, CA 92627

R.C. Plath Co.
Bronze hardware and anchor windlasses
337 N.E. 10th Ave.
Portland, OR 97232

Caseco
All types stainless steel fasteners
1215 S. State College Blvd.
Fullerton, CA 92631

Moritz Foundry
Windlass and other beautiful bronze cast marine hardware
133 Industrial Way
Costa Mesa, CA 92627

Beckson Manufacturing
Pumps, vents, hatches, etc.
Box 3336
Bridgeport, CT 06605

Danforth
Anchors, compasses, instruments
-500 Riverside Industrial Parkway
Portland, ME 04013

Mariner Yacht Hardware
Blocks, deck hardware
1714 Seventeenth
Santa Monica, CA 90404

Nicro-Fico
Complete line of hardware for running rigging
2065 W. Ave 140th
San Leandro, CA 94577

PYHI
ABS plastic portlights and vents
1647 N. Avalon Blvd.
Wilmington, CA 90744

Rostand, Inc.
Ecclesiastical brass and marine hardware
Milford, CT 06460

Seagull Marine
Avon, Whale pumps, CQR anchors and Simpson Lawrence
Windlass and British hardware
1851 McGaw Ave.
Irvine, CA 92705

Wilcox-Crittendon
Complete line of marine hardware
Middletown, CT 06457

Yacht Specialties Co., Inc.
Wheel steering
15 5 E. St. Gertrude Place
Santa Ana, CA 92705

Bomar Company
Hatches
1021 E. State St.
Westport, CT 06880

ELECTRONICS

Dawn Electronics Corp.
Knotmeter and taffrail log
P.O. Box 91736
Los Angeles, CA 90009

Davis Instruments
Navigation supplies
857 Thornton St.
San Leandro, CA 94577

Fisheries Supply
Swoffer knotmeter and log
Pier 55
Seattle, WA 98101

Kenyon Marine
Navigation instruments, hardware
New Whitfield St.
Guilford, CT 06437

Ray Jefferson
Radios, electronics, instruments
Main & Cotton St.
Philadelphia, PA 19127

Signet Scientific Comp.
Yacht instruments
129 E. Tujunga Ave., P.O. Box 6489
Burbank, CA 91510

Telcor Instruments Inc.
Yacht instruments
17785 Sky Park Circle, Box CC
Irvine, CA 92664

VDO Instruments
Knotmeters
116 Victor
Detroit, MI 48203

GENERAL

Ferro Corp.
All fiberglass materials
18811 Fiberglass Road
Huntington Beach, CA 92648

Grove Specialties
Two part polysulfide caulking for teak decks
528 N. State St.
Glendale, CA 91203

Larwyck Development
Windvanes
17330 Raymer St.
Northridge, CA

Marine Vane Gears
Windvanes
Cowes, Isle of Wight
England

Alco Mining
Lead ballast casting
16908 S. Broadway
Gardena, CA

Norcold Inc.
Refrigerators
11121 Weddington
North Hollywood, CA 91601

Norton Products
Holding plate refrigeration systems
173-M Monrovia Ave.
Costa Mesa, CA 92627

Thalco Uniglas Co.
Fiberglass
1212 McGaw Ave.
Santa Ana, CA 92705

Boat Transit
Boat hauling cross-country
P.O. Box 1403
Newport Beach, CA 92663

Fatsco
Beautiful solid fuel ship's stoves
251 N. Fair Ave.
Benton Harbor, MI

Lavender Fasteners
All stainless steel fasteners
884 W. 18th St.
Costa Mesa, CA 92627

Southwest Instruments
*Navigation aids, marine supplies, books and
everything you can dream of*
235 W. 7th St.
San Pedro, CA

Aquadron/Acme
First aid kits
1113 Johnston Building
Charlotte, NC 28281

Atlantis
Foul weather gear
Waitsfield, VT 05673

Canor Plarex
Foul weather gear
4200 23rd Ave. W.
Seattle, WA 98199

Aonolite
Reinforced fiberglass foam
425 Maple Ave.
Carpentersville, IL 60110

Doris Hammond
Canvas bags
260 Kearny St.
San Francisco, CA 94108

Edson
Steering equipment
480 E. Industrial Park Road
New Bedford, MA 02745

Guest
Yacht lights
17 Culbro Drive
West Hartford, C 06110

Interlux Paints
Marine finishes
220 S. Linden Ave.
So. San Francisco, CA 94080

A.B. Optimus
Stoves and lanterns
P.O. Box 907, 1251 Beach Blvd.
La Habra, CA 90631

Paul Luke Inc.
Stoves and cabin heater
East Boothbay, ME 04544

Sailrite Kits
Sail and awning kits
2010 Lincoln Blvd.
Venice, CA 90291

Samson Cordage Works
Dacron and nylon braided line
470 Atlantic Ave.
Boston, MA 02210

Z-Spar Koppers Co. Inc.
Marine finishes
1900 Koppers Building
Pittsburgh, PA 15219

Woolsey Marine Ind.
Marine finishes and winches
201 E. 42nd St.
New York, NY 10017

GLOSSARY OF TERMS

— A —

ABX — A grading system for plywood indicating that one side is flawless (A) and one side is good, but perhaps seamed or patched (B) and the laminating glue is resorcinal (exterior grade (X).

Acetone — A very combustible, fast evaporating cleaning fluid for cleaning surfaces. The only thing that will dissolve and clean polyester resin.

Acid Brush — A small inexpensive brush of about ½'' bristle width with a tin handle; ideal for gluing or cleaning.

Accordian Hose — A flexible rubber hose used to act as a flex unit between a deck fill and tank.

ACX — Same as ABX except the second side holes and flaws are *not* repaired (C).

Aft — Toward the rear or stern of a boat.

Aloft — Upon the mast or rigging.

Ammeter — An indicating gauge that reflects the amount of amps being drawn.

Amp/Hrs. — A rating which reflects the number of amps per hour a device draws or charges.

Anchor Light — An electric or kerosene ''white'' light placed in the rigging during overnight anchoring to advise other boats.

Anchor Roller — A stainless steel or bronze roller over which anchor-chain commutes.

Anchor Windlass — A mechanical winch, manual or electric, which aids in hauling anchors and chain.

Anemometer — An instrument used to measure wind speed.

Aqualift — An exhaust system, usually a small cast iron unit attached directly to the engine.

Arbour — An attachment used with a drill motor; supports hole saws of different sizes. Usually has a drill bit inserted throughout its center.

— B —

Backstay — The wire rope giving aft support to the mast.

Back-Up Plates — Reinforcing plates, usually steel or brass, used when bolting through vulnerable material such as wood or fiberglass.

Baffles — Structural partitions in fuel and water tanks that restrain liquids from gaining momentum during violent boat movement.

Baggywrinkle — Fluffed, short rope ends fabricated to prevent sails from chafing on shrouds.

Ballast — High-density weight (lead, steel, or cement) carried in the lower part of a vessel to give her stability and enable her to right herself.

Band Saw — A large saw with a flexible, thin loop of a blade, used to cut curves or fine finishing angles.

Bar Clamp — A very long adjustable clamp of 24'' or more used to clamp large pieces.

Barograph — A barometer equipped with a moving graph that records barometric changes.

Battens — Flexible plastic fiberglass or wood strips utilized in a reinforced pocket in the leech of a sail, used as an aid to properly set a sail with a roach.

Battens Pockets — Reinforced sheath on the leech of the sail that houses battens.

Battery Box — A protective box, usually plastic, which protects the battery from external damage and also accumulates battery spillage.

Battery Cables — High output cables (usually #4 or lower gauge) that connect the battery with the alternator or generator.

Battery Straps — Strong non-corrosive straps used to lash a battery to its shelf or support to keep it from damage.

Beam — The widest dimension of a vessel.

Bedlog — A set of raised tracks upon which the main hatch slides.

Berth — A bunk or any sleeping accommodations of a vessel.

Berth Rail — A trim piece that keeps berth cushions in place.

Bevel — The act of cutting to a taper.

Bevel Square — An adjustable tool which with two arms and a wingnut can be used to duplicate or record angles.

Bilge — Area of the boat below the cabin sole utilized for tanks, storage, etc.

Bilge Pump — A high capacity manual or electric pump used to pump out bilge water.

Bilge Pump Strainer — A strainer or sieve (hopefully brass) attached to the lower end of a bilge pump hose needed to keep flotsom and jetsom from clogging the pump.

Binnacle — A housing for compasses.

Bobstay — The stay from the tip of the bowsprit to a fitting at the waterline, counteracting the pull of the forestay.

Boiler Punchings — Steel punchings, usually scrap, which because of their small size (thus high density) are commonly used as ballast.

Bolt Rope — Roping around the edge of a sail needed to take the strain off the sailcloth.

Boom Bail — A "U" shaped bracket screwed to booms through which blocks and lines can be led.

Boomgallows — A standard support upon which the boom rests when the sails are stored.

Boomkin — A horizontal extension off the stern of the boat used to accommodate a backstay if the main or mizzen boom length demands.

Boomvang — A rope and block mechanism which controls the upward movement of booms.

Bowsprit — A horizontal extension off the bow of the boat used to accommodate the headstay if the size of the headsails demand.

Bowsuns Chair — A canvas sling used for hoisting one up the mast.

Boot Stripe — A painted stripe above the yacht's waterline to catch oil or dirt; or just for esthetics.

Bridge Deck — A narrow part of the deck between the cockpit and the companionway or cabin.

Bulkheads — Usually structural partitions of a boat. Solid dividers e.g. lazarette bulkhead, chain locker bulkhead, engine room bulkhead.

Bull-Nose — (A) to round off a sharp edge; (B) a concave bladed router bit used to round off a sharp edge; (C) the rounded edge itself.

Bullseye — A high strength plastic eyelet that can be secured to the deck to aid in fairleading lines.

Bulwarks — Raised portion of deck that follows the sheer line, usually used for protection of crew and equipment.

Butt Connector — A metal press fitting that unites two wires end to end without complex splicing.

— C —

California Reefing — Same as slab and jiffy reefing.

Cam Cleat — A piece of deck hardware consisting of two cogs between which line will pass in only one direction.

Cap Nut — A finishing nut with one side sealed off.

Car — A moving fitting attached to a traveler to which a block may be attached.

Carriage Bolt — A smooth-headed bolt with squared shoulders to keep it from turning.

Catalyst — A chemical activator for an otherwise inactive substance.

Caulk — To drive cotton line into the seam of a wood planked vessel.

Ceiling — The lining which keeps things from touching the inside skin of the hull.

Center Bond — The laminations uniting two halves of a twin molded hull.

Center Punch — A pointed tool for making marks on wood or metal.

Charley Noble — A through deck fitting (usually with cap) for a stove pipe.

Cheek Block — A fixed pulley which is attached to a boom, etc. on its side.

Chicken Head — A metal fitting at the top of a mast to which are secured the shrouds, stays & sheaves.

Chocks — Blocks of wood or metal on the deck which act as pads for deck equipment such as a dinghy, spinnaker pole, etc.

Chronometer — A very accurate clock used for navigation.

Circular Saw — Also known as skill saw; a small electric saw with a rotating circular blade.

Clam Cleat — Similar to a cam cleat, but without moving parts.

Clamping — Mechanically holding two parts together.

Cleat — A T-shaped piece of hardware, usually of wood or aluminum attached to the mast deck or caprail for securing items.

Cleat Stock — Square cross-sectioned strips of wood used to join perpendicularly uniting pieces of plywood.

Clevis Pin — A stiff piece of metal rod which secures a joint (e.g. toggel and turnbuckle).

Clew — Lower aft corner of sail.

Clipper Bow — A bow that has a forward curve.

Club Footed Jib — A self-tending jib whose foot is attached to a boom at the clew rather than being free flying.

Coaming — Side of cabin, cockpit, etc.

Cockpit — The sunken area of a deck in which the helmsman and passengers sit.

Cockpit Sole — The floor of the cockpit.

Cold Chisel — A very hard chisel for cutting metal.

Companionway — The entrance by which you pass through when going below from topsides.

Companionway Ladder — The steps in the companionway leading below.

Compression Lever — A lever used by Volvo for releasing compression, thus enabling hand cranking.

Compression Tube — A reinforcing tubing welded into aluminum mast, through which a bolt passes. It prevents the walls from collapsing.

Countersink — To set the head of a screw or bolt below the surface; tool used for this purpose.

Cunningham Hole — A hole and cringle in a sail used to tighten or stretch the luff.

Cutter — A single mast vessel with two headsails.

— D —

Davit — An overhanging fixture from which a dinghy is supported.

Deadeye — Old-fashioned method of rigging adjustment used in combination with lanyards. Replaced by modern turnbuckles.

Dead Light — A non-opening piece of glass in deck, cabin atop, etc. for light.

Deck Beams — Atwartship beams that support the deck.

Deck Bridge — The piece of decking between the cockpit and companionway entrance.

Deck Cap — A metal cap that fits over a deck-pipe to prevent water from entering boat.

Deck Fill — A metal deck fitting with screwdriver top through which water and fuel can be administered to tanks below decks.

Deck Pipe — A metal deck fitting through which chain is fed below.

Displacement — Very close estimate of the vessel's weight.

Dolfinite — A very oily bedding compound best used on fiberglass to wood or wood to wood joints.

Dovetailing — A very positive method of corner joints for wood, using intermeshing wedge shapes of each wood as fasteners.

Dovetail Saw — A very stiff-bladed, hand saw with well reinforced blade for very accurate cutting.

Dowels — Wood turnings used as a common attachment, usually to join boards on end.

Downhaul — Line used to pull down sails. Commonly used in reference to a moveable gooseneck on tracks.

Draft — The vertical distance from waterline to lowest point of keel.

Drop Boards — Removable boards that slide into gallows, usually to shut off companionway opening.

Drops — Wood "doors" usually below cushions that cover access holes to stowage below.

D-Shackle — A "D" shaped shackle with threaded pin.

— **E** —

Echo Sounder — A fathometer.

Elbow Catch — A spring loaded catch for cabinet doors, usually hidden and accessible through a finger hole.

Engine Pan — Usually a fiberglass molding bonded to the hull. The engine mounts fitted onto its shoulders. Below the pan catches oil drippings.

Epoxy Glue and Resin — A high strength synthetic adhesive that will stick anything to anything.

Eye — A closed loop in wire-rope or line.

Eyeband — A fitting on the tip of the bowsprit to which the forestay, bobstay and whiskerstays are attached.

Eyebolt — A bolt with an open loop for a head.

Eyelets — Brass loops sewn into sails for reef points, etc.

— **F** —

Fairlead — A fitting which alters the direction of a line to keep it from fouling.

Fathom — 6 feet of measure.

Feather — To even two levels into each other.

Feeler Gauge — Small metal sheets of given thickness used to measure fine spacings; e.g. coupling to engine alignment.

Fender — A bumper or rubber guard hung from the boat's sides.

Fiddles — Wood or metal guardrails along the perimeter of counters, tables, etc. that keep items from falling.

Flare — Outward curve of a vessel's side. To widen or ream the end of a pipe for coupling purposes.

Flathead — A bevel-shouldered screw.

Flex Coupling — A rubber fitted unit uniting the engine with propeller shaft. The rubber acts as an absorber of engine vibration.

Flex Mounts — Rubber fitted engine mounts that prevent transmission of engine vibration to the hull.

Flux — A cleaning paste used on surface just before soldering.

Foot — The bottom edge of a sail.

Footpump — A water pump operated by foot.

Fore and Aft — In direction of centerline. Stern to bow.

Forecastle — The forward-most accommodations.

Forefoot — The underwater part of the bow from the forward part of the keel to the foremost part of the waterline.

Forepeak — Generally same as forecastle.

Forestay — The forward-most mast supporting rigging.

Fork Wrench — Open ended wrench.

Freeboard — Vertical distance from waterline to sheer.

Fresh Water Cooling — A closed water system which circulates through the engine block to cool it. The fresh water is in turn cooled through a heat exchanger by circulating exterior water.

— G —

Galley — A boat's kitchen.

Gallows — Boom gallows.

Galvanize — A zinc coating put on steel to protect it from corrosion.

Gate Valve — A conventional shut-off mechanism for water and fuel flow.

Gelcoat — A very hard outer coating (usually color pigmented) of a fiberglass boat.

Genoa — A headsail filling the entire fore triangle and more.

Gimbals — A swivel arrangement by which stoves, tables, compasses, etc. are allowed to remain level in spite of the boat movements.

Gooseneck — A swivel fitting that holds the boom onto the mast.

Grabrail — Holed handrail on deck or inside a boat.

Graphite — A mineral base lubricant.

Grinder — A term used sometimes for a belt sander.

Grommet — A brass eye sewn into a sail.

Guard — An adjustable metal fence on a table saw, running parallel with the blade.

Gudgeon — A hull fitting into which the pintle of the rudder fits.

Gypsey — A wheel on the windlass notched for rope.

— H —

Hack Saw — A very fine tooth bladed saw (the blade is removable) made for metal cutting.

Halyard — Lines used for hoisting sails.

Halyard Winches — Winches with a drum for wire or rope used to aid in hoisting the sails.

Hank — The attaching clip of a sail that holds it to the stay but allows it to slide up and down (usually brass).

Hasp — The hinged part of a fitting that combined with an eye and padlock completes a locking unit for hatches, doors, etc.

Hatch — An access hole in the ship's deck; also the cover for this hole.

Hatch Coaming — Built up buffer around a hatch opening to keep out water intruding under the hatch.

Hatch Cover — A fixed housing under which a hatch slides.

Head — The toilet of a boat.

Headsail — Sails such as jib, genoa, staysail, set forward of the mast.

Heat-Exchanger — A cooling unit of an engine which allows circulating raw water to cool captive fresh water.

Helm — Tiller or steering wheel.

Hex (Head or Nut) — A six-sided nut, or six-sided bolt-head.

Hobby Horse — The pitching of the bow and stern of a boat about its athwartship axis.

Hold Downs — Straps of steel or nylon used to fasten tanks to shelves, floor timbers, etc.

Hole Saws — Circular heavy walled saw blades of infinite diameters used in conjunction with a drill motor to cut holes.

Hose Barb — A tapered fitting with terraced ridges that allow a hose to slip on but not off.

Hose Clamp — An adjustable stainless steel ring used to fasten hoses to fittings.

Hose Ties — Plastic ties with a barbed tongue and eye used to fasten hoses to bulkheads, sole, etc.

House Pipe — A fitting in the bulwarks through which mooring lines or anchor lines are led.

— I —

Inboard — Toward the centerline.

Injectors — The device on a diesel engine which turns the fuel from liquid to vapor.

Intermediates — Stays that support the mast at a point between the spreaders and masthead.

— J —

Jack Stays — Spreader lifts.

Jam Cleats — A small cleat with general shape of a mooring cleat but one end is tapered so the line can be wedged with a single run; used for sheets where quick release and quick making-fast is necessary.

Jib — The foremost headsail.

Jiffy Reefing — A method which quickly hauls the luff and leech of the mainsail down to the boom by means of lines and blocks.

Joiner — A mechanical table plane for dressing wood surfaces.

— K —

Keel — The fore and aft underwater members which stabilizes the boat's direction and prevents leeway.

Ketch — Twin masted sailboat with the main forward of the mizzen and the mizzen forward of the stern post.

Key Hole Saw — A very narrow bladed hand saw with one end of the blade unsupported, used for hole or curve cutting.

Kill Switch — A control mechanism on a diesel engine that shuts it off by cutting off fuel supply.

King Plank — The central plank of a deck.

Knot — A vertical speed rating — 1 nautical mile = 6080 ft./hr.

Knotmeter — A boat's speedometer.

— L —

Lag Bolt — Square headed wood screw.

Lay Up — The laminations of fiberglass.

Lazarette — A stowage compartment in the aft-most section of a vessel.

Lead-Fish — Large lead castings used for ballast.

Lead-Pig — Small (1016-10016) lead castings used for ballast.

Lead-Shot — Very small lead chunks used for ballast.

Leeboard — Canvas or plywood slabs used to keep a berth's occupant in the berth in spite of the vessel's roll.

Leech — Aft edge of the sail.

Leeway — Sideways movement of a vessel.

Lifelines — The lines attached to the stanchions providing a ''railing.''

Limber Holes — Holes in bulkheads that allow drainage from one compartment to another.

LOA — Length Over All (not including bowsprit or boomkin or aft hung rudder).

Locker — A stowage compartment.

Log — A mechanical device that records the distance the ship has moved relative to water.

Lowers — The lower shrouds.

Lubber Line — Mark on a compass corresponding to the boat's center line.

Luff — Forward edge of sail.

LWL — Load Water Line — length of hull at marked waterline.

— M —

Machine Screw — A fine threaded, slot headed fastener made to be used with a tapped hole.

Mainsail — Fore and aft sail attached to aft part of main mast.

Make Fast — To attach or secure a line.

Marine Eyes — The looped fitting over a shroud.

Mast Head — Top of the mast.

Mast Step — A fitting on deck or below onto which the foot of the mast is fitted.

Mat — An unwoven fiberglass material made up of randomly layered short fibers.

Miter — To cut on an angle.

Miter Box — A wood or metal frame which is used with a hand saw to cut material at a given angle.

Miter Gauge — The sliding fitting on a table or band saw against which the piece of wood is laid to assure a straight cut. The gauge itself is adjustable to any angle required.

Mish-Mash — A mixture of polyester resin and fibers of asbestos or fiberglass combined to make a thicker putty-like adhesive.

Mizzen — Fore and aft sail attached to aft part of mizzen mast.

Mizzen Mast — The aft mast of a yawl or ketch.

Molding — Trimming pieces of wood or plastic that hide joints or mistakes or both.

Mooring Cleat — A large deck cleat to which mooring lines are attached.

— N —

Negative Roach — A battenless, hollow-cut cruising mainsail.

Non-Skid — A high friction surface for deck and cabin top.

— O —

Open End — A type of mechanic's wrench.

Outboard — Away from center line.

Outhaul — The gear used to stretch the foot of sail along the boom.

Oval Head — A screw with a head of that shape.

Overhang — Stern or bow of hull extending past the LWL.

Overhead — Inside cabin top.

— P —

Pad Eye — A through bolted deck fitting to accommodate blocks, lines, etc.

Pan Head — A type of screw with a head shaped like the bottom of a cooking pan.

Pennant — Short length of wire to which headsails are attached.

Pet Cock — A small 90 degree turn off-on valve ideal for fuel switch off.

Pilot Berth — An elevated single berth.

Pinrail — A rack that houses belaying pins.

Pintle — Rudder fitting that fits into gudgeons to form hinge.

Pitch — Sticky wood rosin.

Plastic Resin Glue — A powder base mixed with water that forms a very strong water resistant glue.

Plug — A tight fitting wood dowel used to fill screw head holes.

Plug Cutter — An attachment for a drill motor that cuts plugs.

Plug Remover — Any sharp tool to split an inserted plug and take it out.

Polysulfide — An unbelievably effective totally waterproof sealing-bedding compound.

Polyurethane Foam — A tight-celled polyester resin resistant insulation.

Poop — An overtaking sea swamping the aft deck and/or cockpit of vessel.

Port — Left side of vessel facing forward.

Portlight — A small cabin side window.

Preventer — Another name for a boomvang.

Pull Rings — Flush fitting swivel rings used to lift hatches.

Purchase — The lines and blocks used to gain mechanical advantage.

— Q —

Quarter Berth — Usually an excellent sea berth located in the aft quarters of the ship.

Quarters — The sections of the vessel from amidships to bow or amidships to stern.

— R —

Rabbet — A groove cut in a plank.

Radio Coax — Radio antenna wire.

Railstripe — A color line along the sheer.

Rake — Fore and aft inclination of mast, sternpost, etc.

Ratlines — Horizontal ropes or strips of wood between shrouds forming a ladder.

Rat Tail — Faired or feathered rope end.

Raw Water Cooling — An engine cooling system that circulates exterior water directly through the block.

Reaching Pole — A light boom for keeping light wind sails full.

Reef — To shorten sails.

Reef Points — Grommets or ties for shortening the sail.

Resorcinal Glue — A two-part completely waterproof glue.

Roach — The outward curve added to a sail to increase its belly.

Rope Tail — A nylon end on a wire halyard.

Roving — A very heavy woven fiberglass material.

Rubrail — Bumper strip of wood or metal on the beams.

Rudder Preventer — A strip between hull and aft-hung rudder that keeps lines from catching on rudder.

Run — To sail before the wind.

Running Rigging — Sheets, halyards, etc. i.e. moveable rigging.

— S —

Sail Track — A track on the mast or boom into or onto which the sail slides are fitted.

Salon — Main living area in vessel.

Samson Post — Strong post in foredeck used as a hitch post for anchor line and mooring line.

Schooner — A rig that sports a smaller mast ahead of the main mast.

Scupper — An opening in the bulwarks allowing deck-drainage.

Scribe — To reproduce the curve of a surface onto another surface by using a compass with pencil.

Seacock — A 90 degree shut-off valve used on through-hull fittings.

Seakindly — Having characteristics which respond well to any sea condition.

Searail — Fencing along table, cabinetry, etc. to guard items from falling.

Seating Cleat — Shelving upon which drop boards sit.

Section — Lines of a vessel as if cut in half looking fore and aft.

Set — To hoist sail.

Shaft-Log — A bearing supporting fitting guiding the propeller-shaft through the hull.

Shank — The shaft of the anchor.

Sheer — Curve of gunwale.

Sheet — A rope used to trim sails.

Sheet Metal Screw — Heavy threaded self-tapping screw.

Shrink Tubes — Plastic tubing slipped over wire splices then shrunk.by heat to seal the splice.

Shroud — Wire rigging giving the most athwartship support.

Silicone Seal — A quick drying non-hardening sealing compound.

Slab Reefing — Jiffy reefing.

Slides — Metal fittings that hold a sail onto the sail track.

Sloop — Single masted rig with single headsail.

Snap Shackle — Hinge bar shackle.

Sole — Cabin floor.

Sole Timber — Floor supporting beams.

Spinnaker Car — A moveable fitting that attaches the spinnaker pole to the spinnaker track.

Spinnaker Pole — A light spar that keeps the clew of the spinnaker well out helping fill the sail.

Spinnaker Track — A track attached to the mast over which the spinnaker car slides.

Spreader — A strut on a mast giving rigidity to rigging.

Spreader Lifts — Wires that keep spreaders in position.

Stanchions — Steel poles attached to deck or bulwarks to support lifelines.

Standing Rigging — Permanently attached wire stays and turnbuckles supporting the mast.

Starboard — The right side of a vessel facing forward.

Stay — A wire rope supporting the mast fore and aft.

Staysail — A triangular hanked sail.

Staysail Pedestal — A deck mounted base footing the staysail boom.

Stops — Moveable fittings on a track that keep a block in place.

Storm Jib — A very small, heavy clothed heavy-weather headsail.

Storm Trysail — Very small heavy clothed heavy-weather sail to replace mainsail.

Stuffing Box — A fitting at the shaft-log preventing the entry of water.

Sump — The lowest point in the keel where water collects.

Swedge — Method of attaching, by pressure, fittings onto a wire rope.

— T —

Tabernacle — A large deck bracket that houses the foot of the mast and the pin which allows it to be lowered.

Tack — The lower forward corner of a sail.

Taffrail — A rail around the stern — usually decorative if you like that sort of thing.

Tang — A metal fitting on mast or hull to which rigging is attached.

Tender — Given to heeling, antonym of "Stiff."

Terminal Blocks — An electrical, insulated block with fittings to unite wires.

Thimble — A round or heart-shaped metal eye chafe protector around which rope can be seized.

Tiller — A bar attached to top of rudder used for steering.

Toggle — A swivel fork uniting the turnbuckle to the chainplate.

Topping Lift — A line supporting aft end of a boom.

Transducer — A fathometer through-hull fitting.

Transom — A chopped stern, opposite of double ender.

Traveller — A moveable attachment that allows control over movement of the boom.

Tumble-Home — Inward curve along the sheer line of some vessels.

Turnbuckle — Adjustable attachment uniting rigging to hull fittings.

— U —

Upper Shroud — That part of the rigging going to to mast head which provides athwartships support.

— V —

Vang — A rope controlling upward movement of a boom.

Vented Loop — A bronze fitting with a valve that prevents siphoning of water into appliances below the waterline.

— W —

Waterline — A horizontal line at the point of designed displacement.

Water Separator — A filter that takes water from diesel fuel by gravity.

Water Strainer — A filter for incoming raw water.

Whiskerstay — Standing rigging which prevents athwartships movement of bowsprit or boomkin.

Winch — A mechanical aid made up of a drum and pin and gears to aid in hoisting and trimming sails.

Winch Bracket — A fabricated mount for sheet winches.

Winch Pad — A welded pad on a mast serving as a base for a halyard winch.

Windlass — A winch to haul up anchor and anchor chain.

— Y —

Yankee Jib — Large foresail, its size between a working jib and genoa.

Yaw — To change bearing from side to side — unadle to maintain course.

Yawl — A twin-masted rig, the mizzen being stepped abaft the sternpost.

INDEX